The World of
STILL WATER
THE LIVING COUNTRYSIDE.

A Reader's Digest selection

THE WORLD OF STILL WATER

Front cover picture: A great crested grebe carries its stripy chicks
pick-a-back. This handsome bird frequents shallow lakes, reservoirs
and gravel pits.

ISBN 0 276 39658 8

The World of
STILL WATER
THE LIVING COUNTRYSIDE

PUBLISHED BY THE READER'S DIGEST ASSOCIATION LIMITED
LONDON   NEW YORK   MONTREAL   SYDNEY   CAPE TOWN

Originally published in partwork form
by Eaglemoss Publications Limited and Orbis Publishing Limited

Consultant

Robert Gibbons

Contributors

Aune Butt	**Paul Hillyard**	**Chris Newbold**
John Clegg	**Nigel Holmes**	**Malcolm Ogilvie**
Thomas A Cope	**Dick Hornby**	**Roberta Peacock**
David Corke	**Richard Lindsay**	**John Sankey**
Carole Devaney	**Roger Lovegrove**	**Marian Short**
Steve Downer	**TT Macan**	**David Sutton**
Euan Dunn	**Nigel Matthews**	**Michael Tweedie**
Jim Flegg	**Chris Mead**	**John Waters**
Pamela Forey	**John Mitchell**	**Susan Wells**
Paul Freeman	**Fred Naggs**	**Alwyne Wheeler**

Contents

The World of
STILL WATER

Introduction

For any plant or animal able to make use of it, the world of still freshwater – lakes, ponds and marshes – is one of the most productive habitats anywhere. You have only to look at the dense, lush growth of vegetation around a lake or pond, or see the swarms of insects, ranging from dragonflies to midges, that are associated with wetland areas to realise just how productive they are.

Even in the damp, cool climate of Britain, lack of water is one of the factors that limits plant and animal survival. Plant growth is frequently slowed drastically in summer for lack of water in dry-land habitats, and many insects fail to colonize land areas because of the risk of desiccation. But in still waters these limits are removed – plant growth is faster for a longer season, and a much greater range of insects survives in summer, while still more insects make use of the abundant soft plant growth. Wherever there are masses of insects and flowering plants, you can be sure that there will be many birds, mammals and other animals to feed on them.

Water has another advantage too – one that becomes apparent in winter. It may warm up more slowly than the ground in spring, but it cools more slowly in winter, especially if fed by underground springs, and so its animals and plants remain available for more species to feed on through winter.

Each water habitat is different in detail, but most consist of a deep layer, little disturbed by the vagaries of the weather above; the surface layers where most light and warmth reaches; the shallows which warm readily, where emergent aquatic plants can root and thrive; and the all-important marginal habitats where land and water meet, giving the best of both worlds to those species adapted to make use of it.

Left: Its small size, sheltered position and nutrient-rich waters enable a multitude of plants and animals to thrive in this pond.

LIFE IN UPLAND LAKES

Not all lakes support the same amount and variety of plants and animals. The key lies in the plant nutrients which are washed into the lakes from the surrounding countryside.

Lakes contain many varied habitats, with a great variety of different features. Some of these are common to all freshwater lakes in Britain, but others are unique to either upland or lowland lakes. Deeper lakes, particularly those in upland Britain, tend to have a more complex and interesting structure. One definition of a lake is a large natural expanse of open water exposed to the full force of the wind – which means that waves break over its exposed shores. Normally the upland lakes are too deep, over most of their area, to permit light to penetrate and enable rooted plants to grow on the bottom.

Lake nutrients Every gardener knows that good crops can be grown only if the land is well-fertilised to provide nitrates, phosphorus, carbonates and other chemicals needed for plant growth. In a lake the plants need the same substances and, in addition to those already there, more are brought in by the waters entering the lake. It is not, however, the large plants that are important in the natural history of a lake but the immense quantities of microscopic plants that float freely in the upper water. These are the primary producers, and on them the food webs of the lake mainly depend.

Lakes in regions of hard (for example, volcanic) rocks, which provide few nutrients, receive poor supplies of these essential substances in the waters flowing into them, and are unproductive of plants and animals. The bottom of these lakes remains stony or rocky.

In areas where the rocks are softer, this often shows in the gentler contours of the country and the presence of good farming land. The drainage waters reaching the lakes are rich in dissolved substances, and also carry particles of soil and other undissolved matter which together are known as silt. The silt sinks to the bottom, and in time provides further nutrients. Such lakes are productive of plants and animals.

Examples of productive lakes are Esthwaite Water and Windermere in the Lake District. Ennerdale, Wastwater and Buttermere are typically unproductive lakes.

Windermere was not always as productive

as it is now, and has changed comparatively recently. Scientists examining samples of mud from the bottom of the lake find that two single-celled plant species, *Asterionella* and *Fragilaria*, indicative of a productive lake, have been present in the lake for only 150 years or so. The cause of the change must have been the great increase in nutrients reaching the lake as the population of the area increased. There are plenty of plant nutrients in sewage, and it may be that modern farming has made the land yield more nutrients into the streams that pass over it.

Windswept margins Even on a productive lake it is not always easy to see a good example of a lake-edge (littoral) community. The shallow water at the edge of a lake that is not sheltered from the wind is a difficult habitat for living things. The chief problem is the backwards and forwards motion of the water created by wave action; it is even more difficult to cope with than the steady flow in one direction of water in a stream. Stones are constantly dislodged and silt is prevented from accumulating, so rooted plants cannot gain a foothold.

Nevertheless, in these inhospitable places the stones become covered with microscopic algae, especially diatoms, and mosses can become established. The diatoms provide food for small animals, and the mosses afford them shelter.

The lake limpet is one animal well-adapted

Above: Surrounded by grazing land and forestry, Loch of the Lowes in Scotland is a productive lake.

Opposite page: Wastwater in the Lake District, whipped to a flurry by the wind. It supports little wildlife.

Lake formation
Most of Britain's upland lakes are glacial in origin. The great sheets of ice during successive ice ages dug out valleys and deposited rock and rubble at the lower end, forming a natural dam.
Lowland lakes such as Loch Leven were created when a melting sheet of ice left a shallow depression.
Loch Ness is an altogether different case. Rock faults running across the whole width of Scotland created its deep basin.
Lough Neagh in Northern Ireland was formed as the result of sagging. A large mass of volcanic lava subsided and created a hollow, which filled with water.

to the turmoil of a wave-swept shore. The broad sole of its foot acts as an efficient sucker to resist being dislodged by the movement of the water. The edges of its shell are soft, and fit into the irregularities of the stones on which it browses, eating diatoms and other algae. The little wandering snail, one of the most widely distributed molluscs in fresh water, is also equipped with a sucker-like foot that it uses to defy the movement of the water.

Other animals of this wave-swept habitat are flatworms, small leeches that can grip with powerful suckers at both ends of their bodies, freshwater shrimps and the larvae of a caddis fly, *Agapetus*, which fix their stone cases to larger stones.

In deeper water where wave action is less pronounced, dense growths of shoreweed and quillwort carpet the bottom and in deeper water there may be stoneworts such as *Nitella*.

Sheltered shores On shores sheltered from the full force of the wind, communities of plants similar to those that form in a small shallow pond may become established, with submerged species such as water milfoil and Canadian pondweed, floating-leaved plants such as the yellow or white water-lilies, swamp plants including the common reed and finally marsh plants such as marsh marigold and yellow flag. The plants provide shelter for a range of small creatures: pond skaters, water bugs and beetles, and nymphs of dragonflies will be seen.

Open water When scientists study the open water community of a lake, they naturally have to row out to reach it. Since most of the plants and animals are extremely small, a plankton net is used. This is made of a fine-meshed material, and at its tip it holds a collecting vessel. When it is trailed through the water behind a boat this net will collect a 'broth' of living organisms which are channelled into the vessel. The organisms are then transferred into jars and dishes to be examined under the microscope.

The tiny floating organisms are called plankton; the plants (phytoplankton) include various kinds of algae, mainly diatoms. The small animals (zooplankton) include rotifers and crustaceans. The commonest of the tiny crustaceans are water-fleas such as *Daphnia* and copepods such as *Cyclops* and *Diaptomus*. Some of the lake fish, including charr, feed on these planktonic animals.

The fish represent the other end of the scale in the open water community. In productive lakes these are usually coarse fish such as roach, perch and pike. In unproductive lakes the game fish such as trout and charr are more characteristic. But if an unproductive lake is made richer by nutrients from man's activities, conditions become suitable for coarse fish.

Seasonal variation In the early part of the year productive lakes are rich in nutrients which have been washed in by winter rains. The first spring sunshine leads to rapid

Above: An *Aeshna* dragonfly nymph, whose prey-catching mask is clearly seen from below. These carnivores are found among the plants in the quieter waters on sheltered lake shores.

Left: The unsheltered lake shore is constantly disturbed by waves. Some animals hold fast to a fixed object by suction. The creature crawling on this sunken leaf skeleton is a freshwater flatworm.

Right: A magnified view of the plant plankton typical of a productive lake. This sample was taken from Windermere. Where these microscopic plants are plentiful, animal life on a similar scale thrives.

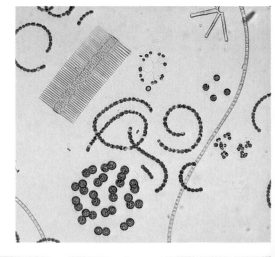

Below: The common eel is one of the larger lake dwellers. It is a coarse fish, but unlike others in this group it is less confined to productive lakes and can adapt to various habitats.

Above: However productive a lake's water may be, a mature lakeside community including a succession of large plants cannot develop without truly sheltered conditions, away from the violence of the wind and waves.

populations of algae in even large lakes such as Windermere.

The lake bottom In time, all living things die and drop to the bottom of the lake where decomposition – largely the work of bacteria and fungi – gradually converts the remains into simple chemicals that become once again the nutrients for further plant life.

The water of a deep lake is arranged in a three-layered structure. In the middle is the thermocline, a layer of still water which prevents movement from the lower to the upper levels. Its main ecological effect is to limit the movement of lake-bottom nutrients up to the layer where plants can use them. This explains why even large lakes do not support as abundant a plankton as might be expected from such a large body of water.

In spite of the inhospitable nature of those remote, cold depths, a few animals can live in the bottom mud of a deep lake. Oxygen is scarce but food, in the form of decomposing material, is abundant. Sludge worms have the same blood pigment as we have – haemoglobin, which enables them to make do with quite small supplies of oxygen. The worm-like larvae of some midges of the chironomid family are called bloodworms because they have the same red pigment in their bodies. They lie in the bottom mud or sometimes – if oxygen supplies grow unusually scarce – float up to join the creatures of the upper lake community.

growth of the plants, and consequently of the animals that feed on them. Some of the algae reach the point where they have used up certain essential nutrients. Silicates, for example, are present in only small quantities in lake water. Other algae are consumed by the small crustaceans, and are also liable to attack by minute fungi. Others fall victim to single-celled animal parasites called Proteomyxa, whose attacks can cut down the

Layers of a deep lake

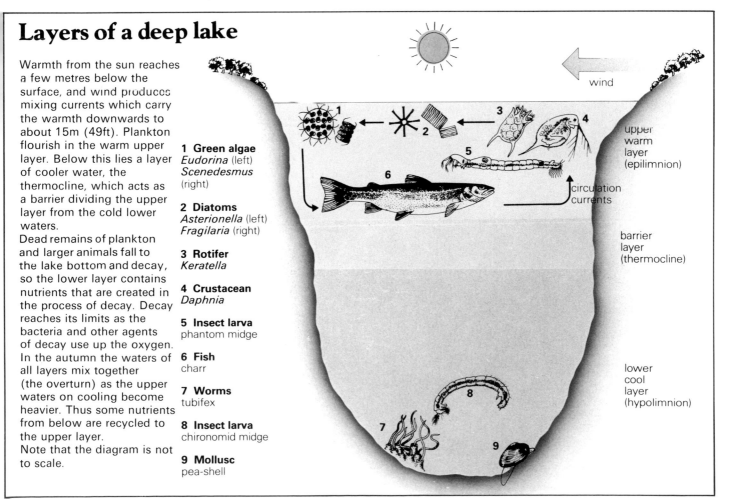

Warmth from the sun reaches a few metres below the surface, and wind produces mixing currents which carry the warmth downwards to about 15m (49ft). Plankton flourish in the warm upper layer. Below this lies a layer of cooler water, the thermocline, which acts as a barrier dividing the upper layer from the cold lower waters.

Dead remains of plankton and larger animals fall to the lake bottom and decay, so the lower layer contains nutrients that are created in the process of decay. Decay reaches its limits as the bacteria and other agents of decay use up the oxygen. In the autumn the waters of all layers mix together (the overturn) as the upper waters on cooling become heavier. Thus some nutrients from below are recycled to the upper layer.
Note that the diagram is not to scale.

1 Green algae
Eudorina (left)
Scenedesmus (right)

2 Diatoms
Asterionella (left)
Fragilaria (right)

3 Rotifer
Keratella

4 Crustacean
Daphnia

5 Insect larva
phantom midge

6 Fish
charr

7 Worms
tubifex

8 Insect larva
chironomid midge

9 Mollusc
pea-shell

wind

upper warm layer (epilimnion)

circulation currents

barrier layer (thermocline)

lower cool layer (hypolimnion)

THE RICH LIFE OF LOWLAND LAKES

Lowland lakes–such as those in Shropshire and Cheshire–differ markedly from those of the Lake District in being nutrient-rich and therefore very productive. Algae in abundance are characteristic of lowland meres and proliferate in early summer.

Below: A mass of yellow flag irises growing along the margins of a small lake. Most lowland lakes have muddy bottoms and are surrounded by soil (rather than by rock); consequently yellow flag and other emergent species, such as reedmace and bulrush, flourish along the edges.

Lakes have been formed in a variety of ways, but what interests the naturalist is the shape of the resulting basin and its location. The Cheshire-Shropshire plain once lay under a sheet of ice that brought with it soil and boulders scraped from the land as it advanced. When the ice melted it left behind hollows that filled with water, thus forming the meres that still exist today. Many–Crose Mere is one–are typical lowland lakes. They are

shallow, for the ice did not excavate deeply, and are not much longer than they are broad. They lie in small drainage areas in a thick layer of soil, now fertile agricultural land, and consequently rain reaches them mainly by seepage, bringing a rich supply of nutrients.

When the rain is heavy in these areas it does not come as a flood, diluting the lake and its inhabitants. This contrasts with the Lake District, where the ice, concentrated by the valleys, gouged long, deep, narrow trenches lying in large rocky drainage areas. Rain dissolves little from the thin superficial soil and, when heavy, may enter the resulting lakes in such volume that a significant portion of the open water inhabitants are carried through to the outflow.

Similar lakes or meres have been formed in other ways, such as by damming, subsidence or human excavation. One example of the latter is the Norfolk Broads–created by digging for peat in medieval times.

Marginal zones versus open water Parts of the margin of a mere may be so exposed that waves erode the bottom and remove all but stones, but most mere edges are, in fact, covered by soil in which grow emergent

plants—reed, clubrush, bulrush, yellow flag and others. Beyond them there is a zone of water-lilies and, in deeper water, various pondweeds and other submerged plants which, however, do not extend far as there is insufficient light. Large numbers of a variety of animal species find food and shelter among this vegetation.

In the open water there is a good supply of such nutrients as nitrates and phosphates, and the production of living matter is prolific. Plant activity is limited to the surface layers because the sun's rays do not penetrate far, even into pure water; and when many organisms crowd the surface, the sun's rays hardly penetrate at all.

There is no anchorage for plants in open water and no plant can keep its place from year to year, as does a reed at the lake edge, for example, with its roots in the mud ready to put forth new shoots in the spring before any competitor starting from seed can take its place. Furthermore, there is no cover to provide shelter for animals from predators, whose activities can be countered only by rapid reproduction.

Only small plants and animals, therefore, can inhabit the open water environment. The plants here are all algae, small to minute in size, often consisting of a single cell, and capable of reproducing by simple division. Among these algae there is a seasonal succession throughout the year, different species attaining great abundance by rapid, often asexual, reproduction and then declining to survive in small numbers or in a resting stage.

Seasonal changes in a mere The changing conditions, favouring first one species and then another, are produced by sun and wind and by the activities of the organisms themselves. The seasonal cycle of the mere begins when the sun warms the upper layers of the water, producing in still weather a sharp gradient, for water warmer than 4°C (39°F) floats on top of colder water. Wind mixes the layers and also sets up vertical turbulence, but after a time a body of warmer water several metres deep is created and remains separate from a lower, colder layer all through the summer. This occurs in all the deeper meres.

The copious production of living matter in the upper layers leads to a rain of dead and dying organisms falling to the bottom. Bottom-dwelling animals and bacteria exploit this food supply. They use oxygen in the process and, if the volume of the lower layer is relatively small, they may deplete it of oxygen, in which state it remains until the water layers mix in the autumn. Lakes where this occurs are termed 'eutrophic'.

Algae and algal bloom The first algae to start rapid reproduction as the sun gains strength in spring belong to a group known as diatoms; they are characterised by a shell made of silica and a lack of swimming organs. The turbulence of the water keeps them in the light but, during a calm, still spell, they may

Above: Algal bloom on Crose Mere in Shropshire. The appearance of blue-green algae in the form of scum on the surface of the lake is called 'the breaking of the meres' and occurs regularly as the community ages.

Right: The larva of the alderfly *Sialis lutaria*—one of many carnivores found in lowland meres.

Below: A water flea with eggs in its brood pouch. Creatures of this type belong to the zooplankton—the animals floating in the open water of lakes.

ink, bringing their activity to an end. If the weather remains windy, however, they may exhaust the supply of silica for making their shells, after which only a small population survives until conditions are favourable again.

Their place is taken by quite different groups of algae which, provided with small lashing organs for movement, can devote some of the available energy not to reproduction but to moving through the water in search of favourable conditions. By this time a short windless spell can result in a dense algal population near the surface, with consequent shallow penetration of the sun's rays and depletion of nutrients. Therefore, the ability to move between lower zones, where nutrients are still to be found, and upper ones in the sunlight, is a great advantage. The proliferation of algae is followed by a proliferation of animals which feed on them – a further factor altering the composition of the community.

Blue-green algae, typical of productive lakes in late summer, can regulate their buoyancy by means of gas vacuoles – probably a more economical way of moving up and down than swimming. As the population ages, the control of gas formation breaks down; too much is produced and the algae come to the surface to form a green scum, a familiar phenomenon known as the 'breaking of the meres' or 'algal bloom'. The scum eventually drifts ashore and decomposes.

Animals of open water The zooplankton (the animals floating in the open water) is composed mainly of small crustaceans such as water-fleas, and rotifers or wheel-animalcules. Many increase rapidly in numbers by asexual reproduction when conditions are favourable which, for most, is, when small algae and bacteria are abundant.

The first flush of herbivorous species is followed by an outburst of carnivores. One such is the phantom larva *Chaoborus*, which gives rise to a fly related to the mosquito. It is the only planktonic insect and is transparent except for two gas-filled bladders whereby, without too great an expenditure of energy, it can seek refuge in the mud by day and rise to seek its prey by night.

Fauna of the mud The mud that covers much of the bottom of a lake provides both cover and food for animals that are adapted to burrow into it. These specialists comprise the nymphs of the mayflies *Ephemera* and *Caenis*, larvae of the alderfly *Sialis* and the larvae of chironomids, pea mussels and worms. Only the last three groups are found in the deep region, where oxygen is scarce in summer.

Chironomids, of which there are some 400 British species, occur in every type of aquatic environment and, in productive waters, give rise to enormous numbers of adult non-biting midges.

Fauna of the vegetation In the vegetation animals are abundant; many species feed on each other, on algae attached to the surfaces

of plants, or on decaying vegetation. Beetles and some bugs, aquatic throughout life, are active hunters, and leeches too catch prey. Flatworms lay down a sticky mucous trail in which prey becomes entangled. Dragonfly nymphs and both stages of some bugs (the water scorpion *Nepa*, for example) lie in wait for their prey and seize anything which comes in reach.

The larger crustaceans, such as the freshwater shrimp *Gammarus* and the hoglouse *Asellus*, feed predominantly on detritus and plants, although *Gammarus* is occasionally seen with living prey in its claws.

Fishes and birds Among the fishes, which can range through the open water of lakes, and penetrate the vegetation where it is not too thick, are perch, pike, carp, roach and eels. Trout are recorded from a few meres.

The meres are noted as haunts of the Canada goose and the great crested grebe, as well as for the various species that frequent reedbeds – the reed bunting, for example. Many kinds of duck, together with the coot and moorhen, can also be seen on the meres.

Above: *Sympetrum flaveolum*, a particularly striking dragonfly, is a frequent migrant from the Continent and favours meres with rushy margins, mainly those in the southern counties.

Opposite page: The lowland lake at Castor Hanglands, near Peterborough, fringed with lush vegetation on all sides.

Below: Pike usually stay close to the banks of meres where weeds are dense, but may stray into deeper water in large lakes. From an early age they feed on other fishes and also prey on waterfowl, small aquatic mammals and even each other. They can grow up to 1.3m (4ft) long.

TURLOUGHS: IRELAND'S DRY LAKES

Turloughs–found in Ireland– are grassy depressions in porous limestone rock where underground water periodically wells up into temporary lakes.

Turloughs are so named for their dramatic habit of 'disappearing': the word is derived from the Irish *tuar loc*, meaning 'dry lake'. This apparent contradiction is scientifically explained by a combination of hydrological and geological factors–a permeable limestone rock, fluctuating water tables and hence fluctuating water levels on the surface. The rise and fall of the water and the duration and frequency of the flooding in turloughs all depend on the peculiar drainage patterns of these limestone regions.

Reported nowhere else in the world in this form, turloughs are most abundant in the limestone pavements of north County Clare and eastern County Galway–the area known

as the Burren. Here, the bare grey rock, with few trees and little surface water, looks like a lunar landscape, apparently devoid of life. But this area is internationally famous and a treasure house for the botanist who can find, within a relatively small area, a rare combination of Arctic, Alpine and Mediterranean plant species.

Types of turlough These 'dry' lakes may be small or large, shallow or deep. They vary from saucer-like depressions in the ground, measuring only a few feet across, to large basins extending over several hundred acres of land. Rahasane Turlough is one of the largest, located between the towns of Kilcogan and Craughwell in eastern Galway. It is a great

Above: A turlough near Gort in County Galway, showing plant zonation from the submerged pondweeds (*Potamogeton* and *Elodea*) to emergent water plantain (*Alisma*). Notice how shallow the water is. In high summer (if there is no rain) it may well dry up altogether.

Below: Brent geese are among the wildfowl species that come to graze in winter on the grass of a dried-up turlough.

flat-bottomed basin, 3.2km (2 miles) long and just under a kilometre (half a mile) wide, with a depth of some 1.5m (5ft). (Some turloughs may be 9m (30ft) deep.)

The impressive Carran Depression, in the heart of the Burren, is another variation. This 60m (200ft) deep valley, with the village of Carran perched above the steep limestone cliffs, is of great interest to geologists and geographers alike. It is probably caused by collapse of a subterranean cave, deepened by further solution and erosion of the carbonate rock by acidic waters.

During the winter months of November to April turloughs are filled with water, fed through the subterranean passages which honeycomb the limestone rock beneath. During the summer months the turloughs empty through the same passages–often quite dramatically within a few days–and assume the appearance of grassy depressions in the surface. This periodic fluctuation in water level is not necessarily a seasonal one but rather related to rainfall patterns; as any visitor to Ireland will know, downpours are not at all uncommon during the summer months.

Some turloughs never dry out and hold a permanent, though shallow, lake throughout the year. Others may have a spring in the floor from which a stream of water flows, only to disappear a few feet further on into a swallow hole–a kind of in/out system. The Castletown River flows through the Carran Depression and provides a dramatic example of such a disappearing trick: the river rises in a group of springs at the northern end of the valley, flows on through and then plunges into a swallow hole at the southern end. The bottom of this valley contains several small turloughs, some permanently filled with water. During wet weather, much of the floor is flooded, often to 1.5m (5ft) deep.

Another interesting variation is Caherglas-saun Lough, near Kinvara in eastern Galway. This turlough remains filled with water during summer and the water level can actually be seen to rise and fall by a few feet or so over a period of several hours. A network of underground passageways connects this tur-lough to the sea at Galway Bay, some 6.4km (4 miles) away, and the twice-daily fluctuation in water level at Caherglassaun is due to tidal influence. The water in the turlough is not, however, salty to the taste, so the seawater is obviously much diluted during its passage through the rock.

Grazing and soils The periodic flooding of the turlough basin and the thin limy deposits left behind promote the development of a rich grassy sward much favoured by local grazing animals, from cattle and sheep to rabbits and hares. During the summer Rahasane Tur-lough is alive with grazing animals–hundreds of horses, cattle and sheep, owned by local farmers and breeders, eat their way down to the last blade of grass. Due to this intensive

Right: Besides the Burren, turloughs are also found wherever limestone rock outcrops on the surface or is covered by a thin layer of soil or vegetation. Thus, turloughs are found scattered throughout western Ireland, in parts of Mayo, Limerick, Roscommon and Donegal. They are also found, though less concentrated, in eastern counties, such as County Meath. Since the central plains of Ireland are underlaid by limestone but covered by a generous layer of peat bog, turloughs are rarely seen here, but a few may exist.

All karst or limestone regions of the world probably have similar features. For example, the tarn lakes of the Ingleborough area in Yorkshire are superficially akin to turloughs, as are the poljes of Yugoslavia. But the exact hydrological conditions, especially the drainage patterns, characteristic of turloughs have only been described in Ireland to date.

Centre right: A brown hare–one of the many animals that graze the turlough grass down to bare soil.

Below: The 'turlough' violet (*Viola stagnina*) covers the slopes of many of the dry lakes in early summer with its pale blue flowers.

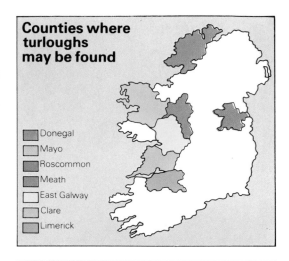

Counties where turloughs may be found

- Donegal
- Mayo
- Roscommon
- Meath
- East Galway
- Clare
- Limerick

ated with turloughs and which are rarely found elsewhere. The critical factors for life in these ephemeral lakes are, of course, the alternate periods of flooding and drying-out and the adaptability to survive under such stresses. Even within a dry period, local variations in the water table may cause a turlough to flood again suddenly and such temporary changes have to be coped with.

From the botanist's point of view, the slopes of a turlough provide a fascinating zonation of plant life. The zones are usually quite distinct, with one type of plant ending abruptly and another taking over.

On the upper slopes of the turlough a few small scrubby trees manage to grow in the shallow soils. The most common are hawthorn, blackthorn and purging blackthorn, sometimes accompanied by ash. Willows and alders, common elsewhere, never grow here. There is some evidence to suggest that there would be more trees were it not for the intense grazing of the turloughs during the year. The dewberry, a relative of the blackberry and with equally edible fruits, is also a common plant associated with turloughs at this level. During winter flooding, the trunks and roots of the trees may be submerged for months at a time.

Below the tree zone, in the middle reaches of the turlough's slopes, carnation sedge and autumn hawkbit are common. The so-called turlough violet (*Viola stagnina*)—the fen violet

Above: A golden plover may come to feed on the insects found in turloughs.

Left: Blackthorn in bloom –this species grows on the upper slopes of turloughs.

Below: A turlough shrinking rapidly–the boulders in the foreground (now high and dry) are submerged in winter and covered with the aquatic moss *Fontinalis*. Any animals and plants in the turloughs must be able to withstand this dramatic change from wet to dry.

grazing, the vegetation of turloughs is nearly always stunted and dwarfed.

Except for isolated pockets, turlough soils are usually thin and poorly developed. They lie either directly on the bedrock or above sediments of varying thickness. These sediments consist of glacial drifts and, below this, typical lake deposits such as marls and silts. Marls are fine limestone, white in colour; on sunny days a soft pearly lightness is imparted to the waters of certain turloughs with marly bottoms. Since water drains away freeely through marls, the soils of such turloughs retain little water and dry out easily. The floor of a turlough may be covered with grassy vegetation or with muddy rocks, which often indicate the position of the turlough's swallow hole. Sometimes, the soil in the very bottom of a turlough remains waterlogged in summer and this has allowed peat to develop over the centuries.

The plant zones Although they do not have a unique flora and fauna, there are a few species of plants and animals closely associ-

of England—is locally abundant. Another violet species, the heath dog violet (*V. canina*), also grows in this zone and where the two species occur together, hybrid violets have developed in great abundance.

Silverweed abounds further down the slopes, and when the turlough dries out this plant, together with creeping bent grass, may cover the entire bottom of the basin. In wetter soils or turloughs which hold a permanent lake, typical aquatic species are present—floating sweet grass, floating fox tail, fool's watercress, shoreweed and amphibious bistort. Other typical marsh plants are also found—pondweed, water crowfoot, large sedges and marsh marigolds. One of the striking features of turlough flora is the abundance of such typical grassland species as creeping buttercup, silverweed and bent grass in situations where these plants are inundated for half the year and yet can withstand drought at other times.

A black moss, called *Cinclodotus fontinaloides*, is another species closely associated with turloughs. In fact, the site of a turlough can often be spotted from a distance by the presence of this black moss growing in a roughly circular pattern around the rim of the basin. It is a most adaptable moss, growing on the tops of the grey limestone boulders almost throughout the depth of the turlough. Those patches lying out of water simply dry up and wait. Another moss, the water moss *Fontinalis antipyretica*, also features in turloughs; it is less tolerant of drying out and forms green patches on the sides of submerged boulders and on the damp floors.

Animal life To the casual observer, turloughs may appear devoid of animal life, with little to be seen in their clear waters. Animal life in these basins depends on many factors, such as the state of the turlough at a particular time of year, the frequency of flooding, the nature of the bottom sediment, the size of the basin and its surroundings. Obviously, the alternate flood and drought conditions in a turlough affect the animal life as much as the plants, suiting neither aquatic nor dry-land species unless they are fast breeders and can complete their life-cycle in a few months. Fish and water snails thus tend to be absent.

However, the numbers of aquatic animals make up for their lack of variety. Large populations of water fleas and related small crustaceans abound in the water, feeding on decomposing faeces (provided by the summer grazers) and decaying plant remains. Winged adult insects, such as water bugs and water beetles, fly to the turlough and feed on the microscopic planktonic life or prey on the crustaceans. Dragonflies and mayflies hover over the water and their nymphs develop to adulthood there. One opportunistic dry-land animal, typical of turloughs, is the ground beetle, a small and active carnivore. It hibernates in winter above the turlough and becomes active in spring when the receding

Water tables

DRY TURLOUGH

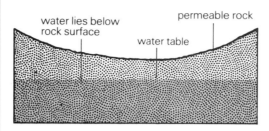

water lies below rock surface

permeable rock

water table

WET TURLOUGH

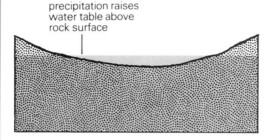

precipitation raises water table above rock surface

PERCHED WATER TABLE

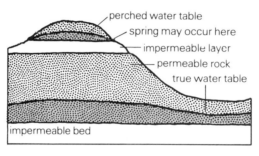

perched water table
spring may occur here
impermeable layer
permeable rock
true water table
impermeable bed

SPRINGS

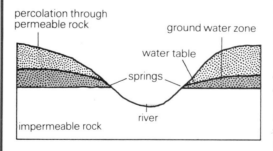

percolation through permeable rock
ground water zone
water table
springs
river
impermeable rock

ARTESIAN BASIN

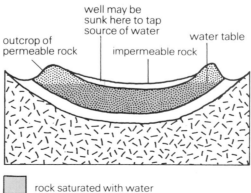

well may be sunk here to tap source of water
outcrop of permeable rock
water table
impermeable rock

rock saturated with water

Water enters the land as precipitation in the form of rain or snow, then seeps downwards through pores in the rocks until it is halted by a layer of impermeable rock. Since it cannot drain down any further, it accumulates above the impermeable layer. The upper surface of this zone of water saturation is called the water table and it may vary from place to place and from season to season.

In the case of the **Irish turlough** the water table lies below the surface of the permeable limestone rock in dry seasons, but rises above the ground surface in wet seasons to form shallow lakes—the turloughs. In localities where there are alternating permeable and impermeable rock layers (for example the Cotswolds), the impermeable beds may form their own water tables, which lie high above the main water table of the region—they are therefore known as **perched water tables**. The occurrence of springs is also related to the position of the water table, and to the shape of the land surface and the character and relationship of the rocks. For instance, in some places a permeable rock is underlaid by an impermeable one, such as clay or shale. Under these conditions ground water in the permeable rock may be forced to emerge as **springs** above the impermeable layer. A more complex system still is that of an **artesian basin**, in which water accumulates and is trapped under pressure between layers of impermeable rock. When permeable rocks outcrop at the surface, water can percolate downwards and become absorbed in the rock strata deep down. If the permeable stratum is sandwiched between two impermeable layers, then the water is trapped and can be tapped by man.

waters leave small crustaceans stranded at the edge and prey to the ground beetle.

The swallow hole is a favourite place for some animals to survive periods of drought in a turlough. Black flatworms, water lice and shrimps may live here; competition for space and food must be extreme in these narrow crevices, which effectively form summer prisons for these animals. When there is a permanent lake present or a river connection to the turlough, sticklebacks are found, living and breeding there all year round.

One animal which has been found only in turloughs is the fairy shrimp *Tanymastix*. Nearly 2.5cm (1in) long, this animal is the largest of the invertebrate fauna and spends its whole life-cycle in the turlough. During dry periods the drought-resistant eggs lie buried in the soil. As soon as the turlough floods, the eggs hatch, releasing tiny shrimps which swim up into the water and become fully grown within two months. The adults die when the waters recede, but first they produce thousands of eggs which will not hatch until they have gone through a period of desiccation, thus ensuring the survival of the species for another generation.

Threats to turlough survival In recent years, due to programmes of draining and reclamation, many turloughs have been destroyed. In fact, Rahasane is the only surviving large turlough in the country and is itself under threat. It has long been a major feeding ground for wildfowl wintering in Ireland, especially the Greenland white-fronted goose. Thousands flock here in winter to feed on the rich grassy vegetation and hence Rahasane is recognised as a site of international importance for environmental conservation.

The pace of damage has slowed partly due to doubts about the value to agriculture of arterial drainage, but turloughs will remain threatened until they get official protection.

Above: Burren limestone with a marl-bottomed, pale pearly blue turlough in the distance. (Marl is a fine white limestone.) Water drains freely through marls so such lakes are often dry.

Below: Amphibious bistort –a typical turlough plant.

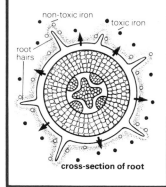

non-toxic iron

toxic iron

root hairs

cross-section of root

Left: A man-made dyke in Woodwalton Fen, East Anglia. This fen is one of the few that have been rescued from the plough and is now in the care of the Nature Conservancy Council who preserve it as a nature reserve. Being surrounded by intensively drained fields Woodwalton Fen is no longer flooded naturally, thereby maintaining the fen conditions. Instead the NCC has installed a water pumping system with which it can periodically flood the fen artificially.

FENS OF LAKE AND FLOOD PLAIN

'The land was either a gloomy waste of waters, or still more a hideous expanse of reeds.' Such was the view once held of fens. Today, with most of our fenlands gone, people are at last beginning to appreciate their wild beauty.

The dismal picture painted by the quote above concerned the Somerset Levels—an area which was once one of the finest expanses of fenland in the country. It was made by a 19th century historian and serves merely to demonstrate the complete lack of appreciation for fenlands that used to exist in the minds of most people.

Right: In Britain the swallowtail butterfly can be seen only in fenland—and even there it is scarce. This swallowtail has just emerged from its chrysalis, which you can see on the right.

Those who lived there, however, and who depended on the fens for their livelihoods, took quite a different view. As an old fensman once said, 'Any fool can appreciate a mountain but it takes a man of real discernment to appreciate the landscape of the fens.'

Fens generally represent a transitional phase in the development of wetlands and are in a constant state of change. The evidence for their transitional nature can be seen in their failure to 'balance the books'. Consider, by contrast, tropical rain-forest. This habitat has, in terms of growth, an extremely high productivity but this entire production of organic material is balanced by the huge army of decomposers in the forest, and the system as a whole remains stable, books perfectly balanced. In a fen, however, productivity far outstrips decomposition because the most efficient decomposers cannot survive in the waterlogged conditions. Partly decomposed material slowly accumulates as fen peat, the increasing depth of which finally brings about changes in the very fen vegetation that produces the peat. Ultimately the fen, doomed by its own inability to balance the books, may be replaced by other habitats more suited to the new conditions.

Water is the life-blood of a fen because it is the high water levels at the start of the growing season—a critical and sensitive time for most plant species—that inhibit potential competitors and give the fen species a head start.

Above: Beds of common reed are a characteristic feature of any fen. In the days when fenland was harvested on a large scale reed, along with various sedges, was the main crop gathered.

Below: Parts of the Somerset Levels and the East Anglian Fens have been given over to the cultivation of osiers for the wickerwork basket industry. Osiers, which are a type of willow, are well suited to the damp fenland conditions.

There are two ways in which high spring levels of water can arise, and each produces its own characteristic type of fen–lake fen and flood plain fen.

Lake fen No picture of a lake or pond is complete without a fringe of reeds, whether the wispy screen of common reed or the solid wall of bulrush. This is the simplest form of lake fen, also called open-water transition fen because it dominates the transition zone between open water and dry land. This type of fen is largely restricted to static water; some of the best examples are found in the Norfolk Broads.

The various zones of vegetation surrounding many of the Broads reflect different stages

Two fen formations

A lake fen, also known as open-water transition fen, typically occurs on the edge of a lake, between the open water and dry land. Such a fen shows a distinct succession of different species, from the most water-tolerant ones (bulrush, clubrush, reed and sedge) actually in the water, through plants needing successively drier conditions such as sallow and alder, to oaks which can only grow in soil that is not too wet.

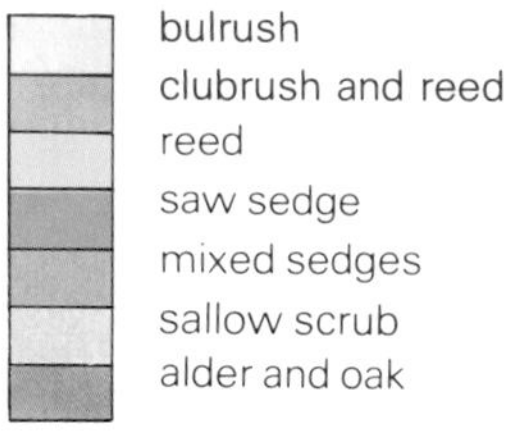

bulrush
clubrush and reed
reed
saw sedge
mixed sedges
sallow scrub
alder and oak

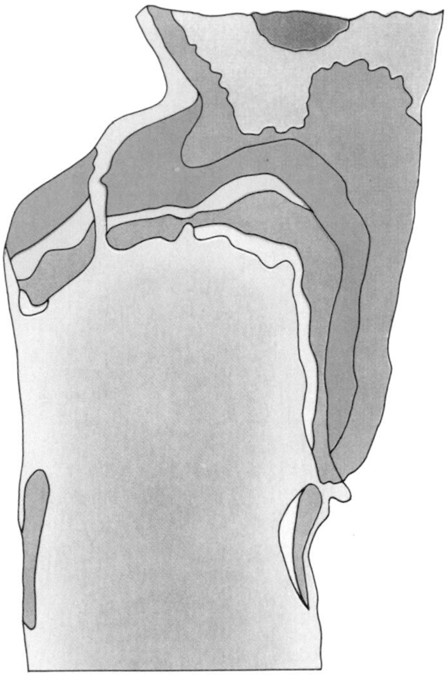

cross-section

plan view

LAKE FEN

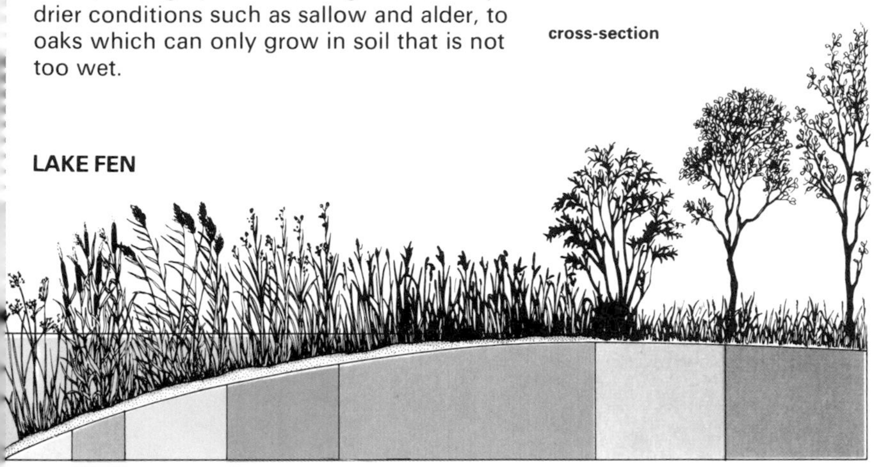

FLOOD PLAIN FEN

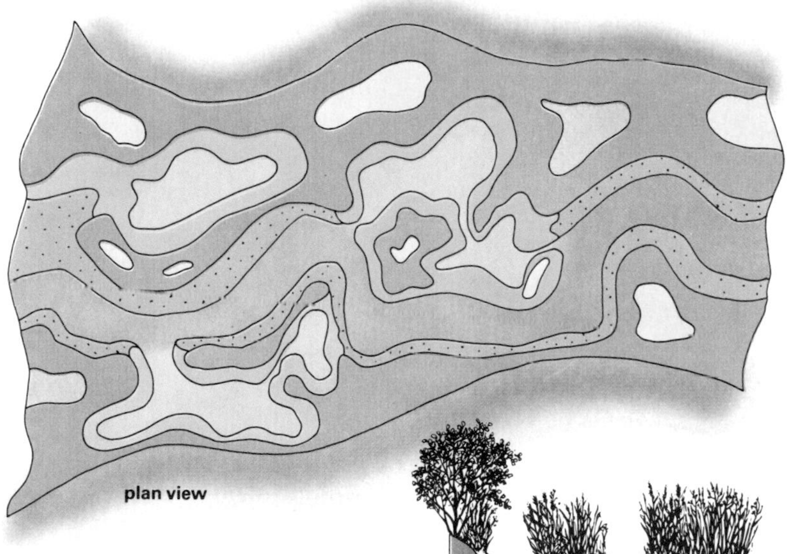

plan view

cross-section

A flood plain fen, or river fen, is formed when a river in its lower reaches opens out into a wide, gently sloping valley—the flood plain. Such a river is prone to flooding (and therefore to the formation of a fen) both from surges of water further upstream and from high tide at sea blocking the river flow and forcing it back upon itself. The succession of species in a flood plain fen is similar to that in a lake fen.

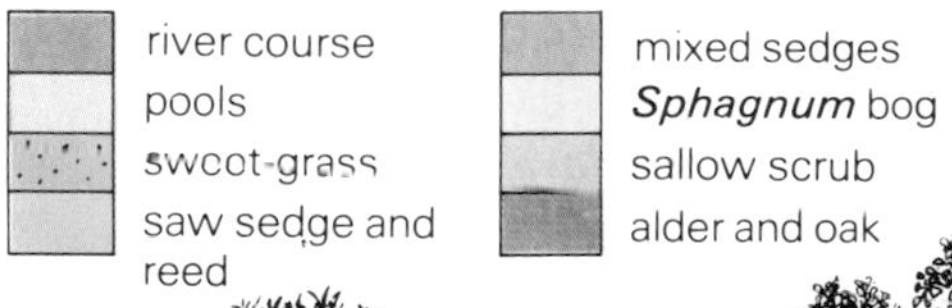

river course
pools
sweet-grass
saw sedge and reed

mixed sedges
Sphagnum bog
sallow scrub
alder and oak

in the accumulation of fen material, clearly demonstrating the effect of this accumulation on the species found there. The first colonizers are common reed and clubrush. In the Broads, and in southern Britain generally, these plants may be accompanied by lesser bulrush while in northern Britain water horsetail may form its own pioneer zone. The resulting mat of stems, roots and rhizomes quickly traps organic material, as well as the decaying remains of the year's growth, to form a loose, spongy reedswamp peat.

Into this rapidly stabilising mat come fen species such as hemp agrimony, water mint, greater spearwort, broad-leaved dock and great willow-herb. As the peat builds up on the bottom of the lake it eventually reaches the surface of the water, and plants that cannot tolerate extremes of flooding are then able to establish themselves. Examples include meadowsweet and yellow and purple loose-strifes. Very occasionally, rare species such as marsh pea, large wintergreen and fen sow-thistle may also be found. At this point the peat surface is flooded for part of the year, but it may experience some dry periods, at least during the summer. But, where the water is still quite deep in early spring, saw sedge is likely to form dominant stands, and once saw sedge is established then another factor usually becomes important in controlling the subsequent stages, namely, man.

Above: The two major types of fen have roughly the same succession of vegetation, though it is formed in quite different circumstances. The essential difference between the two is that lake fen occurs in water that is static or moving only very slowly, whereas flood plain fen occurs around moving water.

Man steps in The natural trend after the arrival of saw sedge would be for the vegetation to continue accumulating peat until its level becomes so high that the spring flooding is no longer sufficient to inhibit saw sedge's competitors. Seedlings of sallow and alder would then become established, followed by birch, ash and oak, until a dense woodland canopy closes over a relatively dry mixed-sedge community.

The 'fen tigers', as the inhabitants of the fens were known, were far more interested in the beds of saw sedge and reeds than in woods. So, under a careful regime of flooding and harvesting they deflected the course of natural succession and prevented the woodland from shading out the economically important fen communities. An entire way of life was sustained in this manner, but sadly the reedcutters have now almost vanished, victims of recession in their industry, and the sedge beds are rapidly being colonized by alder and willow carr. After centuries of being held in check by the fens people, the natural succession to broad-leaved woodland may yet triumph.

Flood plain fen The second major type of fen is flood plain fen. As a river approaches the sea it flows out into a wide, gently sloping valley in which it has room to spread itself when necessary. Before man began to interfere, the lower reaches of most large rivers would have had little in the way of a sharply defined water-course with neat banks; instead there would have been a wide expanse of fen and marsh occupying the whole of the valley floor. In wet periods the river would flood the whole valley floor–the flood plain–and even in the dry summer months when the river would be more clearly confined to a main channel this would have been little more than a clear route through the reeds.

Above: The eerie booming of the bittern can still be heard in the Norfolk Broads, but it is much rarer now than it used to be.

Opposite page: The fens are particularly rich in insect life, including such species as this damselfly.

Right: Once the initial colonists—common reed, bulrush and clubrush—have established themselves, other more colourful plants begin to move in. One such is yellow loosestrife, a member of the primrose family also found along river banks as well as in fens.

Below: An important and characteristic component of fen vegetation is saw sedge, named after the sharp teeth along its edges.

Both the Thames and the Severn once had much wider flood plains than they do now, but the most spectacular of all, rivalling even the broad swathes of oak that covered much of Britain at the time, must have been the two areas which we now know as The Fens and the Somerset Levels. Both are immense flat plains which receive water from a considerable catchment area, yet the gradient across the plains to the sea is so shallow that at high tide the river water became ponded, flooding out across the whole area because it had nowhere else to go.

The Fens and the Somerset Levels were the places to see flood plains in their real glory: a maze of river channels spilling water through the reed-beds, eddying round areas of raised bog, and emptying into meres so large that sailors would feel sea-sick on them during storms. Sadly, today all this can be seen only in the mind's eye because The Fens and the Somerset Levels have all but gone, drained and reclaimed for agriculture, leaving four tiny pockets in Cambridgeshire and some

At Woodwalton Fen the combination of water flow and a somewhat acidic peat has resulted in a purple moor-grass community with saw sedge and sweet gale. There is also an extensive area of mixed fen with common reed, purple small-reed, common meadow-rue and wood small-reed. Wicken Fen has a rich sedge 'litter' with yellow and purple loosestrifes, wild angelica and marsh pea.

Animals of the fens Fens are particularly rich in bird life, probably because they provide so much excellent cover among the reeds and sedges and also because the dense floating vegetation limits the amount of human disturbance. Many of our rarer birds are associated with fens: the bittern, marsh and Montagu's harriers and bearded tit.

Mammal life is more restricted, the water vole and otter being the main species, though coypu escaped from fur farms, but now said to be extinct, used to create havoc. Mink, also an escapee, is reputed to be even more of a pest.

The invertebrates more than make up for the lack of mammals. Deep in the peaty substrates are millions of bright red midge larvae, and water beetles, alder flies, moths, dragonflies and butterflies are all typical of these reed swamps, including such rarities as the Norfolk aeshna and scarce darter dragonflies and the swallowtail and large copper butterflies. The last of these was reintroduced at Woodwalton Fen by the NCC.

In changing the very environment upon which they depend, fens may be said to be their own worst enemy. But man, too, has played a part in their destruction, which is sad and ironic because we also have the ability to maintain these areas and save them from their natural fate. A few tiny sites are being saved but what a shame that people are only now learning to see fenland landscapes through the discerning eye of the fenland tiger.

Above: A stand of reeds lining a water-course in Woodwalton Fen.

Left: Purple loosestrife, seen here with two brimstone butterflies feeding on its flowers. Like yellow loosestrife it is a common plant of fenland and other wet sites, such as river banks. The two species are not closely related, although they share the same common name.

Below: The otter—one of the main fenland mammals but decreasing in numbers.

slightly larger remnants in Somerset. Nevertheless, these fragments are enough to give us some indication of the vegetation that once dominated these vast areas.

Fen reserves Two of the Cambridgeshire fens that have been saved are Woodwalton Fen and Wicken Fen but, because both are now surrounded by intensively drained farmland, they no longer benefit from the regular inundation of a flood plain. However, they are supplied by artificial floods, Woodwalton Fen by virtue of a pumping system installed by the Nature Conservancy Council and Wicken Fen because the National Trust is able to flood the site from a drainage channel running through it.

ALDER CARR: A WET WOODLAND

This fine example of alder carr (below) is at Flitwick Moor in Bedfordshire. The scene is dominated by mature alders, on whose trunks climbing honeysuckle can be seen, while here and there the marsh supports tufts of buckler fern and remote-flowered sedge.

Alder flourishes best in wet places, but also occurs in a variety of dry woodland habitats. It can be seen lining the banks of most lowland rivers, or spreading into swampy places. It is easily recognised by its dark green foliage, the round and slightly clubbed shape of the individual leaves, its dark brown bark and the small cones which bear the seeds.

Alder is the only British deciduous tree with cones, which are otherwise present only on conifers. Through the summer, the fertilised female catkins enlarge to form solid oval cones about 13mm ($\frac{1}{2}$in) long. In winter these gradually become woodier and finally open out to release the seeds. Any seed not

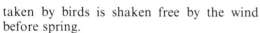

Above: Marsh violet, which is found in the upper parts of alder gullies. In this community you can also find broad buckler fern, wood horsetail, loose-spiked wood sedge, lesser skullcap, yellow archangel and occasionally cyperus sedge.

Left: Cyperus sedge, which can easily be recognised by its yellowish-green colour and the elegantly hanging female spikes.

taken by birds is shaken free by the wind before spring.

Two birds, in particular, have learnt to exploit alder seeds and are largely dependent on them for their survival through the winter. These are the redpoll and the siskin, both finches which, in Europe, breed mainly in the northern forests, but move southwards for the winter.

Alder has evolved to cope with the birds' depredations by producing enormous quantities of seeds. However many are taken, there are always enough left to ensure the survival of the species. The water-resistant seeds float, and rivers and lakes are important agents of dispersal. When the seeds are washed up on shorelines they are eaten by small mammals and birds, particularly wildfowl. From those that are left, where there is not too much competition from other plants, seedlings may grow rapidly to produce new trees.

The vigorous growth of alder is made possible by bacteria contained in small swellings, or nodules, on the roots. These are 'nitrogen fixing' species of bacteria, that have the ability to extract nitrogen directly from the air—something that no higher plant or animal can do. Both bacteria and tree benefit from an exchange of nutrients, and alder obtains a rich supply of nitrogen and the other materials it requires for rapid growth.

Alder carr Alder woodland that has developed by natural succession from marsh-

land is known as alder carr. One of the best places to see it is on the Norfolk Broads, where it covers extensive areas. Pollen records tell us that alder has been present on the Norfolk Broads for thousands of years, but the alder carrs in the floodplains of the meandering rivers are relatively recent.

Broadland carrs have a lush, jungle-like atmosphere—a tangle of differing shades of green, soft black peat underfoot and shimmering hordes of midges dancing in patches of sunlight. Ferns are abundant, particularly the marsh fern, a species now extremely rare outside Broadland, but also buckler ferns and the unmistakable royal fern, which was highly prized and sought after by the Victorians. Climbers, too, are plentiful—most commonly honeysuckle, hedge bindweed, ivy, woody nightshade and wild hops.

Ancient coppice woodland Not far from the Norfolk Broads you can find alder growing in a quite different situation, for it occurs as a component of mixed coppice in a number of ancient woods in Norfolk and Suffolk. Trees that were once coppiced—cut back to stumps to encourage fresh shoots to grow—are easily recognised by their multiple stems. In these sites the distribution of coppice species is likely to be entirely natural. Generations of woodmen took crops of poles from the coppice, without needing either to plant new species or remove trees.

In the old coppice woods in East Anglia,

Formation of alder carr

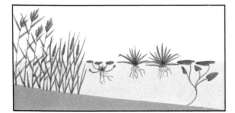  

1 Lake or pond with floating plants such as water soldier, frogbit and duckweed, and rooted plants such as water lilies, becomes choked with **swamp-forming** reeds and bulrush invading from the margins.

2 Invasion of pond causes swamp to form, which becomes filled with decaying plant matter. Habitat thus becomes drier, allowing colonization by marsh-dwelling plants and by **young alder scrub.**

3 Alder competes well with other marshy scrub species, and grows into a mature wood—**alder carr**—on partly or wholly dry ground. Mature alder is now dominant, resisting colonization by other plants.

Below right: The redpoll relies on alder seeds for food in winter.

Below: Sweat Mere, a lake in Shropshire where the margin is invaded by tussock sedges. These develop as massive tufts of vegetation, on which alder seeds germinate. Dead and leaning alders have become too heavy for the tussocks to support. The weight of their trunks has pushed the roots down into the oxygen-starved lower mud, killing the trees.

alder grows with a wide and colourful range of partners—ash, hazel, birch, wych elm, hornbeam, bird cherry and small-leaved lime are all to be found there. Differences in their distribution can usually be attributed to variations in soil or drainage. Alder is generally found growing in the less freely drained and more acid areas.

Tidal alderwood On the other side of England, in Somerset, Devon and Cornwall, alder is not common, except as a riverside tree. It does, however, occur in one particularly striking habitat—tidal alderwood. This was formerly more common but has been almost eliminated from Europe by coast defence works and reclamation of land for grazing. It is best seen today in the estuary of the River Fal in Cornwall. Here you can see a splendid transition from saltmarsh to sallow scrub, then to alder woodland and finally to dry oak-birch woodland. An exceptionally diverse array of plant species grows in this sequence of habitats.

New Forest Alder can be found in countless small valleys and bogs in the New Forest. It would no doubt be more widespread if seedlings and young plants were not continually eaten by livestock, but it is well established in the wetter peaty places, where the grazing animals are wary of treading. Having found a foothold, alder grows rapidly, eventually forming an alder carr. In the wettest places, bog myrtle and sallow are the

only woody species to compete with alder, but on slightly higher ground birch, alder buckthorn, oak, holly and even yew can be found.

Alder carr in Scotland The Mound Alderwoods in Sutherland form the largest expanse of alderwood in the British Isles. Early in the last century a road and rail embankment was constructed across Loch Fleet, cutting an area of saltmarsh off from the sea. Freshwater collected behind the new barrier, and water levels rose. Alder spread rapidly to cover most of the marsh, and natural succession has been allowed to run its course since that time, with virtually no interference from man.

The result has been a large alder swamp with rich vegetation. The populations of birds, mammals and insects are equally rich. Unfortunately it is not at all easy to get into this swampy place to see the fabulous range of wildlife. A few ridges of dry land, clad in Scots pine, lead into the area but it is otherwise impenetrable.

Alder gullies It is common to find alder growing where springs rise in acid soils. A more unusual and interesting habitat is formed when, instead of rising in a spring, the water gradually seeps through the surface because its downward movement is impeded by underlying impermeable clay. This is known as a flushed surface, and sometimes in flushed valleys you can find long-established

woodland, dominated by alder, growing on wet peat. The Weald in Kent has a few such sites, and there is a fine concentration of them in the west of Berkshire. Known as alder gullies, they occur on the edge of elevated land bearing, for the most part, acid gravels of the Reading and Bagshot Beds, overlying London Clay.

A typical gully contains a small stream which has cut a meandering channel through the gravel. The ground on either side is usually wet and peaty, and the water is moderately to highly acid, and low in plant nutrients. Mosses and liverworts are prominent, while the commonest flower is probably the opposite-leaved golden saxifrage; this may be accompanied in small quantities by its close relative, the much rarer alternate leaved species.

Moving down the gully, as the water becomes less acid, you may discover a different range of plants: wavy bitter-cress, redcurrant, wild hops, alder buckthorn, wood speedwell and wood sorrel. The lowest parts of the gullies, where they have not been drained, may contain giant horsetail, tussock sedge, water mint, hemlock water dropwort and, in one or two sites, the rare wood club rush.

Animals in alderwoods A multitude of insect species feed on alder foliage, including the caterpillars of over 40 moths, two of which even derive their name from their foodplant— the alder moth and alder kitten. The caterpillars, and other insects such as leafhoppers, weevils, sawflies and aphids, which also feed on the leaves, are preyed on and parasitised by a host of other species, forming a complex living community.

Above: a water shrew coming down to the waterside to plunge in among the duckweed. In this picture you can just see the edge of the white belly as the shrew turns its body sideways to look round. Beside this tiny mammal, the leaves of water forget-me-not appear enormous. Water shrews can dig their tunnels in banks held firmly together by the roots of alder.

Alder wood may soon become infected by a large number of fungi. Some of these, such as the bracket fungi, produce conspicuous fruiting bodies, but many species may be present in a single tree or coppice stool without showing any external sign. Once fungi have started the process of decay, they open the way for insects that tunnel in dead wood— primarily beetles and flies. The grubs of longhorn beetles, which tunnel in the wood, are a favourite food of the great spotted woodpecker. The willow tit is another insect eating bird which frequents dead wood, usually nesting in the soft trunks of rotted alders, willows and birches.

Another animal which takes advantage of alder is the otter, which is now very rare in England and Wales. Only in the Western Highlands of Scotland is it managing to maintain a healthy population. In the lowlands it frequents unpolluted and undisturbed rivers with natural courses and dense bankside vegetation. Their holts are often located amid the roots of large alders. The otter is probably the species which would suffer most if alder was to disappear from the British countryside.

Above: The caterpillar of the alder moth develops a vivid colouring which may scare off predators. It is the only British caterpillar to have these paddle-shaped black hairs that stick out all along its body.

Left: Tiers of the soft young fruiting bodies of *Inonotus radiatus*, a bracket fungus found mainly on alder. This exceptionally rich crop indicates that the wood is thoroughly infiltrated by the invisible threads of the fungus. The chemical changes brought about by the growth of the fungus make the wood edible for specialist insects and their larvae, some of which live in galleries in the wood for several years.

FERTILE FLOOD MEADOWS THEN AND NOW

Along some of our lowland rivers lie flat meadows – known as flood meadows – which are prone to regular winter flooding. Invertebrates in the mud and floating grass seeds attract flocks of ducks and geese in winter; later, breeding birds feed on insects and butterflies gorge on nectar from the meadow flowers.

This riverside meadow, rich with knapweed, creeping buttercup and grasses such as crested dog's-tail and reed sweet-grass, is part of a 275-acre flood meadow area of West Sedgemoor in Somerset which was recently saved by the Royal Society for the Protection of Birds from the threat of drainage. It is flooded annually by the River Parrett.

Lush green meadows in river plains, dotted with pale pink cuckoo flower, perfumed meadowsweet, white sneezewort and tall clumps of rushes and sedges, form some of the last surviving 'unimproved' grasslands in the country. They have not yet been drained or reseeded or treated with artificial fertilisers or herbicides. They are ancient meadows where once-common plants, insects and birds can still be found.

In recent years many of our river valleys have been extensively drained to prevent winter flooding. The adjacent fields are then converted to perhaps more profitable arable farming at the expense of this natural wetland habitat. However, there are still stretches of some rivers which flood each winter; these include the Hampshire Avon at Ibsley, the Parrett and Axe in Somerset and the Ouse in Yorkshire. There are also smaller areas of land (sometimes just a few fields) which are under water for varying periods each year: some may not flood for very long, others may not do so in very dry years. But in the richest of such meadows there may be up to 60 species of flowering plants, 15 grasses and a similar number of rushes and sedges.

These ancient meadows, undisturbed by ploughing, are distinguished by the diversity of their plant life. Marshland plants such as the bright yellow marsh-marigolds and the blue water forget-me-nots adorn the ditches while patches of great burnet and meadow-rue

grow among the lush grass. The nutrient-laden silt deposited by the winter floods provides a natural fertilizer. If the meadows were left untended through the summer the stronger grasses such as fescues and tufted hair-grass would gradually oust the majority of the flowers. However, grazing by cattle and sheep keeps the grass down and enables a much greater variety of plants to survive. In the summer you might see hares and water voles, but if animals remained for the winter they would drown as the meadows flooded.

Plant feeders The abundance of plant life provides food for many kinds of animals from geese in winter to myriads of insects in summer. The permanent nature of the grassland

Snipe, like many other waders, hollow out their nests in tussocks of grass where they sit tight until you practically walk on them. Then they explode into the air with great speed. They feed at night, probing in the mud with their long beaks for worms and insect larvae.

Above: Clusters of golden marsh-marigold appear in spring, attracting large numbers of insects. They thrive on wet nutrient-rich ground, and continue to flower until July.

Below: For 19 miles along the River Ouse on the Cambridgeshire-Norfolk border the riverside meadows, known as washes, are deliberately flooded for two or three months during the winter. They attract several thousand mallard, teal, and pintail every year.

is also crucial to this diversity, in that the animals of the soil such as mites, worms and insect larvae are able to survive without disturbance by cultivation or the use of pesticides. Various butterflies, moths, beetles, flies, bees and wasps feed on plant parts – the roots, stems, leaves, seeds, flowers and buds of grasses, rushes, sedges and so on.

Many insects depend on a particular plant at various stages in their life cycles. For example the caterpillar of the marbled white butterfly feeds mainly on cock's-foot grass and the adult is able to collect nectar from many of the flowers. Worms are often especially numerous and the waterlogging of the soil forces them – and also insect larvae – to remain near the soil surface to escape drowning. Here they are easily accessible to birds and hence the attractiveness of flood meadows to large numbers of waders, which can easily probe the soft mud to exploit the abundant supply of food.

Wildfowl invasion When the winter floods swell the rivers, filling the meadows with water, flocks of mallard, teal, pintail and other wildfowl move in.

As the floods rise so large numbers of insects are flushed out of the grasses and drown. Quantities of seeds from the flowering plants fall into the water and drift to the edges of the flood. Both insects and seeds are eaten by the ducks. When the water level is low enough flocks of waders such as lapwings and golden plover feed on the insects, probing for them in the mat of grass roots.

Soft mud conditions must last throughout the early summer if meadow birds such as snipe, curlew and redshank are to breed successfully. Parent birds need to be able to extract animal food from the soil from March until May; and then the young birds must be able to feed themselves until they are old enough to fly off in June.

Man's involvement The management of the meadows is also crucial to birds in their search for food: tightly packed tall grasses and flowers cannot be easily penetrated by probing waders. Before the meadow is cut for hay, the birds have to move out to the field edges or nearby arable land to feed. But

The marbled white butterfly

The rich variety of plants growing in the flood meadow in summer support a mass of insects which take advantage of the bounty of root, stem, leaf and flower. One of the most attractive, the marbled white butterfly (*Melanargia galathea*), is about in high summer from the beginning of July to mid-August. The adult feeds on the flowers of such plants as knapweed and thistle.

As they are not strong fliers you might see several resting together on the flowers, wings spread wide open in the sunshine. The female is usually larger than the male and has rounder wings. A pair are shown here mating.

The female scatters her eggs in flight so they land at random on a variety of plants, but the pale, straw-coloured caterpillars which hatch out and go into hibernation almost at once will not survive the winter flooding of the meadow. The marbled white butterfly will only breed successfully in areas of chalk downlands and grassy meadows and roadsides.

The marbled white butterfly belongs to the Satyridae family (which is often known simply as 'the browns') but it is an odd one out since it is coloured white with dark markings. Like other members of its family it walks on four legs only; the front pair are useless and much reduced in size.

once it is cut they can get at the soil again. The traditional rotational method of hay-cutting in some years followed by cattle and sheep grazing opens up feeding sites where the livestock have trampled the vegetation or left patches of dung. Cattle grazing benefits birds in another way: cattle do not eat rushes and sedges, so clumps of these are left which make ideal tussocks for nest sites. Several species breed in them from April onwards, including mallard, teal, snipe, redshank and yellow wagtail.

Deliberate flooding Although man is now trying to reduce these areas which flood naturally, he used to flood meadowland deliberately. As an alternative to uncon-

Above: Cattle are one of the few mammals you are likely to see in a flood meadow. Yellow flags frame the field.

Right: Cuckoo flower is often found in wet meadows. Leaves break off the parent plant in the winter floods, become rooted in the mud, and produce new plants in spring.

Some summer inhabitants
Breeding birds snipe, lapwing, curlew, yellow wagtail, mallard, teal, redshank, skylark, meadow pipit, whinchat
Flowering plants marsh-marigold, ragged-robin, meadowsweet, water forget-me-not, marsh pennywort, marsh-bedstraw, devil's-bit scabious, yellow rattle, great burnet, meadow-rue, marsh valerian, marsh-orchid, greater bird's-foot-trefoil, marsh speedwell, tufted vetch, water mint, lady's-mantle, lousewort, knapweed, marsh thistle
Grasses cock's-foot, tufted hair-grass, creeping bent, yellow oat-grass, meadow fox-tail, sweet vernal-grass, Yorkshire-fog
Rushes and sedges soft rush, sharp-flowered rush, common spikerush, oval sedge, brown sedge, star sedge, hairy sedge
Insects marbled white, common blue, meadow brown, small skipper, small copper butterflies; moths; craneflies; grasshoppers; beetles; bees; dragonflies

trolled winter flooding, special banks were built around a number of meadows. When more water came down the rivers than the banks could contain, it flowed via sluices into these meadows–or washes–and was stored there until the river levels dropped sufficiently for the sluice gate to be opened and the water to flow back into the river. In a normal winter, this would last from October or November through to March or April.

The Ouse Washes form the largest of these areas. Here, the land is divided into many grass fields which are grazed by cattle during the summer. It is a paradise for birds, both in the winter, when the floods attract some of the largest flocks of ducks and swans in the

country, and in the summer when many species breed in the marshy fields.

Irrigation skills In the 17th and 18th centuries the farmers of southern England realised that winter flooding greatly improved the quality of the grass. In Hampshire, Wiltshire and Dorset especially, they developed skilled techniques for flooding the fields deliberately, using the nutrient-rich chalk streams. To ensure that the water flowed evenly over the fields, and did not stand too long to form stagnant pools, parallel ridges were built across each field, at right angles to the stream. The ridges were about 1m (3ft) high and the gap between them anything from 2m (6½ft) to 6m (20ft), depending on the slope of the ground. Along the centre of each ridge ran a shallow water channel fed from the stream through one or more sluices. The channel was stopped at the far end so that the water spilt over and ran down either side of the ridge. It then flowed across the intervening strip of grass before being drained away by a ditch at the base of the next ridge. By operating the sluices carefully the farmer could vary the speed and quantity of water flow.

The key period for irrigation was during January and February. Water in chalk streams is very constant in temperature coming as it does from deep underground and at this time of year is invariably warmer than the surface soil. Thus the irrigation not only fertilised the grass, but warmed it and so further stimulated growth. By March there was enough grass for the farmer to cease flooding and set his sheep to graze, perhaps three or even four weeks earlier than would have been possible on untreated fields. Later in the spring he removed the sheep, recommenced flooding, and then obtained a hay crop; in a dry year further flooding was done in the autumn. The technique gradually declined in the late 19th century and today only the remains of the ridges and furrows can be seen. One of the few working examples left is at Lower Woodford in Wiltshire.

Widespread drainage Careful management of water meadows and the southern chalk streams are now mainly a thing of the past and the washes, for example, are periodically threatened with drainage. Those alongside the river Nene have been drained and ploughed up, although during recent wet winters drainage authorities have been forced to flood the washes deliberately again. However, with the increasing cost of artificial fertilisers conservationists are beginning to think that nature's own fertilising floods–which are free–may be the more attractive long-term proposition.

The value of floods to wildlife is being used as a weapon by conservationists in the fight against indiscriminate drainage. The most recent successful battle was fought over Amberley Wildbrooks, a big area of flood meadows on the river Arun in Sussex, where a flooding plan was turned down.

RICH RESERVOIRS

Britain's huge above-ground reservoirs – built to supply cities with water – have also provided a rich new wetland habitat where wildlife can thrive.

Our modern society expects – and gets – pure water supplied to every home and factory in the land. We accept this unquestioningly, use the water, and probably think little of how it reaches us. Water – readily and instantly available in extremely large quantities – comes to us in some cases from underground

wells and natural storage chambers in the rock, but increasing amounts are now being held in above-ground reservoirs. These catch and retain the flow of streams and rivers, or have water pumped into them from other sources. Nearly all our larger cities and conurbations of people have drinking water reservoirs not too far away.

Water is attractive to all forms of wildlife. Even the smallest garden pond quickly becomes the home for pond-skaters, water-beetles and even frogs, and garden birds come to it to drink. Enlarge that pond many times over and other birds arrive to bathe and swim, plants begin to colonize the water and its banks, insects and other invertebrates fly in, or come down the feeding streams, and before long a whole rich wetland habitat has been created. This is exactly what happens when a new reservoir is built; most reservoirs eventually become havens for birds, fish, insects and plants, though this was far from the minds of the engineers who constructed them.

Types of reservoir Reservoirs can be divided into three main types, which have varying attractions for wildlife. There are upland waters, sometimes completely artificial, but often natural lakes that have been dammed up to increase the depth of water. Secondly, many of the reservoirs near towns and cities are sited on fairly flat land, with earth banks built up and lined with concrete to retain the

water and increase the capacity. Thirdly, there are the more natural lowland reservoirs, with a concrete dam at the end of a shallow valley that traps water draining into it. These last are easily the most attractive to all forms of wildlife.

Habitat for the hardy The upland waters of Britain, in the Lake District or Scotland, form a severe habitat in which only the tougher species of wildlife can survive. The underlying rocks are acid and so do not add much fertility to the water. Plant and insect life is often sparse as a result; so, too, are the numbers of birds that live on them. This is as true of reservoirs in these areas as it is of natural waters. In addition, many upland reservoirs are subject to considerable fluctuations in water level. Water is pumped in or out in large quantities and several feet of mud and rock may be exposed from time to time. These changes are unpredictable, so there is not much chance of plants becoming established around the banks. However, if mud is exposed for a season, a single species of pioneer plant – thistles or purple loosestrife, for instance – can become established on the banks.

Gradual enrichment The lack of natural shores in concrete-lined reservoirs inhibits the growth of plants, most of which need shallow water and shelving banks. The water does not, however, remain sterile for long, provided it contains some natural goodness

Previous page: Craig Goch Reservoir, Elan Valley, in Wales. An alien fish, the American brook trout (*Salmo fontinalis*) was introduced to this reservoir, and many others, in the late 1970s – mainly for the benefit of a growing number of keen anglers—and though depleted, it still survives.

Below: Purple loosestrife (*Lythrum salicaria*) growing in spiky purple masses on the banks of Dowdeswell Reservoir in Gloucestershire. The lack of natural shores in concrete-lined reservoirs inhibits the growth of plants, but if there is sufficient soil on the banks pioneer plants such as loosestrife and thistles soon establish themselves.

from the surrounding soil. Quite a number of plants can live in water without being rooted. The tiny green leaves of duckweed and frog-bit form extensive mats floating on the surface and the plants obtain nutrients directly from the water with their many fine rootlets that hang underneath the leaves. The rafts of vegetation often form floating homes for small snails and other animals.

Although the bottom of the reservoir probably starts off as hard-packed earth, it gradually acquires a layer of silt in which other plants can become established. Pond-weeds of several different species, including the introduced Canadian pondweed, water mil-foil and water lilies are all bottom-rooted but send up leaves and flowering spikes to the surface.

Invertebrate life will arrive and colonize any stretch of water, but most kinds flourish only when there are enough plants there to provide food and resting places. The larvae of many flying insects – midges, damselflies and mayflies – all live in the mud at the bottom, or on the underwater parts of plants. Water boatmen, water-beetles and many different kinds of snails swim and crawl among the vegetation and pond-skaters and whirligig beetles scurry over the surface. All these plants and animals are food for birds; once they are established, then the birds arrive to feed on them. A barren area may be used by birds as a roosting place, or for drinking and bathing, but if there is plenty of food available, large numbers of birds begin to use the reservoir regularly. Some of the concrete-lined drinking water reservoirs in West London, near Heathrow Airport, hold the largest flocks of tufted duck and pochard in the country, often being thousands strong. Both species of duck feed by diving for plant leaves and stems, small snails and other underwater animals. Coots also feed in this way and large flocks of them can be seen on many urban reservoirs.

Lowland reservoirs There is no doubt that the lowland valley reservoirs, particularly those in southern England, are the richest for wildlife. The greater pond sedge and the beautiful flowering rush form dense stands, together with the familiar reed mace. They extend from the shallow water up the natural banks on to dry land where they mix with willowherbs and water dropwort. If the area is left completely alone, willows and alders will appear, eventually producing woodland.

The plants provide food, shelter for insects and nesting sites for many small birds as well as the ducks, coots and grebes. Some fairly large reed beds exist on a few reservoirs, while in shallow water, emergent vegetation creates virtual islands.

The water flowing into these reservoirs from the streams is rich in nutrients such as nitrogen and phosphorus. Much of this comes from the natural fertility of the soils of lowland Britain. More is added by farmers

Above: Gulls flying over Lliedi Reservoir in Wales. Gulls frequently roost on reservoirs at night, bathing and drinking on their arrival in the evening, but not feeding there. They probably spend the day taking insects from playing fields and parks, or scavenging on rubbish tips. You can also see thousands of swifts flying over reservoirs in summer, hawking for insects over the water.

Above: Tufted duck (Aythya fuligula). The reeds and other waterside vegetation found in lowland reservoirs with natural banks provide food, shelter for insects and nesting sites for the ducks, and for other birds such as coots and grebes.

to fertilise their crops, the surplus being washed out by rain and eventually finding its way to the reservoirs. In excellent conditions such as these, plants flourish, the tiny plankton and algae in the water proliferate, and a considerable richness and diversity of wildlife builds up.

Wildfowl counts Numbers of birds on the lowland reservoirs, particularly the ducks, reflect the abundance of food. There are many reservoirs that hold several thousand ducks each winter, of many different species. Several of our larger reservoirs, for example Chew Valley in Avon, Blithfield in Staffordshire, Grafham Water in Huntingdon, and Rutland Water in Leicestershire, are visited

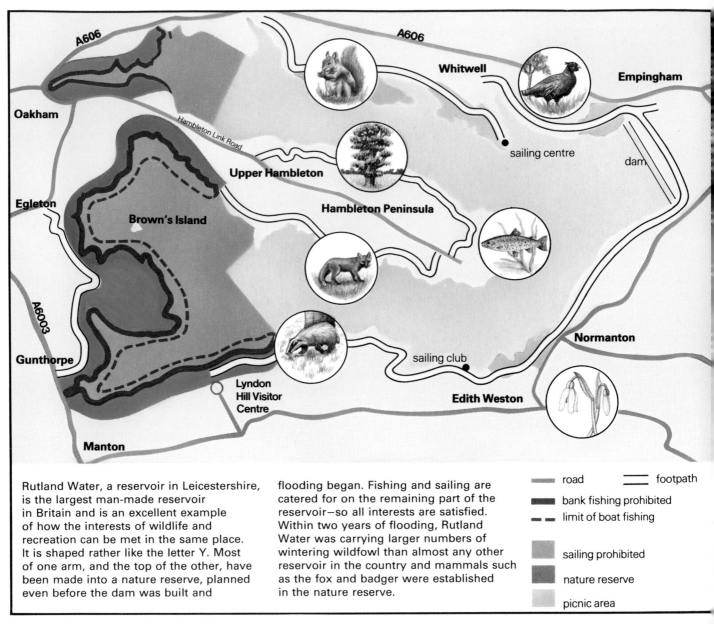

road		footpath	
bank fishing prohibited			
limit of boat fishing			
sailing prohibited			
nature reserve			
picnic area			

Rutland Water, a reservoir in Leicestershire, is the largest man-made reservoir in Britain and is an excellent example of how the interests of wildlife and recreation can be met in the same place. It is shaped rather like the letter Y. Most of one arm, and the top of the other, have been made into a nature reserve, planned even before the dam was built and flooding began. Fishing and sailing are catered for on the remaining part of the reservoir—so all interests are satisfied. Within two years of flooding, Rutland Water was carrying larger numbers of wintering wildfowl than almost any other reservoir in the country and mammals such as the fox and badger were established in the nature reserve.

by large numbers of birds every winter.

Wetlands of all types in Britain have been rated according to the numbers of wildfowl that visit them regularly. If a water holds more than 1% of the national total of a particular species, then it is rated as of national importance to that species. On this basis several reservoirs are of national importance, for tufted duck, shoveler, pochard, mallard, wigeon and teal. One reservoir, Abberton in Essex, though partly concrete-banked, regularly holds over 10,000 ducks of different species, and this qualifies it to be rated as of international importance as a wetland site, comparable to waters throughout Europe and further afield.

Policy change Until fairly recently, people were not allowed near the majority of drinking water reservoirs. The authorities concerned were worried about safety and health risks. Fishing was permitted at just a few reservoirs, usually for trout which were reared and put into the water for the purpose. At other sites, birdwatchers were allowed to visit in small numbers, but any other kind of recreation was prohibited.

This attitude has now been completely relaxed, and various sports—especially sailing—are encouraged. This is not always compatible with the wildlife of the reservoir; many species are frightened off by boats on the water, and fishermen lining the banks trample vegetation and disturb nesting birds. Even walkers can discourage wildlife.

When reservoirs were opened up for recreation in the 1970s, there was no doubt that the value of some of them for wildlife was seriously diminished. More recently, however, there have been a number of successful schemes for fitting both recreational and wildlife interests into the same reservoir. For example, at Chew Valley in Avon the area within which the sailing boats can operate is strictly limited, as is the total number of boats permitted on the water at any one time. The boats are not allowed into the shallow areas and sheltered bays that are the preferred spots for the water birds and which have the best growths of plant and animal life.

Substitute habitat

The drinking water reservoirs created by man for the purpose of supplying water in large quantities to towns and cities also benefit wildlife greatly by providing a new habitat for plants and animals to colonize. However, it is ironical that, at the same time as creating this new habitat, man has been trying to rid lowland Britain of almost all its natural freshwater wetlands. Marshes have been drained, rivers straightened and embanked to prevent winter flooding, and even large numbers of small ponds have been filled up. The building of the reservoirs has not, of course, been a deliberate replacement for all the destroyed wetlands, but it has been at least some recompense and substitute for them.

GRAVEL PITS: A NEW HABITAT

With so many habitats dwindling, it is at least reassuring to know that one industry – gravel extraction – actually creates new ones. After the digging and dredging work is completed, the site is returned to nature, and wildlife takes over.

Below: A gravel pit during the first years after the end of excavation. In the foreground, rose bay willowherb is the most successful among various colonizing plants on the bare gravel. You can also see the low yellow spikes of wild mignonette, the upright stem of teasel and, on the right, a tall-stemmed ragwort with its yellow flowering heads.

Gravel occurs naturally in the ground and is dug out to provide materials for road-making and other building work. When the excavation of a gravel pit is completed, the draglines and other machinery are taken away and the open pit usually fills with water. Often this occurs as rain falls and water seeps in from the ground all around the pit; but sometimes the last task of the contractors is to pump water in, to form a lake for amenity purposes. Plants and animals are presented with a brand-new habitat.

This habitat then becomes the scene of a natural process of colonization. If this is to be successful, one important condition is needed: that the pit has gently sloping (not sheer) sides. This ensures that there is a large area of shallow water, which has two advantages for wildlife: it supports prolific water plants, and it also warms up quickly in fine weather. The warmth and the plentiful supply of plants then provide an ideal breeding environment for many species of invertebrates, as well as for frogs and other amphibians. Fishes, too, spawn in the shallows.

First comers Colonization is an ordered process, following the simple but ruthless rules of competition. At first, the strongest competitors in a gravel pit are the algae.

A certain number of these tiny plants – many of them microscopically small – are present in almost any water. Once the pit is filled, they begin to multiply by cell division, thriving on the dissolved nutrients that the water naturally contains.

The higher plants are slower to make their appearance. Seeds are blown in by the wind or brought by birds and animals and, since the water is usually taken from a river, it may already contain fragments of water plants such as pondweeds or water lilies. Both seeds and fragments are capable of developing into whole plants, but their growth is slow, and so it is the advanced algae, known as stoneworts, which are the first rooted plants to become well established. Rooted or free-floating, the algae dominate the pit during the first year.

Often the dense mass of microscopic plants

Gravel pit birds

Dabbling ducks, such as gadwall and shoveler, feed in shallow water, while diving ducks feed in deeper water. If waterside plants are scarce, mallard, coot and moorhen will not be present, for they seek shelter among reeds and other plants. The vegetation provides nesting sites for great crested grebes. Yellow wagtails may breed on the wasteland of old spoil from the gravel workings. In small, sandy cliffs a few feet high, sand martins make nest holes. As the seasons pass, the increasing variety of plants offers a winter harvest of seed and the winter buds of water lilies and other plants. This is a plentiful food supply for overwintering wildfowl. Pochard, teal, tufted duck, mallard, wigeon and goldeneye are regular winter occupants of mature pits.

gives the water a light green colour. They form a natural light filter that reduces the brightness of the light reaching the deeper water, and therefore its capacity to support life. The seeds or fragments of higher plants, having sunk to the bottom and started to grow their first shoots, are starved of light and can develop no further. So, in the natural contest for a place in the gravel pit, the algae are clear winners of the first round. Their light-filtering effect proves to be a subtle but ruthless means of controlling competitors.

Round two The reign of the algae is, however, short-lived in a gravel pit where shallow water offers a habitat for plentiful aquatic plants. The growth of the algae produces abundant oxygen which enables tiny animals, the zooplankton, to thrive; many of these are plant-eaters, and their feeding checks the prolific growth of the algae.

As the seasons pass, the slow, steady progress of the higher plants takes on a new vigour. Their root stocks, established in the initial phase, produce more shoots. Early growing species, such as Canadian pondweed and water crowfoot, develop rapidly in February and March, extracting quantities of nutrients from the water and leaving less for the spring growth of algae.

With less prolific growth of algae, more light penetrates to the deeper water where most of the higher plants grow. This allows the later-growing plants – water milfoils,

pondweeds, hornworts and water lilies–to thrive.

Plant zonation As they appear in the gravel pit, the aquatic plants occupy their range of new habitats in a characteristic pattern. The shallow water up to a depth of 1m (3ft) is suitable for crowfoots and Canadian pondweed. Further out, to a depth of 2m (6ft), are the hornworts, which float beneath the surface. Pondweeds and water lilies grow in water up to 4.5m (14ft) deep, their tall stalks rising from roots in the bottom of the gravel pit. In deeper water still are the water milfoils, which can grow at a depth of up to 6.5m (20ft).

In a steep-sided gravel pit, most of these habitats are either missing or reduced to the narrowest band as the bottom slopes sharply away. Gravel pits of this type tend not to progress beyond the stage of an open pool containing few plants besides algae and perhaps the deep water species.

The marsh plants, too, depend on the habitat offered by shallow water. These are the waterside plants, whose roots can be submerged but can also stand on ground that is dry for part of the year. Soft and hard rushes, or bulrush, soon appear. In succeeding years, a reedbed may grow along the water's edge, leaving room for bulrush only on its outer fringe. Clubrush, and mare's tail, may appear on the outer fringe of the reedbed.

Left: Marsh plants spreading on the margin of Ellingham Lake in Hampshire. Near the water's edge are reed sweetgrass and water dock. Bulrush, which typically grows farther from the bank, can be seen in the centre of the picture.

Right: A pair of mating damselflies on the emerging flowers of spiked water milfoil.

Below: A great crested grebe sits alert on its nest of rotting vegetation, partly concealed in the invading reedbed.

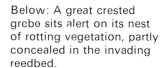

Arrival of the animals As plant diversity increases, conditions become more favourable for invertebrates. One by one, various species of dragonfly and damselfly, as well as aquatic beetles and other insects, spread to the new habitat. The pace of this invasion slows down as time passes, until the gravel pit has stable plant and animal communities.

After some years, gravel pits are often found to contain fish. Minnows and stickle-backs are common, and bottom-feeding fish such as gudgeon and tench also appear, along with those that feed at all levels in the water, such as roach. Rudd, a plant-eating species, is found, and even pike, which prey on other fish. These species, all coarse fish, colonize the gravel pit naturally, but little is known for certain about how the coarse fish arrive. One possible explanation is that their fertilized eggs may stick to the feathers and feet of wildfowl, and thus travel by air. Game fish, mainly trout, are often artificially introduced to provide sport for anglers.

Frogs and newts colonize gravel pits only where the banks slope gently or where separate shallow pools lie close by. These amphibians depend more than any other group of vertebrates on the warmth and prolific plant growth of the shallow water. Many species of wildfowl come either to rest or to stay for the winter, feasting on the aquatic plants.

Essential variety The community of the gravel pit can only become stable if it has a wide diversity of species. If there are few insect species, any carnivore that lives on them would undergo periods of food shortage. If many species are present, a constant food supply is assured and the community will not lose its carnivorous species.

Some animals that change their diet as

they grow to maturity are faced with special difficulties in an environment with few species. Fish may feed on bloodworms, water fleas and beetle larvae when young, but as adults they need a supply of larger creatures – water snails, water boatmen, caddis fly larvae and adult beetles. Without these, the fish continue to eat the smaller creatures and deplete the supply; they are then unable to grow to full size, remaining stunted.

Web of aquatic life In the community that gradually forms in a gravel pit, all the members depend on one another for their survival. Herbivores feed on plants and in turn are the prey of carnivores. Larger or more aggressive carnivores hunt the smaller carnivores, and so the numbers of each species are regulated by the other species that feed on them.

This relationship between a community of organisms is known as a food web. As a gravel pit matures, the water plants form a dense forest beneath the surface. Water fleas clinging to the plants venture out at nightfall to feed on algae, moving upwards towards the surface where the algae are concentrated and descending in a cloud at dawn to hide among the plants once more. The predators they hide from are minnows, three-spined sticklebacks, insect larvae and young fish.

Eat and be eaten is the rule, and yet even in death nothing is wasted. Uneaten remains of plants and animals rain down and settle on the mud floor, where they are greedily consumed by such insects as the lesser water boatman, whose sucking mouthparts take in the debris like a vacuum cleaner. Mud-dwelling chironomid larvae and bacteria complete the breakdown of tissue into basic chemical compounds. These contain elements such as nitrogen and phosphorus, essential nutrients for plant growth, and so the cycle is complete.

Above: The sedge warbler nests in the base of a reedbed or other waterside vegetation.

Opposite page: A duckling resting among tall vegetation. Such birds colonize gravel pits very readily.

Left: Spiked water milfoil, an underwater plant with flowers emerging above the surface. There are three British species of water milfoil: alternate-flowered spiked and whorled. They are capable of growing in deeper water than almost any other water plants, being adapted to survive with a minimum of light.

The freshwater food cycle

The food cycle begins when plants manufacture food by absorbing carbon dioxide and nutrients, utilising the energy of sunlight in the process. The nutrients are taken from the mud (**1**) or from the water (**2**). These plants are then grazed on by animals such as snails (**3**) and daphnia (**4**). The herbivores may then be eaten by carnivores such as dragonfly larvae (**5**) and fish (**6**). Thus nutrients pass from the plants through a chain of feeding animals. Plants and animals continually die and decompose. Decomposition is aided by scavenging animals (**7**) as well as by bacteria (**8**),

reducing the materials to soluble chemicals which become available to plants at the start of the food cycle.

sunlight

carbon dioxide

rainwater washes nutrients in

nutrients produced by breakdown recirculated

1 **Rooted plant**
  (*Elodea*)
2 **Floating plants**
  (*Chlorella* **and**
  Spirogyra)
3 **Pond snails**

4 **Daphnia**
5 **Dragonfly larva**
6 **Roach**
7 **Lesser water boatman and chironomid worms**
8 **Bacteria**

animal and plant remains broken down by scavengers and bacteria

BRITAIN'S VARIED VALLEY BOGS

Although the most extensive areas of bog are to be found in the wild, remote uplands of Britain, parts of the drier, gentler south–Surrey's Thursley Common, for instance, or the New Forest–also have bogs, in particular the type known as 'valley' bog.

Opposite right: The formation of valley bogs, as their name suggests, depends mainly on terrain. Where water collects along a valley, conditions are right for peat formation, provided the flow is fairly sluggish or impeded at times. This proviso still allows a wide variety of conditions to occur in valley bogs, with the result that they are, perhaps, the most variable of all our types of bog. Unlike raised and blanket bogs, valley bogs do not rely purely on rainfall and are therefore not restricted to north and west Britain.

Below: The central watercourse of a valley bog may be picked out by a line of the strangely shaped hummocks of tussock sedge.

While the high rainfall and cool climate of the north and west of the British Isles give rise to our most widespread development of raised and blanket bogs, you can also find something of the untamed, primeval atmosphere of these places in parts of southern Britain. However, while the blanket bogs of upland Britain are entirely dependent upon rainfall for their formation, the bogs of the south are a product of both climate and topography, and are therefore not restricted solely to the wetter parts of the country. Thursley Common National Nature Reserve in Surrey and the bogs of the New Forest in Hampshire are examples of just such southern bogs, of a type known as valley bog. (Visitors to Thursley Common, for their own safety, are advised to follow the clearly defined series of track-ways constructed by the NCC.)

At its simplest, a valley bog is formed when water collecting along a valley induces peat to flourish. In practice, this concept is much more complex; nevertheless, this very com-plexity tends to produce a much wider range of conditions than is possible among the simpler blanket and raised bog systems. Consequently, valley bogs are possibly our most varied and widespread type of bog.

Valley bogs vary in size from small seepage lines only a few metres wide to huge systems several miles long and a mile or so wide. However, the huge flood-plain mires which represent the upper range of valley bogs are generally regarded as a type of bog in their own right. By convention, valley bogs are usually fairly small–rarely exceeding an area of 500 hectares (1235 acres)–and are characterised by a central watercourse.

The distinction between valley bog and flood-plain mire is that the central watercourse of the latter tends to be a major river whereas in a valley bog the water-course is never more than a small stream. This feature also separates valley bogs from the fen reed swamps that occur around the margins of lakes–valley bogs are formed where there is moving water, lake reedswamps where the water is static.

Topography and water sources For valley bog formation, a valley is obviously the first requirement, but its shape is also extremely

oxygen). Although the constant flow of water provides a certain level of oxygenation, it is insufficient to bring about complete decomposition of the year's plant growth before the next growing season. The build-up of this undecomposed material (as peat) results in the release of humic acids which further inhibit decomposition.

However, balanced against this is the nutrient content of the water flowing through the system. If it is rich in minerals, these counteract the acidification process and allow a certain amount of decomposition to continue. When the nutrient levels are low and conditions are markedly acidic (pH4-pH5), the peat formed is moss peat–consisting of the remains of the bog moss *Sphagnum*. Somewhat richer conditions (pH6-pH8) encourage a sedge-dominated community which gives rise to a rather amorphous type of peat known as fen peat. Although in general sphagnum peats form the deepest deposits, even the richest fen peats can result in depths of up to 5m (16ft), and it is quite common to find a long history of peat-cutting for fuel over such areas. Indeed, a Government Report of 1789 concerned with the management of the New Forest states: '. . . those who make a trade of cutting turf and peat, for sale, are becoming so daring as to threaten the burning of the Forest if they are interrupted.'

Plants of the central water-track Looked at in cross-section, a valley bog can be seen to consist of distinct zones, which reflect the three separate sources of water flowing into the site. In the centre is the water-track, which may be a broad stream or no more than a seepage line. It is usually the zone with the highest levels of oxygen and is often the richest part of the site, unless the flow is particularly sluggish and the water has been forced to percolate along a sphagnum-rich seepage line.

Under conditions of faster flow, the central water-course is often picked out by a line of alder and willow trees, the latter occurring

important. Peat formation is encouraged by sluggish or impeded water movement, so a steep valley with a tumbling mountain torrent offers little possibility of bog development, whereas a broad, gently sloping valley provides ideal conditions. Blanket and raised bogs occur in a fairly simple set of climatic conditions, but for valley bogs the conditions vary with such factors as the permeability and nutrient status of the bedrock and the size of the catchment area.

The final nature of the individual bog depends on the interactions between these various elements, but by far the most important factor is the nutrient status of the various water sources. There are three sources of water: rainfall, the valley sides and the central water-course. The first two are often not immediately apparent or easily determined, particularly if the valley is shallow and with a barely perceptible slope, but the flow rate and nutrient status of the central water-course is more easily established.

How a valley bog develops Peat formation– the accumulation of dead plant material– occurs because constant waterlogging prevents the normal processes of bacterial decay – the most efficient bacteria are those that need

Below: Water from the sides of a valley bog tends to be fairly nutrient-rich; the plant community here is dominated by herbs, among them this beautiful insectivorous butterwort.

Above: A plant species sometimes found growing near the central water-course of valley bogs, the marsh cinquefoil can be recognised by its reddish-purple petals framed by wider, longer sepals. It can reach as much as 45cm (18in) in height and prefers fairly acidic conditions.

Below: Another plant to look for in valley bogs is the attractive grass of Parnassus—not a grass at all but a white-flowered herb. It reaches 10-30cm (4-12in) in height.

particularly where the water is nutrient-poor. Under slightly richer conditions it is common to find the large humpy tussocks of the greater tussock sedge flourishing along the water-course and dominating the areas of regular inundation. Under rather poorer conditions, however, the water-track is clearly picked out by the small shrubby sweet gale which gives off a heady scent whenever the leaves or buds are slightly bruised.

Where the flow is reduced to little more than a seepage, but is nevertheless mineral-rich, a carpet of so-called 'brown mosses' dominates the zone of water movement. This more open community consists of such mosses as the bright yellow *Philonotis fontanum*, the golden, star-like *Campylium stellatum*, the strange claw-shaped *Scorpidium scorpioides* and the robust *Acrocladium cus-*

pidatum, all of which form dense mats within which such species as mud sedge, black bog rush and bog pondweed are found. Also to be seen here are the delicate white flowers of grass of Parnassus and the strange pink flowers of the marsh cinquefoil, as well as the insectivorous common butterwort and the bladderwort.

Other plants Away from the immediate effects of the water-track, conditions generally become more acidic. Small nuclei of sphagnum moss hummocks rise above the water table to become largely rain-fed, and such species as common sundew, bog asphodel and cross-leaved heath dominate the vegetation.

Such an association clearly demonstrates that the most important source of water for this zone is rainfall, although the presence of other species, such as bottle sedge, bog pimpernel, marsh pennywort and marsh arrowgrass, scattered within this zone, highlight the fact that even here water flow from the surrounding slopes plays a significant part in shaping the structure of the community.

The outer zones, fed by run-off from the surrounding slopes, depend almost entirely on the nature of their soils. Where these are rich, a limited form of 'brown moss' community grades into a wet-meadow type of vegetation which is often extremely rich in herb species, although it is unusual for this part of the bog system to have survived intact because it is so easily drained. Where water forms in ponds at the foot of the steep valley slopes, a not uncommon sight is a fringe of alder, willow and common reed, or—particularly where there has been a certain amount of agricultural enrichment—stands of bulrush.

Birds and insects From the north of Shetland to the south of England perhaps the most characteristic bird of the valley bog habitat is the snipe. Nothing is more guaranteed to shatter the quiet of an early morning walk across a valley bog than the explosive launch of a startled snipe from beneath your feet. Like a little brown bullet the snipe streaks away on a whirr of wings, uttering a short sharp cry of alarm, then jinks left and right

Below: Typical vegetation of the more nutrient-rich parts of valley bogs. Species visible here include bog pimpernel, marsh pennywort and water dropwort. They show up as bright green areas among the brown of the sphagnum moss.

t high speed before diving to the ground behind a convenient tussock. In the evening the same bird can be heard 'drumming' as it circles around its territory. Climbing a couple of hundred feet, it dives to the ground, extending two stiff tail feathers which vibrate in the rushing air. The sound is almost a bleat, like the cry of a distant lamb, and blends perfectly with the other sounds of the evening.

Less ethereal than the sound of the snipe is the sharp scolding of the redshank, another bird sometimes found in southern valley bogs (although more particularly a bird of the north). With its bright red legs it perches on a convenient fence post and chatters away in an indignant manner to anyone approaching its territory. Like the snipe's young, the redshank chicks can run as soon as they hatch, but the raucous chattering of the parent birds causes them to lie still, allowing their efficient camouflage to blend with the tangle of sedges and dwarf shrubs.

Both redshank and snipe are waders, equipped with long bills to probe the peat for insects, of which there are a great many, particularly in the southern valley bogs. Here an abundance of water combines with warm summers to provide a habitat for some of our rarest and most spectacular insects.

Extreme rarities, such as the dragonflies *Leucorrhina dubia* and *Ceriagrion tenellum*, mingle with the commoner libellulas and aeshnas, swooping and hawking over the areas of open water. However, they themselves fall prey to yet another rare and spectacular species – the hobby. Attracted by the ready source of insect food, this acrobatic bird can often be seen performing tumbling cartwheels through the sky while chasing dragonflies, or even swifts and swallows – birds also attracted by the rich insect life of our valley bogs.

Above: Typical valley bog topography. Three main sources of water feed the bog – the central water-track, the sloping valley sides and rainfall – but the formation of the bog also depends on rate of water movement, the nutrient status of the water, flooding frequency and the size of the catchment area.

Left: The raft spider – our largest species – may be found among the sphagnum mosses of a valley bog.

Formation of a valley bog

Peat formation in valley bogs occurs as a result of waterlogging. The type of peat may be moss peat in nutrient-poor conditions or, in richer waters, fen peat. In both cases depths of 5m (16ft) or more can occur. Different plant communities may develop in different parts of the bog, depending on nutrient flow and level of water.

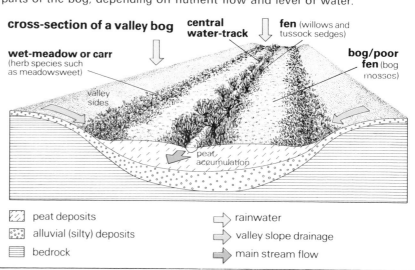

cross-section of a valley bog

central water-track

fen (willows and tussock sedges)

wet-meadow or carr (herb species such as meadowsweet)

valley sides

bog/poor fen (bog mosses)

peat accumulation

peat deposits		rainwater
alluvial (silty) deposits		valley slope drainage
bedrock		main stream flow

TEEMING POND LIFE

Ponds, with their clearly defined margins, are one of the easiest habitats to observe and understand. They are crammed with plants and animals, from masses of microscopic algae to roaming carnivorous fish.

It is difficult to highlight the characteristics of a pond since these mostly man-made areas of water vary so much in detail. From a biological point of view the important features are that they are all small areas of still water, little troubled by wind-generated waves beating on their margins and shallow enough all over for light to penetrate to the bottom to enable rooted plants to grow. Lakes, on the other hand, are too deep for rooted plants to grow in the middle, and are exposed to the full force of winds.

Water plants Apart from the truly aquatic plants such as algae that grow in profusion, pond vegetation consists mainly of representatives of widely differing families of terrestrial flowering plants that have colonised aquatic habitats, displaying differing degrees of adaptation to an alien environment. Examine the vegetation in and around a pond in summer and you will notice that the plants are not haphazardly positioned but occupy more or less distinct zones.

In the marshy area as one approaches a pond, among the rushes and sedges, will be found tall, lush plants such as great willow-herb, meadowsweet, purple loosestrife, the bur-marigolds and yellow iris. They live not in water but in waterlogged soil, in which water instead of air occupies the spaces between the soil particles. The resulting scarcity of oxygen is compensated for by the spongy structure of the plant with many air-spaces for the storage and passage of air.

At the edge of the pond, where the ground is covered with water except in times of drought, you find the second zone – the reed-swamp community – named after one of the characteristic plants at the margin of larger ponds, the common reed. Most of the plants in this zone are tall and thus able to cope with changing water levels. Firmly embedded in the mud, their long creeping stems (rhizomes) keep the plants upright in high winds. Bulrushes or clubrushes, bur-reeds, water plantain and the beautiful flowering rush are common plants of the reedswamp.

In the shallow water at the margins, sheltered by the reedswamp, is a community of plants rooted in the mud but with floating leaves. Of these the best known and most beautiful of all water plants are the white and yellow water-lilies. Other plants in the floating-leaves zone are the various species of pondweed, water-crowfoot and fringed water-lily.

Further out, in the deeper water, are the totally submerged plants such as the water-milfoils, Canadian pondweed and hornworts. Although some are attached to the bottom, they are not dependent on the soil for their mineral nutrients as they can absorb both gases and dissolved salts from the surrounding water through their skin (epidermis) which is thin and delicate. Water plants, supported as they are on all sides by water, have no need for the strong, toughened stems of land plants. The submerged plants are the most completely adapted to an aquatic life and hornwort even flowers underwater, the pollen reaching the stigmas through the water.

Independent of the bottom mud are the floating plants of which the duckweeds are the most common, often covering the whole surface of a pond with their tiny 'leaves', more correctly called thalli. Other floating plants are frogbit and bladder-worts, which trap small animals in the bladders on their leaves.

Finally, there are the truly aquatic plants, the algae, most of which are microscopic in size and either float freely as plankton in the water or are attached to higher plants or other objects. Spirogyra, however, and other filamentous algae, gather together in great masses and are clearly visible in the water as green cotton-wool. In spring these masses rise to the surface buoyed up by bubbles of oxygen, a useful reminder of the value of all green plants in the pond as oxygenators.

Animal life With all this richness of vegetation it is not surprising that the animal life of a pond is similarly abundant and varied. Representatives of nearly every main group from single-celled protozoans to vertebrates can be found. As with the plants, not all the animals are primarily aquatic: some are secondarily aquatic, that is as land animals they have adopted water as their habitat to

Above: A pond is not just an area of still, shallow water: it includes all the plants at the edges and rooted to the bottom which attract the wealth of creatures. Here you see the rare dark red Hampshire purslane and green floating pondweed in the foreground. Water-lilies bloom in the shallower water, fringed by bur-reed and leaves of yellow iris.

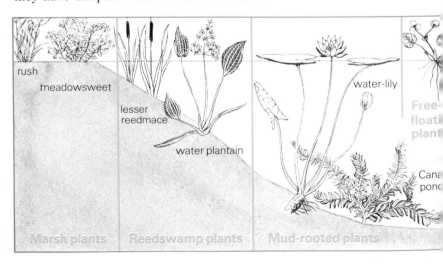

rush
meadowsweet
lesser reedmace
water plantain
water-lily
Free-floating plant
Cana pond

Marsh plants | Reedswamp plants | Mud-rooted plants

ake advantage of the abundant food available. Some are herbivores feeding directly on the plants; others are carnivores. Among the secondarily aquatic animals are some of the snails, 11 orders of insects, some mites and one spider, the water spider. Although they live underwater, they have solved the problem of taking in air in varying and ingenious ways. Most beetles, for instance, have velvety piles of fine hairs on parts of the body which can hold a reservoir of air in a silvery bubble, thus limiting frequent journeys to the surface

to renew their air supply.

Pond animals live in four well-defined zones imposed on them by their particular way of life.

Surface film The surface of the water is in a state of tension and acts like an elastic skin, supporting small creatures both above and below it. The animals living on it are the least adapted of aquatic animals since they hardly ever descend into the water. These include a group of water bugs – pond skaters, water crickets and the water measurer. They feed on

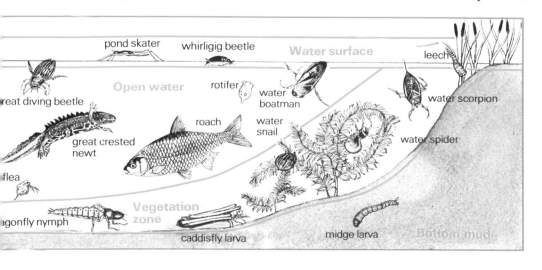

Animal and plant zones
Most ponds fall into distinct animal and plant zones – ranging from the marshy margins to the bottom mud. The diagram (left), which is not drawn to scale, shows plant zones on the left and animal zones on the right, with free floating plants and fish and crustaceans in the deeper water.

49

Above: Frogbit is one of the floating pond plants which do not need to root themselves in the mud at the bottom. The leaves of the frogbit are similar in shape to those of a water-lily but are considerably smaller.

Right: The great diving beetle lives in the vegetation zone and is a voracious carnivore. It preys on any small pond creature and, although only 3cm (1¼in) long, can even attack and kill roach.

Above: These water snails are probably feeding on algae which are attached to the water-milfoil. They respire through lungs and so have to surface frequently to take in air.

Opposite page: A turtle dove by the side of a pond. The usual habitat of this bird is woodland, but it and many other birds visit ponds and lakes occasionally to drink and bathe.

the abundant supply of dead and dying insects that fall on the surface during the warmer parts of the year.

Whirligig beetles also skim over the surface, but can descend below when hunting prey or when alarmed. The larvae and pupae of some flies such as gnats and mosquitoes use the underside of the surface film as a support when they surface to take in air.

Vegetation zone Here live the largest number of easily observed animals. Among the herbivores are the larvae of some species of caddis fly, which make their portable homes from pieces of leaf or stem. The caterpillars of the china mark moths also use

the plants for making shelters as well as feeding on them. Neat oval holes, a few centimetres long, cut out of floating leaves betray their presence in a pond. Water snails are also plant-eaters but feed mostly on the algae, especially diatoms that are attached in great numbers to larger plants and stones.

Preying on all these herbivores are the carnivorous animals: several species of water beetle such as the great diving beetle; water bugs, including the water boatmen and the water scorpion; the nymphs of dragonflies and the smaller damselflies; and several species of leeches. Not all the leeches are blood-suckers; some, including the largest the horse leech, swallow the whole of their prey.

Open water Away from the bank and marginal vegetation is the open water in which live both the largest and smallest pond animals—the fish and the planktonic crustaceans such as the water-fleas and the even smaller rotifers, which are seen with the naked eye only as a cloud in the water of a plankton net, a fine-meshed net with a transparent glass tube at the bottom.

Some fish, such as the little 3-spined sticklebacks, are exclusively carnivorous and feed mainly on living animals. Others, including the roach, take both plant and animal food.

Bottom mud In this apparently unpromising habitat a surprisingly large population exist even if it consists of only a few species. The main problem is a shortage of oxygen which is used up in large quantities by the bacterial decomposition of the remains of animals and plants (detritus). On the other hand, there is abundance of food for animals that feed on these remains. Most common are the 'blood worm' larvae of midges of the Chironomidae family. The red appearance of some of them is due to the presence in their blood of the same pigment, haemoglobin, that is in human blood.

In larger ponds there may be specimens of mussels, including the swan and duck mussels. They dig their fleshy 'feet' into the mud, open their jointed shells and take in large quantities of water through a siphon tube, extracting the oxygen they need and planktonic organisms for food and then pass out the spent water through another siphon tube.

Pond visitors Ponds attract many animals either to drink, feed or clean themselves. Grass snakes swim in search of frogs and fish; water voles feed on the marginal plants; water shrews hunt for insects. Moorhens nest in the reeds, kingfishers dive for fish; swallows skim the water for insects, and house martins gather mud for their nests. These visitors play an important role: birds carry fragments of water plants and seeds, and sometimes aquatic animals and their eggs, on their beaks, feet or plumage from one stretch of water to another. So pond animals and plants become widely distributed.

TEMPORARY POOLS: A CHANGING REGIME

Many slight depressions in the ground hold rainwater all through the short, cold days of winter and lie empty in the warmer months, when evaporation exceeds precipitation. The wildlife in these temporary pools has, therefore, to be highly adaptable.

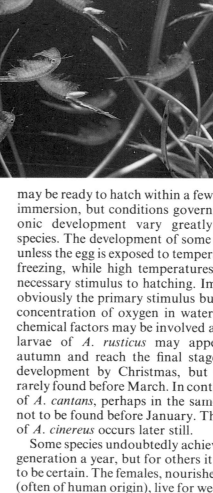

Right: This species of caddisfly—*Glyphotaelius pellucidus*—is often abundant in temporary pools.

The advantage of inhabiting a temporary pool lies in the relative freedom from predation. No fish of the European fauna can withstand the disappearance of water. Some carnivores, mainly beetles, regularly invade temporary pools and sometimes breed in them, but when they do so their active life must start with that of their prey. The result is that species which might provide a copious supply of food in a permanent pond are too large to attack.

Mosquito life-cycles The fauna of temporary pools is surprisingly diverse, but interest has centred on those animals whose way of life confines them to such places. Larvae of the mosquito genus *Aedes*, whose adults attack man fiercely, abound in the smaller pools. The larvae of *Aedes cantans* occur in pools in woodland, often with *A. rusticus* which, however, also inhabits water that is not densely shaded. *A. cinereus*, another species, is associated with fens and low-lying meadows.

The female mosquito in this genus lays her eggs on damp ground and has been observed to crawl beneath dead leaves to do so. The eggs perish if they become too dry, but survive for a long time in the damp atmosphere generally found at the surface of the soil. The embryo develops within the damp egg and

Above: Fairy shrimps—crustaceans of a primitive type and an inch or more in length—can sometimes be seen in the larger temporary pools.

Opposite page: A temporary pool in a Surrey woodland. In our relatively warm climate, with no clear-cut rainy season, there is great variation from year to year in the water regime of such a pool. Nevertheless, some species of animals have adapted to this habitat. For instance, adult bugs and beetles may fly in and leave again before the pond dries up, while other insects breed in the temporary pool and then repair to more permanent water for the next generation.

Left: *Triops cancriformis*, an extremely rare crustacean, may occasionally be found in temporary pools.

may be ready to hatch within a few minutes of immersion, but conditions governing embryonic development vary greatly with the species. The development of some is retarded unless the egg is exposed to temperatures near freezing, while high temperatures may be a necessary stimulus to hatching. Immersion is obviously the primary stimulus but the lower concentration of oxygen in water and other chemical factors may be involved as well. The larvae of *A. rusticus* may appear in the autumn and reach the final stage of larval development by Christmas, but pupae are rarely found before March. In contrast, larvae of *A. cantans*, perhaps in the same pool, are not to be found before January. The hatching of *A. cinereus* occurs later still.

Some species undoubtedly achieve only one generation a year, but for others it is not easy to be certain. The females, nourished by blood (often of human origin), live for weeks or even months and mature a batch of eggs after each meal. If the eggs are laid near the edge of the shrinking pool, larvae will appear at intervals as the water level subsequently rises, and so all stages may occur together.

In the British climate a pool can be filled by heavy rain at any time of year, but the water

Above: An algae-choked temporary pool adjacent to arable farmland in Cheshire. Temporary pools in the vicinity of farmland are not all that common. It is evident that many aquatic organisms which have no winged stage can survive for a time in the damp conditions at the bottom of a waterless pool. Pulmonate, or air-breathing, snails, such as the commonly seen ram's-horn snail (opposite), often do this. Three species are found regularly in temporary water, one of them being *Lymnaea truncatula*, the alternative host of the liver fluke which, a serious menace to sheep, sometimes infests man. Farmers therefore usually fill or drain such possible breeding places which, together with the lower rate of evaporation, is why temporary pools are seen most often in woodland.

may be gone before a generation of mosquitoes is completed. Some species guard against this possible total loss by producing eggs that require different strengths of stimulus to induce hatching. Some respond to a weak stimulus by hatching when first submerged, but others do not hatch at the first contact with water and survive to populate the pool later if earlier inundations did not last long enough.

Mosquito larvae breathe air, which they take in through two spiracles at the end of a tube, and are independent of dissolved oxygen—a substance often in short supply in a pool floored with decomposing leaves. Brushes on the front of the head keep a current of water flowing over the larvae's mouthparts, the larvae feeding on microorganisms in the water. They also descend to the bottom and scrape the surface of the dead leaves.

Unusual inhabitants In temporary pools somewhat larger than those in which mosquito larvae abound, the fairy shrimp (*Chirocephalus diaphanus*) may occasionally be seen. It is a beautiful creature and one of the most spectacular of freshwater organisms for, unlike most, it does not lie concealed in cover but swims perpetually. It must keep swimming for the rhythmical beating of its limbs not only propels it but drives a current of water forwards between the bases of the limbs

to the mouthparts. There small food organisms are filtered, manipulated and swallowed. Clearly an animal with this way of life can survive only in places never permanent enough to harbour fish. Some of the fairy shrimp's eggs hatch without exposure to air but most lie on the bottom until the pool has dried and refilled.

Another crustacean of primitive type, though not closely related to the fairy shrimp, is *Triops cancriformis*. Its characteristic fea-

ture is the broad shield-shaped carapace covering the forepart of the body. It is extremely rare in Britain, possibly because the temperature rarely reaches its optimum. The late Professor H Munro Fox wrote that there were but five published records between 1738 and 1943, though manuscript records suggest that it may have been a little more numerous early in the last century. Fox obtained specimens by placing in water dry mud from the pool where the creature had last been reported. This practice continues today from a secret source in southern England, where live *Triops* have also been seen. But the pool is unique and, hence, a closely guarded secret. *Triops*, unlike the fairy shrimp, swims right way up but resembles its relative in the possession of a series of limbs in constant rippling movement. The animals feed, however, by dabbling in the mud in search of worms, chironomid larvae and other small organisms.

One more unusual animal, *Mochlonyx culicidiformis*, is found only in temporary pools. It is related to the mosquitoes and structurally the larva is intermediate between *Aedes* and the phantom larva *Chaoborus*. The respiratory system terminates in a structure like that of a mosquito, but also comprises hydrostatic air sacs, which enable the larva to hang motionless in mid water. The other feature besides air sacs in which *Mochlonyx* resembles the phantom larva is in the antennae, which are modified for seizing prey. According to a Danish author, it feeds mainly on small crustaceans but takes mosquito larvae as well. Its life history is similar to that of *Aedes* and the larvae are found in March and April. This short, early larval life may partly explain why records of the animal are so few.

Small crustaceans are numerous in the open water of lakes and large ponds, where their only protection against predators–fishes and a variety of arthropods–is their diminutive size, coupled with an ability to reproduce very rapidly when conditions are fair and to lie dormant on the bottom in a resting stage when they are not. Tactics like these are also appropriate for life in temporary pools, and these organisms flourish in such places.

Carnivorous life in temporary pools Beetles are the main carnivores in temporary pools. Many of the adult individuals have probably dropped in during the course of casual wandering, but larvae also occur. As their development is rapid (provided, of course, that the food supply is good), and as they leave the water to pupate, a generation can be completed if the eggs are laid early enough. Some adult beetles have been found in the dead leaves and other vegetation at the bottom of a dry pond, and one species –*Agabus chalconatus*–inserts its eggs into the peat at the bottom of moorland ponds and pools; it may be able to tide over a dry period in this stage. Other beetles found in temporary pools include such species as the black *Agabus*

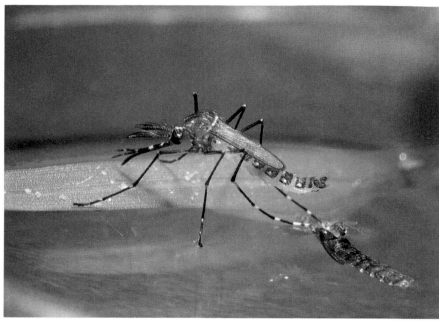

bipustulatus, and *Hydroporus palustris*, a smaller species with yellow marks on the wing covers.

Caddisflies, too, are to be found in temporary pools. *Glyphotaelius pellucidus*, for instance, is often abundant in such places. The adult life of these caddisflies is exceptionally long. They emerge in the summer but their eggs do not start to mature until the autumn, stimulated by the rapidly shortening days. This, it is believed, is an adaptation to life in small bodies of water which, even if they do not dry up completely in the summer, may be deficient in oxygen as high temperatures increase the rate of decomposition of dead organisms and of the respiration of living ones. Hatching in autumn is clearly, therefore, of great survival value.

Such lists as have been published of the animals found in temporary pools are long. In addition to those particularly adapted to this habitat, a whole variety of bugs and beetles may fly in and stay briefly, only to leave again when the pool dries.

Above: An adult mosquito of the genus *Aedes*. Larvae of this genus abound in the smaller temporary pools. The adults attack man fiercely. There are 14 British species of *Aedes*, though a number of these are rare. Two of the species breed in brackish water and are found only in coastal regions and a few inland saline areas. The larvae of a third species are hardly ever found except in the rot-holes in trees.

Below: Apart from the creatures living within the pool itself, visitors to the water edges are frequent. For instance, woodland birds–such as this chaffinch–come to drink and bathe and perhaps to catch any insects hovering over or near the water.

WILDLIFE DOWN IN THE DITCH

A ditch can be a fabulous store of plant and animal life; the natural communities found in ditches today once flourished in the vast wetland areas of lowland Britain, before the wholesale draining of fens and marshes turned them into arable or grazing land.

The humble ditch might seem an unimportant part of the country landscape, yet it plays a valuable role as a reserve for the plants and animals of water and marsh that might otherwise be extremely rare, or even absent from our countryside. Over the past 300 years, as huge areas of marsh and fen were drained and reclaimed as farm land, seven species of wetland plants have become extinct, along with the large copper butterfly. Other creatures have lost so much of their habitat that today they are found in only very small areas: the rosy marsh moth, the swallowtail butterfly and, among birds, the red kite, are just a few examples.

As the wetlands declined, the ditches that were dug to drain them increased, with the result that today we have 130,000km (80,000 miles) of ditches, some of which are of great value in preserving wildlife communities that once existed on a vast scale, before the fens and marshes were drained.

Three main types of ditch are seen in our countryside, depending on the kind of farming that is practised on the surrounding land: arable farm ditches, grassland ditches and grazing marsh dykes.

Right: A ditch in a typical grassland scene on Biggleswade Common in Bedfordshire. The yellow masses of ragwort, the thistles growing on the field, and the *Calamagrostis* grass at the waterside, have probably taken about a year to become established as they are in the picture; this tells us that the ditch is not rigorously trimmed of its vegetation, in the way that ditches on arable land are.

Below: A common toad sits among young rushes and broadleaved pondweed. It is able to survive in almost any ditch, but if it chooses a drier one it must migrate at the end of winter to deeper water where it can breed.

Arable farm ditches If a farmer is to plough the land and grow crops, the level of water in the ground (the water table) needs to be kept well below the surface, and so ditches are dug deep. The water is always kept as shallow as possible, and often these ditches dry out in summer, destroying the conditions needed by marsh plants and animals.

The vegetation in these ditches is usually trimmed, to ensure that in times of heavy rain a sudden torrent will be able to flow away freely down the ditch, instead of overflowing into the field where it could damage the crop seriously.

Under these conditions only a few of the most robust species survive, and these do not include the rarities. The remaining (relic) Cambridgeshire Fens (all of which are nature reserves) are extremely rich in wetland plants and animals, but the ditches that drain them run across arable land. Here they cannot support the same natural communities as the fens.

Grassland ditches Areas of grassland or mixed farming have a relatively high water table, and ditches that drain these are less subject to drying out. The farmer may not take the trouble to cut back their vegetation so thoroughly, since grazing land is not damaged by short-term flooding.

Such ditches certainly contain many common marsh plants and animals, and may even harbour the occasional rarity. In the Mid-

either side. These solitary gates stand on small bridges that cross the dykes, barring the way to livestock.

The grazing marshes are our best preserved relics of that long past era before the wetlands were drained so extensively; and the most interesting parts for wildlife are the dykes themselves.

Plant communities In all types of ditch, common plants of the shallow water are hard and soft rushes, branched bur-reed, greater water plantain, common water crowfoot, water cress and yellow flag. In deeper water spiked water milfoil, hornwort and fennel-leaved and broad-leaved pondweed are often found, although these may be totally absent in a ditch draining arable land. In all ditches, the starworts and all three species of duckweed can so dominate the habitat that they prevent the growth of most forms of underwater vegetation. However, this may be compensated for by prolific bankside plants which include the flowering rush, the hanging cyperus sedge and greater water dock.

Invertebrate life The water in most ditches is shallow and slow-flowing; for much of the year it is a relatively warm habitat, in which invertebrate life can flourish. Snails, beetles, water boatmen, water scorpions, water stick insects, mayflies and small crustaceans such as freshwater shrimps are abundant. These are preyed on by various species of coarse

ands, these ditches are often made more attractive by boundary hedges that run alongside them. Blackbirds, wrens, moorhens, yellowhammers and even corn buntings use these as nesting sites or singing posts. Kingfishers perch in the hedges, diving down to catch sticklebacks in the clear water. In autumn the banks and muddy spurs of these ditches attract grey wagtail and green sandpiper, which come to find worms and other small animals living in the mud.

Grazing marsh dykes Grazing marshes are areas of farmland close to water that are flooded during the winter. In summer the land is relatively dry and is excellent for grazing. In winter it may bring no yield to the farmer, although in the past a crop of reeds or other marsh vegetation may have been cut.

Because hedges could not be grown on land that was regularly flooded, and fences could only be made of wood, which would quickly rot away, ditches were the traditional markers of farm or field boundaries. They were sometimes known as 'wet fences' or, more usually, dykes. In Somerset and neighbouring counties they are called rhynes, pronounced 'reens'.

The grazing marsh is an open landscape, in which pollarded willows are characteristic. Their gnarled and twisted trunks offer the only protection from the wind and rain that sweep across the low-lying marshes. No hedges or other obstacles are seen, but here and there a gate stands without a fence on

Right: Bladderwort is a typical plant of ditches where the soil is more acid and deficient in nutrients, for it can survive here by feeding on small invertebrates trapped in its underwater bladders.

Below: Such insects as this backswimmer can often be found in ditches where the water is shallow and slow moving. The backswimmer swims upside down, but it has well-developed wings and can fly strongly.

Right: The great water dock is typical in the ditches that preserve the plant communities of ancient wetlands.

Opposite page: The harvest mouse can sometimes be found among the reeds in dykes and ditches.

Below right: The bank vole inhabits the drier ditches, such as those on arable land.

Below: A dyke at Woodwalton Fen in Cambridgeshire. The tall foliage on the left is reed canary grass, while on the right is a dense fringe of common reed. Choking the water in the dyke is water violet, a typical plant of the nutrient-rich peaty soils common in the fens.

fish. Sticklebacks, however, are themselves preyed on by invertebrates – dragonfly nymphs or the great silvery water beetle.

Larger life Ditches other than those in intensively farmed arable areas remain the stronghold of the common frog which despite its name, is now declining in numbers. The common toad is still abundant in ditches of all areas, being less dependent on a constant level of water. The palmate and crested newts have fared particularly badly in the south-east of England, but the smooth newt is relatively abundant in all types of ditch.

The most obvious and abundant mammals found in our ditches are the water vole and the bank vole; the bank vole is common in drier parts of ditches, especially those flanked by a hedge. Another mammal that frequently inhabits the ditch is the water shrew, a secretive animal which incidentally cannot resist eating water cress. In dykes with a margin of reeds you may be lucky enough to find a harvest mouse, for this was probably the original habitat of the harvest mouse before cereals were grown by man.

One hunter of the ditch is the heron, which stands motionless, its hypnotic yellow eyes staring down at the water. Quietly it waits for a frog, a water vole or even a large insect such as a dragonfly, to appear. Another predator is the otter, which in small numbers inhabits the dykes of the Norfolk Broads, but is slightly more common in the rhynes of the Somerset Levels.

Some ditches on arable land are overgrown with the tall stems of common reed, for example in the area of Essex where salt marshes have been reclaimed. These ditches are enlivened by the chatter of reed and sedge warbler, while the explosive song of Cetti's warbler is now increasingly heard.

In other ditches, where the water is retained throughout the year, shoveler and mallard breed, while the subtle colours of the dabchick are a less commonplace sight. At night when the mist hangs over the reeds, you can sometimes hear the raucous call of the water rail, a sound that recalls the far-off days when the wildlife of our ditches used to roam through vast regions of wetland.

Plants of lake, pond and marsh

The stable water regime provided by a lake or pond is essential to the survival of many hundreds of plant species. The plants of still water come in many forms, each making use of the aquatic habitat in a different way. First, there are the free-living algae that spread through the body of the water as deep as the light penetrates. Some are single-celled plants, occurring in millions, while others are larger filaments or colonies. Among them are the primitive blue-green algae. In some conditions any of these can become so abundant as to turn the water into a thick green 'soup'.

Other plants, such as the duckweeds, pondweeds and water starworts, are not rooted, but need to be at or very close to the surface to spread their leaves to receive the sun. These are all flowering plants, but their tissues are adapted to the aquatic way of life with air spaces to buoy them up and allow oxygen to filter through to where it is needed.

Shallower water is colonized by a whole new range of plants which have the best of everything – abundant water and nutrients and protection from most grazing animals. Plants like bogbean, water forget-me-not, reedmace and reeds thrive here, producing a lush, dense fringing and floating vegetation.

Beyond this again there are the marginal plants, which are happiest close to water but which cannot tolerate prolonged immersion. Many of these, such as alders and willows, have their seeds dispersed by water so that they naturally end up where they grow best – at the water's edge.

Left: Hogweed is often to be found growing along lake and river banks, in ditches and wet woods and also in rich meadows. It can reach a height of 1.5m (5ft). Here the leaves and brown seed heads are shown.

CHECKLIST

This checklist is a guide to some of the plants you can find in and around lakes, ponds and marshes. Although you will not see them all in the same place, you should be able to spot many of them throughout the changing seasons. The species listed in **bold** *type are described in detail.*

Alder
Algae
Amphibious bistort
Awlwort
Bladderwort
Bogbean
Clubrush
Common reed
Duckweeds
Early marsh orchid
Fringed water-lily
Frog-bit
Great water dock
Hornwort
Indian balsam
Lesser spearwort
Loch Lomond dock
Mare's-tail
Marsh cinquefoil
Marsh marigold
Marsh pea
Marsh valerian
Marsh violet
Marshwort
Meadowsweet
Monkey flower
Osiers
Pillwort
Pipewort
Pondweeds
Purple loosestrife
Quillwort
Ragged robin
Sedges
Shoreweed
Sweet flag
Water crowfoot
Water lobelia
Water milfoils
Water soldier
Water starwort
Water violet
Waterworts
White water-lily
Yellow flag
Yellow water-lily

Left: Beds of the common reed can vary in size from narrow waterside fringes to large areas that extend over many acres. Reeds need water in the soil if they are to grow, so they often stand with their roots submerged.

PLENTIFUL POND ALGAE

There are many kinds of pond algae, which play an important part in providing food for the other pond inhabitants. The algae are not all microscopic— some such as *Spirogyra* build up into dense masses, while others can actually swim or move around.

Above: Water lilies surrounded by an algal mat on the surface of a pond. Many types of algae, such as *Spirogyra* and blanket weed, float in open ponds, where they may form a scum or bloom as they multiply rapidly in sunny conditions.

The algae that live in ponds and other fresh water are related to the familiar seaweeds of the seashore. Many freshwater algae belong to the same group (the Chlorophyceae) as the sea lettuce–a common shore weed. Other common freshwater algae belong to the primitive Cyanophyceae (blue-green algae), and the Bacillariophyceae. The latter includes the diatoms, which also have marine representatives.

Pond algae, unlike their larger marine relatives, are mostly one-celled, or thread-like, filamentous plants. They are usually found floating on the sunlit surface waters of the pond, although some attach themselves to rocks or to the stems and roots of larger plants.

Together with vegetable debris such as leaves that fall into the water, these algae form the basis of food webs in all the fresh waters of the world. Like all photosynthetic plants, the algae produce food by using the energy of the sun to make sugars for growth. The algae are then eaten by animals, which derive energy from them. Some of the larger algae contribute indirectly to the food web when they die, by sinking to the bottom where they become part of the debris. This then provides food for many animals, as well as bacteria.

Microscopic diatoms Diatoms consist of either a single cell enclosed by a cell wall made of silica, or a group of such cells and their walls, joined together. The wall is separated into two halves which fit together like a box and its lid. Under a microscope, diatoms exhibit a fascinating range of shapes and cell wall sculpturing. One of the most common forms is *Asterionella* in which the cells are joined to form a star-shape. *Fragilaria* and the rectangular *Tabellaria* form zig-zag chains while *Pinnularia* has single boat-shaped cells.

Their skeletons fall to the bottom of the pond where they die. In many parts of the world, hundreds of tons of these skeletons have collected and become fossilised to form deposits called diatomaceous earths. These deposits – also known as fuller's earth – are mined and used as ingredients in paints, polishes, toothpastes and in industrial filtration systems.

Fresh water desmids Sharing the surface waters of the ponds with diatoms are the microscopic green algae, known as desmids. Also found on the surface of mud where they sometimes form a green film, they differ from the diatoms in being found in fresh water only. Along with other members of the same family (the Chlorophyceae) such as *Spirogyra*, *Chlamydomonas*, *Volvox* and *Cladophora*, they contain only the green pigment chlorophyll.

In the desmids each cell is divided into halves by a horizontal constriction. They are a very variable group, the cell walls of some such as *Staurastrum*, having long, spiky projections, while others, such as *Micrasterias*, are smoother in outline. Species such as *Desmidium* have the cells joined together in short filaments.

Swimmers and rollers *Chlamydomonas* is one of the simplest of the green algae. It is microscopic and consists of one cell, which is pear-shaped and contains a large green chloroplast, containing chlorophyll, which is used in photosynthesis. It has two whip-like flagella which enable it to swim round in the water and it can multiply very quickly by cell division, the increase in numbers making the water turn green within a few days.

Many green algae are banded together in colonies or groups. In some species there are only a few cells in each colony. *Eudorina*, for

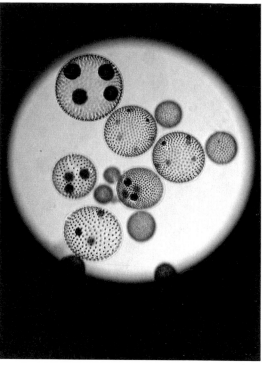

xample, has 32 cells. Each colonial cell esembles a *Chlamydomonas* cell, with a U-haped chloroplast and two flagella, with the ells always arranged in a definite order. The lobular-looking *Volvox* is a colonial form on a grand scale, with thousands of cells arranged round the outside of a hollow ball, generally connected by a strand of protoplasm to make one individual. About the size of a pinhead, it is just apparent to the naked eye but beneath a microscope it can be seen to move by rolling slowly along, rotating as it does so.

Filamentous green algae Not all green algae are planktonic or colonial. *Spirogyra* is a familiar algae which consists of tangled masses of long green filaments, which are covered in mucilage, making them slimy to the touch. These filaments float in the water or may be attached to the bottom of a pond. *Cladophora* (flannel or blanket weed), is superficially similar to *Spirogyra*, but its hair-like masses of tangled filaments are not slimy and are always found floating, sometimes in such numbers that they choke the pond or slow-moving stream where they grow.

The best time of year to see any of these algae is in the spring, for during the winter the numbers remain low due to the low light intensity and short days. When spring arrives, longer days and increased light intensity

Above: *Spirogyra* can reproduce by conjugation. The nucleii in opposite cells in separate strands fuse to form a new cell.

Right: *Volvox* colonies, as seen through a microscope.

cause the algae to multiply rapidly. The numbers may increase to such an extent that the water turns green and cloudy–an algal 'bloom' has occurred. Often one particular species becomes dominant, such as the diatom *Asterionella* which is a common constituent of an algal bloom.

Blue-green algae Frequently found in polluted ponds, blue-green algae are among the most simple and primitive organisms living on the earth. A few of them are unicellular, but they are usually filamentous or colonial. The cells are held together not only by the cell walls sticking to each other, but also by a thick gelatinous envelope which surrounds the whole organism. *Oscillatoria* is a filamentous form, growing as a blue-green slime on stones, and moving about by gliding through the water. Others, such as *Anabaena* and *Nostoc* form gelatinous masses containing many tangled filaments which may be floating in the water or attached to the bottom.

Pollution in ponds

Ponds, ditches and reservoirs are affected in many ways by our way of life today. One important factor is the increasing amount of phosphate found in ponds. A constituent of fertilisers and detergents, it washes into fresh waters from fertilised arable land. Phosphate is an essential factor in algal growth, and lack of it causes the bulk of the algal population to die, while large amounts have the effect of removing the limiting factor on algal growth, causing the plants to multiply rapidly. Blue-green algae in particular can increase uncontrollably, choking a pond and creating anaerobic (oxygen deficient) conditions. Hydrogen sulphide gas, smelling like rotten eggs, is given off by the bacteria in such a pond. The pond may take a very long time to recover from the effects of the pollution since the gas is very poisonous.

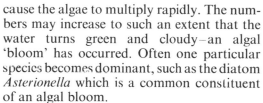

Left: Bubbles of oxygen among the blanket weed are evidence of photosynthesis taking place. Dense masses of this algae can form in ponds, stifling the other vegetation.

FLOATING CARPETS OF DUCKWEED

Duckweeds–a group of tiny floating plants which can cover still waters in a carpet of green–include Britain's smallest flowering plant.

The still waters found in many parts of lowland Britain are rich in dissolved salts, rich enough indeed for aquatic plants to grow in these waters and absorb enough salts for their needs.

Some aquatics are anchored to the bed of the water via their roots, but others are free-floating and have the advantage that they can grow in areas where the water is too deep for bottom-rooted plants, thus avoiding the competition for space that so often occurs in shallower waters. Also, by floating on the surface of the water they are not competing for light with submerged water-weeds or the numerous types of algae that abound in rich waters.

Tiny duckweeds The smallest aquatic flowering plants in Britain are the duckweeds. They can flourish where the water is much too shallow for other aquatics, for example in shallow drainage ditches at the edges of fields or in water-filled wheel ruts. They can even be found in a tiny pool formed in the muddy depression of a cow's hoof-print.

Duckweed is often seen forming an unbroken carpet of green over a stretch of still water, usually one with a muddy bottom rich in decomposing organic matter. The danger of duckweed hiding water of some uncertain depth probably accounts for some of its less savoury local names, given to it to frighten children away. For example in the west of England duckweed is known as Jenny Green-

Above: The covering of duckweed over this stretch of water is so complete that it looks at first glance like a lawn.

Below: Gibbous duckweed, here with the small green or reddish domed thalli, is fairly widespread in Britain, though absent from the far north and parts of the south-west. The rosettes of larger, darker green leaves belong to a quite different species of aquatic, water starwort, a bottom-rooting plant.

teeth, who was also a pond-elf supposed to lurk hidden from view in duckweed-covered waters.

Duckweed structure If you examine a carpet of duckweed you will find that it consists of innumerable small leaf-like structures called 'platelets'. Each platelet has some of the properties of both a leaf and a stem, and so is given a distinct name: 'thallus' (plural thalli). Each thallus usually has one or more roots hanging from its under-surface.

The flowers are not often recorded in Britain, partly because they are inconspicuous. Indeed, some species of duckweed have never been recorded in flower in this country. When flowers do form, they usually appear on plants that are fully exposed to the sun. The flowers are extremely tiny, sometimes less than 1mm across, and consist of a single female flower with just one ovary, and two male flowers each with one or two stamens. Both male and female parts are enclosed in a hood-like sheath borne in a shallow pocket on the edge of the thallus.

Great duckweed The largest British duckweed is the great duckweed, a plant that is fairly widespread in this country, though not particularly common, and is absent from the far north and parts of the south-west.

Each thallus of the great duckweed is up to 15mm ($\frac{3}{5}$in) long, green on top and often reddish-purple beneath. In the autumn, the plants produce specialised purplish thal-

alled turions, which become detached and ink to the bottom of the water. Here, they tand a much better chance of surviving the igours of winter than does a floating plant ecause they are less likely to be frozen into he ice. In the spring, the turions become uoyant and rise to the surface, where they esume growth and start producing normal reen thalli.

Commonest and smallest By far the commonest of the British duckweeds is the common duckweed, which can be found on almost ny body of still water in Britain, often covering the surface of the water almost to the total xclusion of other aquatics. The thalli are up o 4mm across and more or less flat with a ingle root. Among British duckweeds this is he species most likely to flower, bearing its mall greenish blooms in June and July.

Another species, rootless duckweed, has he distinction of being Britain's smallest owering plant. Each minute thallus, scarcely mm across, is a blob of tissue barely recogisable as a flowering plant and looking more ke an alga. Unfortunately, rootless duckeed is close to the limits of its range in Britain nd does not flower here. It spreads by a new hallus budding from one end of an old hallus. This species occurs only in southern ngland and Wales, and even here it is ecoming rarer as more and more of our etlands are being drained.

Submerged duckweed Ivy duckweed is an

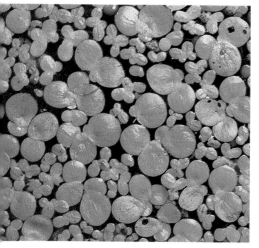

oddity among British duckweeds because it is normally completely submerged. It differs in many other ways, too. The thalli are more elongated than other species of duckweed, and taper at the base into a short stalk. At the base of the stalk two more thalli arise opposite each other and at right-angles to the original thallus. In this manner, a three-dimensional pattern is built up of several interconnecting thalli.

The plants are also a much darker green than other duckweeds and their thalli are translucent, but when ivy duckweed is ready to flower its similarity to the other duckweeds becomes apparent. It sends up fertile thalli to float on the surface of the water. These thalli are smaller, oval and a paler green than the submerged thalli, and altogether much more like the typical duckweed thalli.

Duckweed look-alike A plant very similar to the duckweeds, though it is a fern rather than a flowering plant, is *Azolla filiculoides*. This, an introduced species from North America, is becoming increasingly common in southern Britain. It floats on the surface of still waters, forming carpets of foliage in a similar manner to duckweeds. During a long hot summer it grows at a prodigious rate and, in a small pond, serious overcrowding can push plants at either the middle or the edge right out of the water.

Above: As well as being an aquatic, *Azolla* can also survive for some time on sites that are merely damp, for example among mud or wet moss.

Though superficially similar to duckweeds, *Azolla* has a quite different structure, its branched stems bearing two ranks of leaves.

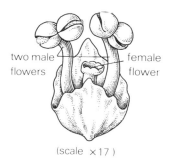

two male flowers — female flower

(scale ×17)

Above: Male and female flowers of common duckweed, the species most likely to flower in Britain.

Opposite: The common and the great duckweeds, the latter having the larger thalli, about 15mm across.

British duckweeds

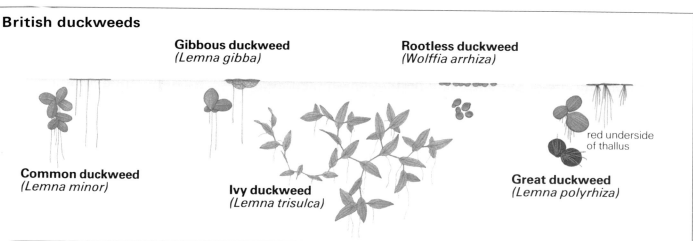

Gibbous duckweed
(*Lemna gibba*)

Rootless duckweed
(*Wolffia arrhiza*)

Common duckweed
(*Lemna minor*)

Ivy duckweed
(*Lemna trisulca*)

red underside of thallus

Great duckweed
(*Lemna polyrhiza*)

THE MUDDY WORLD OF WATERWORTS

Among our smallest flowering plants are two species of waterworts that spring up suddenly and irregularly to colonize muddy lake-sides.

stems creep across the mud, rooting at every node (leaf joint). In deeper water, however, the plants assume a more straggly growth as the stems–which are only barely anchored in the lake bed–reach up towards the surface of the water.

Structure and life-cycle The flowers of both species are extremely small, no more than 3-4mm across. They are borne in the axils between the leaves and the stem from July to September. Flowers of *hexandra* have three delicate petals, while those of *hydropiper* have four. In both species, the petals are usually pale pink but may sometimes be white. Normally the flowers are self-pollinating, and if they are submerged in water they remain

Above: An unusually dry summer caused the water level of this loch in West Stirlingshire to fall and the exposed muddy fringe to be colonized by waterworts and other aquatic plants.

Below: As the exposed mud begins to dry out and crack, numerous small plants of eight-stamened waterwort appear on the surface. Not only is this mud organically rich, its dark colour readily absorbs heat from the sun, promoting rapid germination and growth.

For such diminutive plants Britain's two species of waterworts have unimaginatively long and cumbersome English names: the six-stamened waterwort and the eight-stamened waterwort. Both belong to the same genus, *Elatine*, and botanists usually prefer to distinguish between the two species by their scientific names, *hexandra* for the six-stamened species and *hydropiper* for the eight-stamened.

Waterworts are small plants, rarely exceeding 10cm (4in) in length and usually considerably smaller. They are pioneer colonists of bare mud and silty sand just above and below the water's edge. When exposed to the air, or just lightly covered with water, the slender

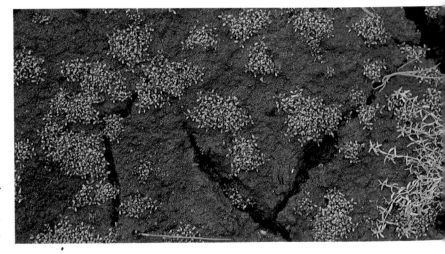

unopened. Yet if the flowers are exposed above the water surface they may sometimes be visited by pollinating insects and cross-pollination might occur. Indeed, the flowers have nectar-producing glands, which implies that the waterwort family was once terrestrial.

The seeds are small and weigh very little, so they are readily dispersed short distances by the flow of the water. Long-range dispersal, on the other hand, seems to be assisted by water fowl, the seeds becoming embedded in mud which then sticks to the birds' feet and feathers. The appearance and establishment of *hydropiper* at an Anglesey reservoir within 8 years of its being built almost certainly resulted from the seeds being transferred there by birds. Similarly, it is surely no coincidence that the ten or so lochs in central Scotland where *hydropiper* has been found since its discovery at Loch Lomond in 1968 are all noted for their wildfowl populations.

Once the seeds have become buried in the mud they can remain viable for many years, waiting for the right conditions in which to germinate: a fall in the water level occurring at the right time of year. As the intensity of light increases the seeds are triggered into germination.

Habitat and associates Waterworts are unable to compete for living space with the much larger perennial plants such as common reed and sedges, which follow in the wake of the first mud colonists. In Britain, these larger plants are sometimes prevented from becoming established around the edge of a lake by the effect of waves breaking upon wind-exposed shores. Another deterrent is farm animals trampling along the muddy fringes and the regular beaching of small boats on the shore. Both will erode the thickest aquatic plant growth, yet leave the tiny waterworts largely unaffected.

The waterworts' inability to compete with large aquatic plants is shared by other small or weak-growing inhabitants of the water's edge. Among the plants most often seen with *hexandra* and *hydropiper* are water purslane, common and autumnal water-starworts, needle spike-rush and shoreweed. A combination, or 'community', of several of these plants growing together in shallow water or on exposed mud is a good indication that one or both waterworts is growing close by.

Neither waterwort is found in lakes whose water originates in areas underlaid with limestone. In the nutrient-poor waters of the Lake District and the Scottish Highlands, only *hexandra* occurs. Conversely, *hydropiper* thrives at several sites moderately rich in nutrients. These are sites that *hexandra* seems to avoid though there is a definite overlap in the distributions of the two species.

In Finland, and perhaps in other northern European countries, *hydropiper* grows in brackish water by the sea. The nearest example in Britain to this type of habitat is a small lake at the head of an estuary in north

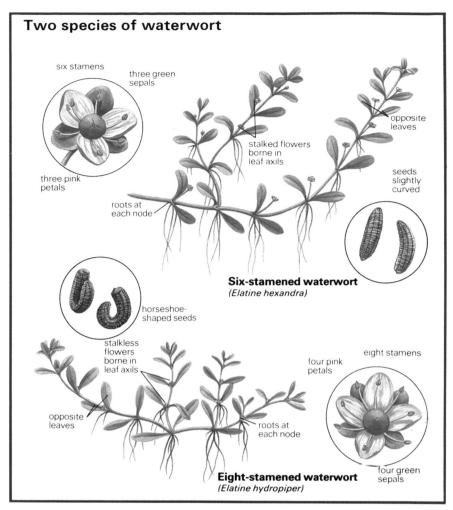

Two species of waterwort

six stamens
three green sepals
opposite leaves
stalked flowers borne in leaf axils
three pink petals
roots at each node
seeds slightly curved

Six-stamened waterwort
(*Elatine hexandra*)

horseshoe-shaped seeds
stalkless flowers borne in leaf axils
opposite leaves
roots at each node

four pink petals
eight stamens
four green sepals

Eight-stamened waterwort
(*Elatine hydropiper*)

Wales, where *hydropiper* has been reported growing alongside the coastal species, beaked tassel-weed.

The outlook A serious threat to the future of our waterwort colonies comes from agricultural fertilisers finding their way into lakes. Even the additional nutrients stemming from modern fish farms can be enough to tip the balance towards prolific algal growth, their dense mass near the surface of the water preventing light from penetrating to plants such as waterworts lying below. Experience, however, has shown us that we should never write off waterworts too soon, for they have a habit of reappearing unexpectedly in numbers at sites where they were presumed extinct.

Above: A comparison of the six-stamened and the eight-stamened waterworts, showing differences in their flower structure and seeds.

Below: With the aid of a hand lens the six-stamened species can be distinguished by the petals and sepals being in threes, the eight-stamened having them in fours. The normally green fruiting capsules and leaves of both species frequently turn red when exposed above the water line for any length of time.

AQUATIC PLANTS: A LIFE UNDERWATER

Many plants flourish in still or slow-moving water in ponds, the shallow margins of lakes and in man-made habitats such as gravel pits and canals. The attractive flowers and foliage of some of the species are familiar sights in ornamental ponds.

Below: The water violet (*Hottonia palustris*) grows in scattered localities throughout England and Wales. Its attractive, yellow-throated lilac flowers, carried on erect stems up to 30cm (12in) high, bloom in May and June.

The water's edge is a boundary between two quite different environments: the land, where plants obtain water and nutrients mainly from below, and must find their own support; and water, where plants are surrounded and supported by the water itself and where nutrients are often available all around. Between the dry land and free water, all kinds of plants have found a home, adapting to their situation in various ways. Some species hardly differ from land plants; others are partially submerged, many with underwater leaves which differ from those on the surface and yet others float on the surface or are completely submerged.

Adaptations to underwater life Underwater species often look very different from their land-dwelling counterparts. Since most of the plants' weight is supported by the water, they may have slender, weak and easily broken stems. In nutrient-rich waters, the minerals essential to plant growth can be absorbed over much of the plant's surface so the roots play a relatively minor role, often doing little more than anchoring the plant.

Carbon dioxide, essential for photosynthesis, is dissolved in the water and can be taken up directly through the leaves. Oxygen is a by-product of photosynthesis and appears as small silvery bubbles among the foliage on a sunny day. Gas exchange under water is less efficient than in the air, so the leaves are usually finely divided, or thin and very

LAKE AND POND PLANTS

numerous to give the maximum surface area. Finely divided leaves also cut down resistance to water movement and so minimise damage to the plants in moving water.

Aquatic reproduction Most of our aquatic flowering plants produce their flowers above the surface of the water to take advantage of the wind or insects to effect pollination. In some species, pollen is carried by the water, while in others new plants can be produced by fragmentation, an asexual method of reproduction. Stem fragments may be broken off by passing waterfowl or the drag of the current and carried to new localities by wave action or in mud on the feet of wading birds. Each fragment is capable of independent growth

Above: The mare's-tail (*Hippuris vulgaris*) owes its name to early botanists who believed it to be the female form of the horsetail, a relative of the ferns. The inconspicuous flowers produced by the mare's-tail in summer help to distinguish it—the horsetail is a spore-bearing species, not a flowering plant. Water starwort (*Callitriche stagnalis*), shown at the bottom of the page, is aptly-named from its floating, star-shaped rosettes of leaves.

the water surface. The lower flowers are female and the upper ones, with larger petals, are male, although flowers in between usually have both male and female parts.

Mare's-tail, a relative of the water-milfoils, grows in ponds, ditches and slow-moving streams throughout Britain, particularly where the water flows over chalk or limestone. A creeping rootstock in the bottom mud gives rise to unbranched stems that rise above the water surface, producing tiny greenish flowers during the summer.

The aquatic primrose The feathery underwater foliage of the water-milfoils can be confused with that of the water violet but the species are easily distinguished when the flowers appear. The water violet is not, in fact, a violet at all but the only fully aquatic member of the primrose family in the British Isles. Although well adapted to life in the water, the flowers of this species need to be raised above the surface if successful cross-pollination is to occur. Nectar is produced by the flowers to attract the various insects that pollinate them.

Water pollinated plants The branching stems of hornwort, most commonly seen in still or slow-moving water, are covered with dense, bristle-like, forked leaves. The inconspicuous flowers, borne under water in the axils of the leaves, are found only on plants growing in warm, well-lit waters. The anthers of the male flowers, which contain the pollen,

| Spiked water-milfoil (*Myriophyllum spicatum*). Flowers June-July. | Alternate-flowered water-milfoil (*Myriophyllum alterniflorum*). May-Aug. | Hornwort (*Ceratophyllum demersum*). Found S and E England to depths of up to 8m (26ft). | Curled pondweed (*Potamogeton crispus*). Often grows in ponds and streams with Canadian pondweed. |

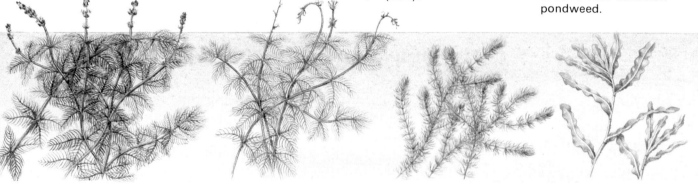

and can start a new colony. In this manner, aquatics can spread very rapidly, even if seed is not produced.

Water-milfoils Several species of water-milfoil grow in the British Isles, some native and some introduced. The two commonest native species are spiked water-milfoil, generally found in lime-rich waters, and alternate-flowered water-milfoil, which grows in peaty, lime-free water. The common name 'milfoil' probably derives from the French for 'a thousand leaves' and aptly describes how the whorled leaves of these species are finely divided into numerous segments.

In summer, water-milfoils produce inconspicuous flowers, carried in a spike above

detach themselves and float to the surface where they burst and release the tiny pollen grains. The pollen slowly sinks back down through the water and if it should land on a female flower, pollination can occur.

In cooler waters, propagation of this species more usually occurs when pieces of the fragile stem break off and the fragments continue growing into larger plants.

Water starworts produce narrow, undivided leaves in opposite pairs under water, and most of the commoner species also produce rosettes of broader, floating leaves. The flowers are minute, green and without petals, arising singly or in pairs at the base of the leaves, usually only in the floating rosettes, from April to September. Pollen usually drifts from the male flowers to the female flowers on the water's surface, or is borne by the wind.

Plenty of pondweeds The dense, dark green foliage of the Canadian pondweed is completely submerged and is composed of undivided, stalkless leaves arranged in whorls of three around the stems. Canadian pondweed has separate male and female plants. The female flowers are commonly seen floating on the surface of the water, borne on long, slender stalks, while the male flowers are inconspicuous and produced at the base of underwater leaves. They are seldom recorded as the male plant is rare in this country.

A closely related species which is becoming

Above: Frog bit (*Hydrocharis morsus-ranae*) overwinters as a turion (bud), resting on the bottom of the pond. Here it is sprouting in spring.

Right: The rounded, kidney shaped leaves of frog bit floating on the water surface.

Above: The small, greenish flowers of broad-leaved pondweed are held above the water in a spike, supported by the floating leaves below. They are wind-pollinated and the fruits that develop may float a considerable distance from the parent plant on the water currents. Amphibious bistort (*Polygonum amphibium*), shown right, is sometimes confused with broad-leaved pondweed but the flowers on its spike are pink or red and insect-pollinated.

much more common each year is *Elodea nuttallii*. This species is very variable in appearance, with leaves in whorls of up to six. It can be distinguished from Canadian pondweed by its slender, narrowly pointed leaf tips and female flowers which are half the size of those of Canadian pondweed.

There are many varieties of the true pondweeds (*Potamogeton* species). Some species produce all their leaves under water, while others have leaves floating at the surface. The leaf shape varies according to the depth.

Curled pondweed is one of the most distinctive species. Its delicate, translucent leaves are crisped and curled at the margin and all submerged. Usually pale green, the leaves may become reddish-brown in deeper waters.

One of the commonest species, broad-leaved pondweed, has wide leaves that float on the surface of the water and are jointed at the base where they join the stalk. It can be confused with the amphibious bistort, which also has broad, floating leaves when growing in ponds or canals.

However, amphibious bistort has a different leaf structure, veins arising along the length of the midrib, not all from near the base as in the broad-leaved pondweed. As its name implies, amphibious bistort is just as much at home on land as in water, and has a terrestrial form with more erect, stouter stems and narrower leaves with shorter stalks.

BROAD LEAVED PONDWEEDS

Look beneath the floating leaves of a pondweed and you may find that the leaves below have a quite different shape from the ones on top.

Above: The large floating leaves of the broad-leaved pondweed (*Potamogeton natans*), here seen with the much smaller, lobed leaves of the common water-crowfoot (*Ranunculus aquatilis*). The much narrower submerged leaves, which cannot be seen here, appear in the spring before the floating leaves unfurl. Once the latter start to develop, however, they may shade out the submerged leaves and become the predominant source of chlorophyll.

In Britain, broad-leaved pondweeds (as distinct from the less important narrow-leaved pondweeds) can be found in a wide range of aquatic habitats: from natural lakes and rivers to man-made reservoirs, canals, drainage ditches and ponds. They are the primary source of food for many insects and fishes, and they improve the quality of the water they inhabit by oxygenating it and absorbing excess nutrients. Pondweeds are also important as sites for fishes to lay their eggs and for microscopic algae to colonize. The eggs and algae are often eaten by insect larvae which, in turn, fall prey to larger insects, amphibians, fishes and birds. Pondweeds are, therefore, important not only as a source of food in themselves but also as a 'larder' to be raided by hunters.

Aquatic herbs Broad-leaved pondweeds belong to the genus *Potamogeton*, a group of aquatic herbaceous plants with representatives in all five Continents. They inhabit fresh water and are known to live in brackish conditions as well, though this is rare. Some species are occasionally capable of surviving out of water if the river or pond dries up, though they cannot normally complete their life-cycle in such an environment.

The flowers of a pondweed are small and insignificant, borne on flower spikes that appear above the surface of the water. Pollination may be via wind, water or insects. Once fertilisation has occurred the fruit stalks often bend back into the water, allowing the fruits to mature at or below the water surface.

There are 11 species of broad-leaved pondweed in Britain. Four of these are submerged species, the only time they appear at the surface being during the flowering season. The other seven species all have some floating leaves and some submerged leaves and, in all but one case, these are two different shapes – a phenomenon known as heterophylly.

Variable leaves All the British species of pondweed that exhibit heterophylly have broad floating leaves and much narrower submerged leaves since these are the most efficient shapes for their particular situations. Broad leaves float better, while narrow leaves are better under water because they offer less resistance to water flow. Furthermore, the broad shape of a floating leaf allows it to catch the maximum amount of sunlight and so makes it more efficient at photosynthesis. Narrow leaves, however, are more efficient photosynthesisers in the often murky waters below the surface.

Among Britain's six pondweeds showing heterophylly, three tend to have more submerged leaves than floating ones. These species are the reddish pondweed, the various-leaved pondweed and the leafy pondweed. Two species–the bog and broad-leaved pondweeds–have more floating leaves than submerged. In the remaining species, the Lodden pondweed, neither type of leaf predominates.

Types of heterophylly

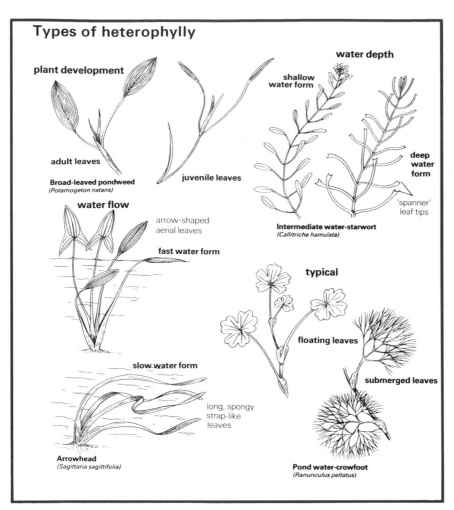

plant development

adult leaves

Broad-leaved pondweed
(Potamogeton natans)

juvenile leaves

water depth

shallow water form

deep water form

'spanner' leaf tips

Intermediate water-starwort
(Callitriche hamulata)

water flow

arrow-shaped aerial leaves

fast water form

slow water form

long, spongy strap-like leaves

Arrowhead
(Sagittaria sagittifolia)

typical

floating leaves

submerged leaves

Pond water-crowfoot
(Ranunculus peltatus)

young submerged leaves are strap-shaped and membranous; as they age they elongate, sometimes reaching up to 20cm (8in) long. The floating leaves appear only during the summer and are much more opaque than the submerged ones.

Superficially, the various-leaved pondweed is similar to the reddish species, but it exhibits heterophylly much more readily—hence its name. It also has a similar distribution, and the two species are quite often found together, though it shows an even greater preference for acid water.

The leafy pondweed, which is also known as the American pondweed, is native in Europe to just one area—the Outer Hebrides, where it was discovered only during the last few decades. It is a very distinct species, with flattened stems and translucent leaves which are about 20 times longer than they are wide.

The broad-leaved pondweed is the most common member of this group in Europe. It can grow in a wide range of habitats, being equally at home in both acid and alkaline waters. Its submerged leaves are long, narrow and opaque—unlike those of other pondweeds, which are translucent. The floating leaves are perfectly adapted to sitting on the water surface because they have two flexible, jointed wings where the leaf blade meets the stalk.

The two remaining species showing heterophylly are the bog and Lodden pondweeds.

The proportion of the different leaf types varies, however, with the depth of water in which the plant lives. The proportion of submerged leaves becomes greater in deep water, while in shallow water the floating leaves become more numerous and the submerged leaves may even be lacking.

Plants with heterophylly The reddish pondweed, named after the reddish tinge sometimes found on its leaves, occurs in scattered locations throughout Britain, though it is rarely common. It prefers slightly acid, peaty water and thrives in lakes, rivers and ponds with a large amount of organic matter on their beds. The plant dies back in late summer and then begins to grow again in early winter. The

Six pondweeds

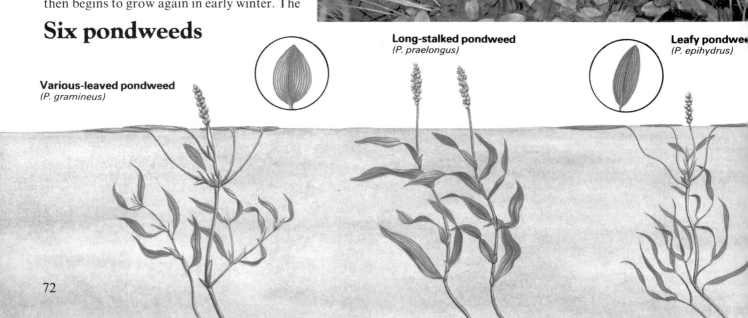

Various-leaved pondweed
(P. gramineus)

Long-stalked pondweed
(P. praelongus)

Leafy pondweed
(P. epihydrus)

The former prefers upland or acid water and is most often found in bog pools and shallow flushes. The latter plant is one of the most beautiful of the large British pondweeds, having very thin translucent leaves and an attractive pattern of veins. The Lodden pondweed is found in certain tributaries of the Thames, the Dorset Stour and the Bristol Avon, and has a high resistance to pollution.

Submerged species Of the five British broad-leaved pondweeds not displaying heterophylly, four are submerged species. The smallest and most easily identifiable of these is the curly pondweed because its leaves have distinct teeth along the margins. A robust species, it is well able to resist pollution and other disturbances to the environment.

The three larger submerged species are the shining, long-stalked and perfoliate pondweeds. The perfoliate prefers deep water and is common in slow-flowing rivers, canals, ponds and lakes, particularly in central England. The long-stalked species is named after the way in which the flowers are borne on very long stalks well clear of the water. The shining pondweed is the commonest pondweed in lowland rivers of southern England but it is rare elsewhere.

Fen pondweed The odd one out among British broad-leaved pondweeds is the fen pondweed, which is neither a submerged species nor does it exhibit heterophylly. It shows a distinct preference for the Fens.

Above: The parallel veins on the leaves of this pondweed are typical of the group.

Right: A flower-spike of broad-leaved pondweed. Each tiny flower is no more than about 4mm across.

Below left: The bog pondweed (*Potamogeton polygonifolius*).

Below: Reddish pondweed (*Potamogeton alpinus*). Note how its submerged leaves are much narrower than the floating ones.

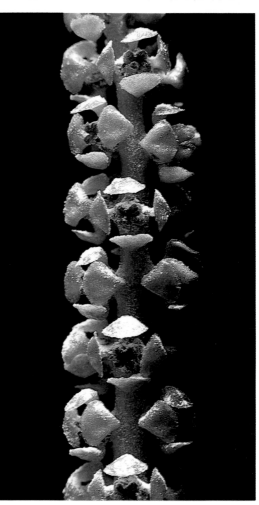

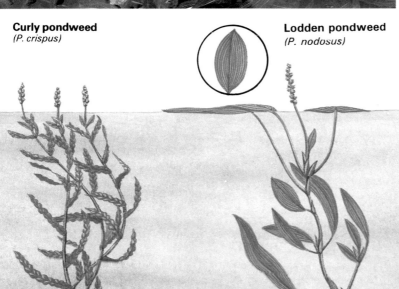

Curly pondweed
(*P. crispus*)

Lodden pondweed
(*P. nodosus*)

Shining pondweed
(*P. luceus*)

AQUATIC ROSETTES

In mountain lakes and pools where conditions can be harsh, many of the aquatic plants grow in a standard rosette shape, sometimes forming thick carpets underwater.

In the mountainous northern and western counties of the British Isles, lakes, tarns and boggy pools are common. These are low in mineral salts, although occasionally peat collects there and gives the water a brown coloration, as well as making it acid. The water is generally shallow, but its level is maintained by the high rainfall of these regions. In exceptionally hot weather the lakes or ponds may recede or dry out, while during the long, cold winters experienced in these parts of Britain, the shallower waters may freeze completely.

Environmental adaptations The plants which grow here have had to adapt to this exacting environment and, as a result, have all evolved a very similar appearance. They have narrow, undivided leaves produced in a stiff tuft or rosette from the base of the plant, and the stems are short and generally well-rooted.

The root performs two main functions. The first is to take up mineral salts from the ground as these aquatics are not able to take advantage of the water-borne supply available to other aquatics in richer waters. The second function is to guard against the effects of wave action by anchoring the plants firmly on the lake bed, which is usually composed of fine gravel from rocks such as granite, sometimes overlaid with peat.

Above: The underwater rosettes of the perennial water lobelia (*Lobelia dortmanna*).

Below: The flowers of water lobelia are produced on slender stalks, well above the water's surface, from July to August.

Opposite page: Loch Awe in Scotland is one of the largest lakes in Britain. Its clear water contains such plants as stonewort and quillwort.

As bottom-dwelling plants, these aquatics are dependent on light filtering through from the surface and so tend to be restricted to shallower lakes, or the margins of deeper ones. Some of the species produce flowers above the surface and are found nearest the edge of the water. These marginal species may be found growing out of the water at different times of year, as the water level fluctuates.

Essential light Rosette-aquatics have been affected by the drainage and agricultural utilisation of the wetlands. Artificial fertilisation of pastures and crop fields has caused 'run-off' into ponds and lakes and altered the mineral balance of the water (a process known as eutrophication). The dense growth of algae or algal bloom, which flourishes under these conditions drastically reduces the quantity and quality of light reaching the lake floor. The green 'soup' of algae effectively filters out those wavelengths of light essential for photosynthesis. The bottom-dwelling plants are particularly affected by these conditions, more so than those aquatics that have stems or leaves floating on or near the surface. As rosette-aquatics cannot tolerate pollution of their waters, they are now extinct in many counties of the British Isles.

Zonation of species These aquatic species form different zones or bands of plants around the margin of the lakes. Shoreweed, as its name suggests, grows in the shallow water nearest the shores of lakes and at the margins

of ponds and reservoirs. Although flowers are only found on the terrestrial forms, this species does not rely solely on seed for the production of new plants. Abundant creeping stems, called stolons, grow away from the plant, producing rosettes of new leaves at intervals. Each rosette forms its own roots and in time becomes an independent plant. Shoreweed can thus colonize large areas quite rapidly, excluding more delicate species such as awlwort.

Beyond the zone of shoreweed, the handsome, nodding, pale lilac flowers of water lobelia appear. While this species prefers water no deeper than 30cm (1ft), sterile rosettes have been found at depths of 3m (10ft). Water lobelia is less capable than shoreweed of withstanding a drought, during which many plants may die.

This species lacks shoreweed's method of rapid propagation, although buds at the base of the leaves may produce new rosettes after the old one has flowered. These new rosettes become detached and are carried away by the water to new localities. However, water lobelia mostly reproduces by seeds, and it is one of the few true aquatics that produces its seeds above the water's surface.

The flowers of awlwort can be successfully pollinated even when totally submerged, so this species is often found growing with water lobelia or further out with the quillworts. A relative of radishes and cabbages, it is an

Oxygen uptake in aquatics

The active growth of roots and uptake of mineral salts depends on energy released during respiration, a process requiring oxygen. This is present in small amounts, dissolved in water, but the green leaves of plants can manufacture oxygen from carbon dioxide during photosynthesis, transporting it to the roots via the air spaces found in the stems and leaves of many aquatics.

The distribution of air spaces varies—numerous spaces are scattered through the leaves of both forms of shoreweed. The two-lobed water lobelia leaf has a large air space in each half, and there are four air spaces, divided by cross walls, in the rounded leaf of quillwort.

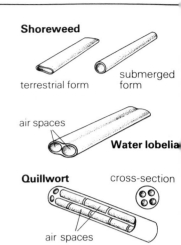

Shoreweed
terrestrial form
submerged form

air spaces
Water lobelia

Quillwort
cross-section
air spaces

Below: Shoreweed (*Littorella uniflora*) can tolerate drought by becoming terrestrial if the water level drops considerably. The flowers are formed only under dry conditions, separate male and female flowers being produced on the same plant. The male flowers are borne on stalks to expose the long anthers to the wind. The wind carries the pollen to the elongated stigmas of the stalkless female flowers.

annual, producing four-petalled flowers in the shape of a cross from June to August. These are often completely submerged and pollinate themselves, although flowers produced in the air on plants near the water's edge may be insect-pollinated. The species takes its name from its slender, grass-like leaves which taper to a point at the tip, resembling the end of a shoemaker's awl.

Quillwort is not a flowering plant, but a spore-bearing species related to the horsetails and ferns. It produces its spores in sporangia on the swollen leaf bases and reproduction is carried out under water. These plants usually grow furthest from the water's edge, although rarely at depths of more than 8m (26ft).

Fellow aquatics Pipewort is another species that favours the same types of habitat as shoreweed, water lobelia and quillwort. It is found on lake margins or in shallow water in parts of the Scottish Islands and western Ireland only, so it is rarely encountered. A more common species is pillwort, an unusual relative of the ferns. The 'leaves' or fronds are produced singly along a creeping stem, often in such profusion that the plant forms a dense 'turf' like the rosette-aquatics. Pillwort is found on the edges of pools, in or out of the water, often on acid soils. While the leaves are still young, they are curled at the tip in the shape of a typical fern crozier.

Below: **Awlwort** (*Subularia aquatica*). Flowers June-August. Ht to 7.5cm (3in). May be submerged.

Right: **Pipewort** (*Eriocaulon aquaticum*). Flowers July-Sept. Ht to 10cm (4in). Found in shallow water.

Right: **Pillwort** (*Pilularia globulifera*). Spores ripen June-Sept. Ht to 10cm (4in). Found at water's edge.

Above: **Quillwort** (*Isoetes lacustris*). Spores ripen May-July. Ht to 30cm (12in). Submerged, to 8m (26ft).

PLANTS WITH FLOATING LEAVES

Some of our most handsome flowering plants have adapted to their aquatic existence by developing differently structured leaves above and below the surface of the water, and flexible, air-filled stems to keep them buoyant.

The fringed water-lily (*Nymphoides peltata*) is fairly uncommon and usually grows in ponds and slow-flowing rivers. It gets its name from the yellow flowers which have feathery fringed margins, and bloom from June to August.

Most flowering plants have evolved for millions of years on dry land. However, some have adapted to water where their primitive ancestors existed. Among these aquatic plant species there are those with leaves that float on the water surface.

Water-lilies are the most familiar aquatic plants, with their showy flowers and large round leaves which spread out over the water. Their structure is similar to many other aquatic plants: because they are supported in the water their stems do not need to be as rigid as those of land plants. Instead, they are soft and filled with spongy, air-filled tissue which keeps the stems buoyant, so holding the leaves at the surface. The stems are flexible and rise and fall in response to the changes in water level. The leaves are tough and leathery and can resist being battered and torn by wave action and heavy rain storms.

There are three species of named water-lilies in the British Isles – the true white and yellow water-lilies, and the fringed water-lily which belongs to a different genus.

The flowers of the white water-lily are up to 12cm (5in) across and are the largest of any wild flowers in the British Isles. Four or five green sepals surround the numerous pure white petals which are arranged spirally around the central mass of yellow anthers. The flowers open by mid-day and give off a fruity scent which attracts pollinating insects. Towards dusk the flowers fold shut and sink slightly into the water.

The yellow water-lily is the most common species, growing in lakes, ponds, canals and in the slow-flowing eddies, bays and back-waters of rivers. It is anchored to the mud by a stout fleshy rhizome which may grow as thick as a man's arm and up to 3m (10ft) long. The waxy yellow flowers smell strongly like alcohol, but it is from the green, bottle-shaped fruiting capsule that it gets its other familiar name – brandy-bottle. In common with some other aquatic plants, the yellow water-lily produces two distinct types of leaf: round floating leaves and submerged cabbage-like leaves which are softer in texture

Above: Amphibious bistort is a common water plant, but it also grows on dry land where it has smaller, stalkless leaves and fewer flowers.

and curly in outline.

Two kinds of leaves Water-crowfoot has flat, lobed leaves that float on the surface of the water, and fine hair-like submerged leaves which offer less resistance to the current of fast-flowing rivers .and streams. The white, five-petalled flowers are borne on stalks held out of the water, but this species also flowers successfully underwater where self-pollination takes place in an air bubble formed within the petals. Marshwort displays a similar difference between its submerged and its floating foliage, and sends up a compact head of tiny white flowers.

Amphibious bistort also has two kinds of leaves but of a different kind: floating leaves which are leathery, smooth and glossy, and aerial leaves which are wrinkled and hairy. A compact spike of delicate pink flowers is borne at the tip of the stem, and the entire shoot system can grow to great lengths—over 12m (40ft) long. The amphibious bistort is aptly named, for it survives well in ponds and ditches which may dry out in summer when it temporarily becomes a land plant.

Free-floating plants Some species are not anchored to the ground and float freely drifting along with the current or being blown about by the wind. They draw mineral nutrients from the water through a thick mat of root hairs which sprout from the base of the stem.

The frog bit is rather like a mini-water-lily and it has a rosette of almost circular leaves

Below: **Water soldier** (*Stratiotes aloides*) flowers June-Aug in broads, dykes and ponds, mainly in East Anglia but also Wales and Scotland. Becoming rare. Ht 30cm (12in).

Below: **Frog bit** (*Hydrocharis morsus-ranae*) flowers July-Aug in shallow, still water.

Below: **Amphibious bistort** (*Polygonum amphibium*) flowers July-Sept in and around shallow and slow-moving water. Ht 50cm (20in).

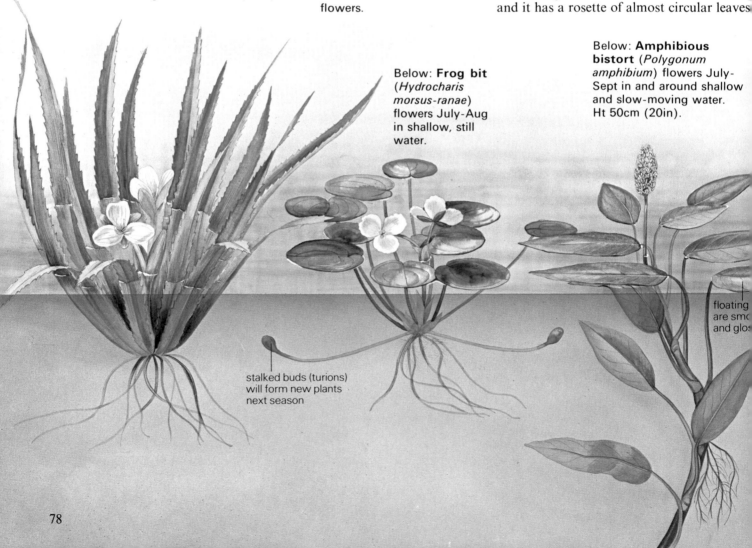

stalked buds (turions) will form new plants next season

floating
are sm
and glo

he flowers have three petals which are reaked with pink to guide visiting insects the supply of nectar. However the seed rarely sets in the British Isles so the species elies mostly on vegetative reproduction. It verwinters by vegetative stalked buds urions) which sink to the bottom in autumn, avoiding the danger of being frozen in the urface ice during winter. In spring the rions sprout and produce new plants which oat to the surface.

The water soldier survives winter in the ater by sinking in autumn, weighed down by e chalky deposit that has accumulated on e young leaves throughout the summer. In oring new green leaves that are free of crustation help the plant to become buoy- nt and reflate itself.

In its wider distribution the water soldier ears male and female flowers on separate lants. However, the species rarely sets seed this country because the populations onsist almost entirely of female flowers. nstead, it spreads vegetatively, sending out ong runners from the squat, bulbous stem. ew shoots form at the tips of these runners, id eventually an independent young plant formed.

Seed dispersal River plants are easily oread because their seeds are dispersed by e flow of water. Some can be animal ispersed. Birds such as waders and water- owl play a vital role in spreading water lants; they pick up seeds on their mud-caked feet and carry them long distances over dry land before they drop off—with luck, over a new watery habitat. For example, when the fruits of the white water-lily are ripe, they burst open and the seeds, embedded in a mass of jelly, float to the surface.

Above: **White water-lily** (*Nymphae alba*) flowers from June to August in sheltered lakes and ponds. Flowers up to 12cm (5in) across.

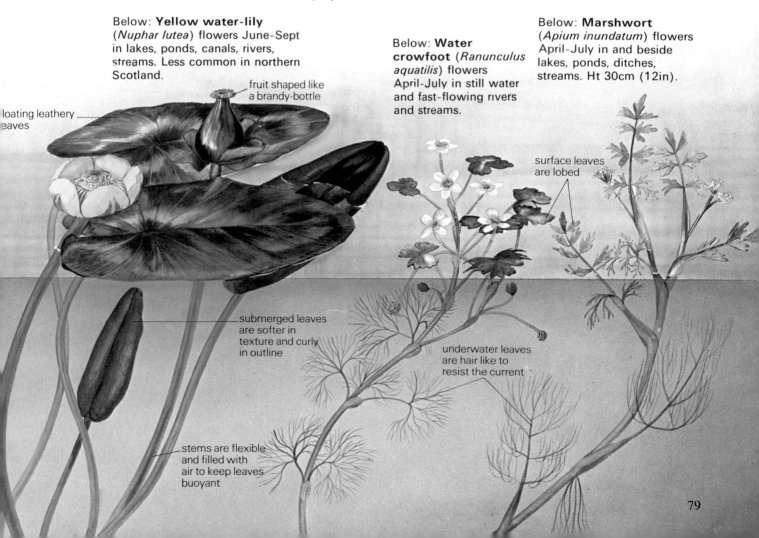

Below: **Yellow water-lily** (*Nuphar lutea*) flowers June-Sept in lakes, ponds, canals, rivers, streams. Less common in northern Scotland.

fruit shaped like a brandy-bottle

loating leathery eaves

submerged leaves are softer in texture and curly in outline

stems are flexible and filled with air to keep leaves buoyant

Below: **Water crowfoot** (*Ranunculus aquatilis*) flowers April-July in still water and fast-flowing rivers and streams.

underwater leaves are hair like to resist the current

Below: **Marshwort** (*Apium inundatum*) flowers April-July in and beside lakes, ponds, ditches, streams. Ht 30cm (12in).

surface leaves are lobed

WATERSIDE PLANT COMMUNITIES

On the banks of slowly moving rivers and canals, by the sides of ponds and lakes, and in the ditches separating low-lying meadows is an ever-changing community of waterside plants, including such attractive species as yellow flag and purple loosestrife.

Opposite page: Common reeds fringing a lake on which white water lilies are floating.

Below: Purple loosestrife (*Lythrum salicaria*) and meadowsweet (*Filipendula ulmaria*), two tall plant species that can often be seen growing beside ponds and lakes. They are perennials, flowering in the summer, and reach a height of 1.2m (4ft).

Any pond or ditch, if it is not fed by a supply stream, is gradually invaded by larger and larger plants until it becomes silted up and boggy. The same would be true of water margins if they were left alone, but they rarely are. Most canals, rivers and ponds are maintained regularly, either by the local council or by the local water authority. The vegetation is cut and the silt removed. If this maintenance is done properly and not too frequently then a rich and balanced flora is achieved.

Pioneer plants The first species to colonize recently cleared shallow water is the common reed. The reeds grow by means of creeping underground rhizomes, from which arise erect hollow stems up to 3m (10ft) tall. The stems support long graceful inflorescences up to 20cm (8in) in length. With time an extensive reed swamp may build up, providing a home for a multitude of water birds, amphibians, insects and other creatures.

The reeds often share a water margin with clubrushes, especially where the silt contains a high percentage of decaying vegetation. Unless cut back, these plants grow too tall to allow much competition from smaller species. Their aerial parts die back each winter, falling into the water where they decompose and form a layer of peat. The water becomes increasingly shallow and the reed swamp is transformed into fen. However, if the reeds are cut regularly for thatch, or if the plants are growing along the banks of a canal or ditch where they are often cut and cleared away, then other species have a chance to establish themselves.

Reed swamp species Reed swamps often contain large colonies of purple loosestrife. This clump-forming perennial has large, somewhat lance-shaped, entire leaves borne on stout stems which may grow to a height of 1m (3ft). Small purple flowers grow in the axils of the upper leaves.

A quite different species associated with reed swamps is the sweet flag. This plant is not native to the British Isles. It was introduced here during the Middle Ages, when it was used to strew the floors of halls and churches: if bruised its leaves give off a sweet scent reminiscent of oranges. It is an easy plant to recognise because its leaves have characteristically crinkled margins. The flower heads consist of a cigar-shaped spike (called a spadix) bearing clusters of tiny greenish-yellow flowers, males on the upper part of the spadix and females on the lower part. The flower heads bear some resemblance to those of cuckoo pint, which belongs to the same family, the arum family.

Outside a reed swamp Even when the reeds are cut back periodically, a reed swamp nevertheless contains only a fairly narrow range of plant species. Most of our prettiest waterside flowers are found outside reed swamps, often as part of a very mixed community of plants.

The yellow flag, which is a species of iris, is a spectacular member of such communities. It grows in ditches and water margins all over the British Isles, and its large clumps of linear (grass-shaped) leaves can transform a waterside bank in early summer.

Other aquatic irises found in Britain include the blue iris, a blue-flowered species which grows in the ditches of Lincolnshire, and the purple flag, an introduced species from North America with pale purplish flowers. It has grown on the banks of Ullswater and other lakes of northern Britain for more than 4 years.

Another familiar plant of river banks, ditches and pondsides is meadowsweet. This large clump-forming perennial has stout

Left: Indian balsam (*Impatiens glandulifera*), naturalised beside a duckweed-covered pond. Introduced to Britain from its native Himalayas, this species has now escaped from gardens and established itself by waterways. Balsams are also known as touch-me-nots, a reference to the explosive nature of their fruits (seen here as pinkish-green hanging capsules). When ripe the fruits rupture violently at a touch, spitting out their seeds, which are then dispersed by water. The Indian balsam grows to a height of 2m (6ft), despite being an annual, and flowers from July to October.

Right: The monkey flower (*Mimulus guttatus*) is another introduced species that has successfully established itself in the wild here. Its common name comes from its flowers which, when seen from the front, can resemble a comical monkey's face. Seen close to, the flowers have red spots in their centres, which is a useful identifying feature, though they are not visible in this picture. This species flowers throughout summer.

Below: Flowering head of giant hogweed (*Heracleum mantegazzianum*). This plant grows in damp places and can reach a height of 5m (16¼ft). The heads measure up to 50cm (20in) across.

stems, growing up to 1.2m (4ft) high and clothed in dark green leaves. In mid-summer the tops of the stems become covered with a froth-like mass of creamy-white, sweet-scented flowers.

Smaller species The plants described so far—meadowsweet, irises, reeds and clubrushes—are all tall, but a great variety of smaller plants can also be found along a water margin. Whenever a gap develops along the edge of a pond or in a ditch you are likely to find a riot of small plants competing for space.

Several species of mints grow by the waterside, for instance the water mint, a species that looks rather similar to our own garden mint though it has a different scent, more akin to that of peppermint. Pennyroyal is another species of mint sometimes found along the waterside. It, too, smells strongly of peppermint. Neither species grows to a height much more than 50cm (20in).

One of the glories of the river bank is the monkey flower. This is an introduced species, native to the western part of North America. It is now extensively naturalised in Britain, largely because it spread along canals during the 19th century. A creeping perennial, its stems are rather brittle and much branched. In spring they send up flowering shoots and, by early summer, the whole plant is covered with distinctive red-spotted yellow flowers.

City colonizer Sadly, not all river and canal banks are attractive. In industrialised areas with polluted waters the waterways and the banks are often dead or dying. However, in recent years, these ugly sterile areas have become colonized by a plant from the Himalayas. This is the Indian balsam or policeman's helmet, a garden plant that has escaped into the wild and seems to thrive beside the inhospitable city waterways.

Several other balsam species grow along our riversides. Touch-me-not balsam is probably native to Britain and grows beside streams in the Lake District and Wales. It has bright yellow flowers. Orange balsam is an introduced species found along the Thames

Above: The yellow flag is one of our most widespread and attractive wetland species. As long as the plant receives plenty of sun it produces numerous flowers, but in shady places all you will see are the stiff sword-like leaves. The yellow flag grows to a height of 1.5m (5ft) and spreads by means of thick rhizomes to form large colonies.

JEWEL-LIKE FLOWERS OF THE WETLANDS

Inland wetlands, marshes, fens and bogs contain one of the richest assortments of plants found anywhere in the British Isles. Some, like the marsh pea, are now rare. Others, like the yellow flag (sometimes called Queen of the Marshes), are both colourful and widespread, forming ever-spreading clumps at the edge of freshwater habitats.

Inland wetlands, as opposed to coastal salt-marshes, can be broadly divided into marshes, fens and bogs. They develop on water-logged ground with a high water table; in summer the water level is at or just below the surface but in winter these habitats may be flooded.

Of the three, marshes are the most widespread. They develop on wet mineral or inorganic soil which is often largely composed of alluvial silt washed down by rivers and deposited during flooding. Typical marshes are found in low-lying land such as river valley floodplains, beside lakes, ponds and streams.

Queen of the Marshes The yellow flag is one of our most stately wetland plants with its erect, sword-shaped leaves and large yellow flowers. The flowers are pollinated by bumble bees. The bee lands on one of the three large petal-like sepals and crawls right into the flower, following the dark brown lines or honey guides which radiate from the nectar source. As it does so, pollen grains that are clinging to its furry body from previous visits to other yellow flags are rubbed on to the female stigma attached to the upper petal-like style.

Further down the tube the bee comes to the nectar and as it drinks, pollen from the anthers is brushed on to its back. When the bee crawls backwards out of the flower tube the stigma curls up out of the way to avoid receiving its own pollen. This system encourages cross-pollination between plants but self-pollination may occur.

Members of the Buttercup Family are found in most habitats. In water-logged ground one of their representatives is the

Above: The marsh violet is common throughout Britain. It grows close to the ground, its slender rhizome anchoring it in wet soils.

Left: **Lesser spearwort** (*Ranunculus flammula*) flowers June-Sept in wet places throughout the British Isles. Very common. Ht 50cm (20in).

Below: **Marsh valerian** (*Valeriana dioica*) flowers May-June in wet meadows, marshes, fens in England, Wales and S Scotland. Ht 30cm (12in).

Below: **Marsh violet** (*Viola palustris*) flowers April-June in waterlogged acid soils of woods, marshes and bogs. Ht 10cm (4in).

Left: **Marsh pea** (*Lathyrus palustris*) flowers June-July in E England and Ireland in fens and in damp grassy and bushy places. Rare. Ht 90cm (35in).

Left: **Early marsh orchid** (*Dactylorhiza incarnata*) flowers May-July in marshes, fens, bogs and ponds. Ht 50cm (20in).

lesser spearwort. Its bright yellow flowers attract insects, but pollination by rain is also thought to occur. The theory is that a raindrop splashing into the flower-cup leaves a film of water upon which pollen grains from the anthers float and engage with the nearby stigmas.

Flowers of marsh and fen The majority of marsh plants also thrive in fens. Fens develop on peat composed of layers of dead plant matter. It accumulates because the normal processes of bacterial decay are slowed down in water-logged conditions. Fens tend to be alkaline or basic in nature because they receive water that has drained off surrounding hills with calcareous or basic soils.

The marsh pea is adapted to live in fens as well as marshes. It has a twisted winged stem which is too weak to hold it upright among tall fen vegetation. Instead of sprawling low over the ground it climbs with the help of tendrils at the tips of its leaves. These twist around the stems of surrounding plants and so support it in its growth towards the light. In summer stalked clusters of bluish-purple flowers appear, and after fertilisation the seeds develop into tiny green pods. The marsh pea is now a rarity and, like most wetland plants, has suffered from loss of habitat through continuing drainage to improve the land for agriculture.

Bog vegetation develops on, and continues to form, a peat which is acidic in nature. The best examples are concentrated in the north and west of the British Isles, especially in Scotland and Ireland where the harder rocks are found. Bog plants therefore have to be adapted to an environment which is poor in nutrients. Bogs are either watered directly by rainfall, which is mostly retained because the drainage is poor, or from rainwater running over hard rocks from which only small amounts of minerals, such as soluble salts, can be washed off.

Some plants grow in all three types of wetland habitats—marshes, fens and bogs—(although most bog vegetation differs markedly in composition from that of marshes and fens). Bogbean and marsh cinquefoil are two that grow in marshes, fens and bogs. Bogbean flowers have a delicate beauty with their fringed white petals tinged pale pink. The trefoil leaves, similar in appearance to broad-bean foliage (hence the name), were used in beer-brewing as a substitute for hops.

Right: **Ragged robin** (*Lychnis flos-cuculi*) flowers May-June in wet meadows, marshes, fens in England and Wales. Ht 50cm (20in).

Below: **Marsh cinquefoil** (*Potentilla palustris*) flowers May-July in marshes, fens, bogs, wet heaths and moors. Ht 30cm (12in).

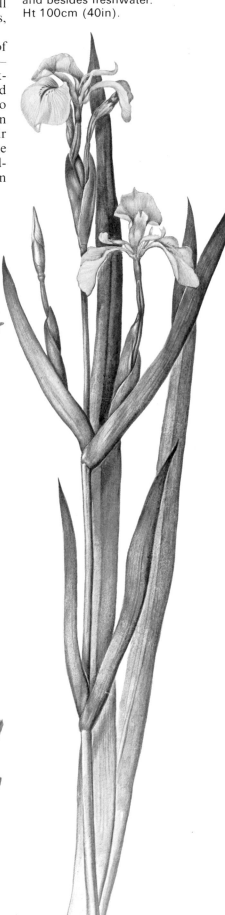

Below: **Yellow flag** (*Iris pseudacorus*) flowers June-August in marshes, ditches and besides freshwater. Ht 100cm (40in).

Above: **Bogbean** (*Menyanthes trifoliata*) flowers May-July in shallow water of ponds, fens, marshes, the edges of lakes. Ht 20cm (8in).

THE DOCK OF LOCH LOMOND

Just over 50 years ago a new native species of dock, previously unknown in Britain, was discovered growing near the banks of Loch Lomond.

As a result of the unprecedented upsurge of interest in natural history pursuits during the Victorian era, Great Britain had, by the turn of the last century, become the most intensively 'botanised' country in the world. Since then, the few additional native species added to the British list have tended to be very small, inconspicuous at flowering or hidden away in some remote, rarely visited locality.

A notable exception to this rule was found in 1935, when a Glasgow botanist, R Mackechnie, collected a tall fruiting species of dock growing near Balmaha, a popular weekend spot on the east side of Loch Lomond. Specimens were sent to the leading authority on docks, who identified the plant as *Rumex aquaticus*, a waterside dock widely distributed throughout central and northern Europe but previously unrecorded in Britain.

Top-heavy stems Popularly known today as the Loch Lomond dock, *R. aquaticus* is a striking plant when fully grown. The tallest specimens can be nearly 2m (6½ft) in height, the pale green flowering heads turning a distinctive golden-brown as the fruits ripen in late summer. Some of the fuller heads make the stems top heavy and they often topple over in the face of strong autumn winds. The large triangular basal leaves (those at the base of the stem) are at their best in early summer for, like other docks, they die back as the fruiting heads mature.

A close relative for which the Loch Lomond dock could be mistaken is the great water dock. However, the spear-shaped leaves and swollen protuberances on the fruits readily distinguish the latter species. The great water dock is most common in the southern half of Britain, whereas the Loch Lomond dock is evidently better adapted to a more northerly environment – in Continental Europe it extends well north of the Arctic Circle.

Distribution past and present Remains of Loch Lomond dock found preserved in peat samples collected in Cornwall and Wales seem to indicate that the species once enjoyed a widespread distribution in Britain. No

Above: The Loch Lomond dock – seen here in fruit – is one of Britain's largest native herbaceous plants, some individuals growing to be 2m (6½ft) tall. As its scientific name, *aquaticus*, implies, this dock grows only where its roots can find a permanent supply of water. On Loch Lomondside the two major habitats are the banks of the River Endrick and its feeder streams, and swampy clearings in wet woods. Occasionally, Loch Lomond dock invades poorly drained meadows, and one lochside colony is growing on a gravelly beach partially covered with silt and sand. Without exception, all the sites are subject to periodic floodings during the winter months.

Right: Loch Lomond dock in flower. Although most easily seen alongside water courses, the largest stands of this plant occur in damp woodland clearings. One such wood has an extensive colony of several hundred plants.

single explanation has been offered why the plant disappeared from its former haunts, but climatic change, a loss of suitable wetland habitats and even hybridisation with a more dominant species have all probably played their parts.

For a while it was thought that the Loch Lomond dock was totally confined to a number of sites scattered around the lower reaches of the River Endrick in the south-east corner of Loch Lomond. Then, in the 1970s, two small colonies were discovered some distance away in the grounds of a country house on the west side of the Loch. And, most recently, in 1982, another well-established population was found beside the River Endrick, but 18km (10 miles) upstream from the mouth.

Hybridisation The Loch Lomond dock is vulnerable in one respect – the readiness with which it hybridises with the common dock, something that the great dock manages to avoid. In general, the drier the site the greater the chance of contact between the two species and subsequent hybridisation.

Hybrids between the two species are not always easy to recognise. However, a combination of intermediate characters – such as less triangular duller-green leaves and reddish rather than golden-brown fruits which, furthermore, have jagged 'teeth' along their lower edges – serve to separate hybrids from pure specimens.

Above: The fruits of the great water dock bear swollen protuberances called tubercles, a feature that serves to distinguish this species from the closely related Loch Lomond dock.

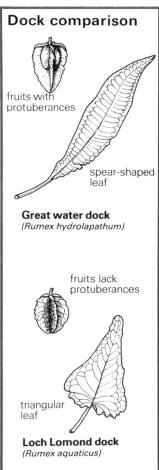

Dock comparison

fruits with protuberances

spear-shaped leaf

Great water dock
(Rumex hydrolapathum)

fruits lack protuberances

triangular leaf

Loch Lomond dock
(Rumex aquaticus)

Another difference between the Loch Lomond dock and its hybrid with the common dock is that the former is a long-lived, freely fruiting plant, whereas the hybrid produces partially sterile pollen and its seeds have a lower fertility rate. The replacement of the Loch Lomond dock by the hybrid is, therefore, likely to be a slow process, but surveys show that this is taking place at several sites.

A mystery resolved? A question often asked is why such an eye-catching species took so long to be detected on Loch Lomondside, an internationally famous tourist area.

One answer is the private nature of the country estates where most of the colonies occur. But this is probably only half the story. During the 18th century, the Endrick's flood plain was drained, and there seems to be every likelihood that this caused the population of the Loch Lomond dock to fall considerably, its numbers gradually recovering after the drainage system fell into disrepair. Many of the low-lying arable fields reverted to marshy grazings and damp woods, giving the dock ample opportunity slowly to recolonize some of its lost ground. It is significant that the marshes near Balmaha, where this conspicuous plant was first discovered, had been visited by botanists more than once.

The future The *British Red Data Book* divides up Britain into 10km (6-mile) squares. All those species that occur in 15 or fewer squares are listed as rare. The Loch Lomond dock qualifies for inclusion because it is found in just three squares, though most of the colonies are not faced with any immediate threat. Provided all the important wetland habitats are maintained the future of Loch Lomondside's very own dock seems assured.

There are two groups of rushes in the British Isles. The first, the true rushes, have hairless leaves and many seeds in a fruit that is divided internally into three compartments. The second, the woodrushes, have hairy leaves and only three quite large seeds in a fruit that lacks internal divisions.

The true rushes are found in all shapes and sizes from small, inconspicuous annuals growing as garden weeds, to huge, tussocky perennials with spiny leaves growing on the seashore. Some species even grow in the exposed environment of the serpentine rocks of the Lizard, or on the rocky mountain tops in Scotland.

Looking at the leaf The problem with identifying rushes is that, unlike most groups, the flowers are less useful than the growth habit and leaf structure. While the flowers of most rushes are very much alike, the leaves exhibit a wide range of forms.

The simplest leaf is more or less flat, with several parallel veins running along its full length. In some species, however, the upper surface is much narrower than the lower so that the leaf is almost circular in section, but with a shallow groove along the top. In other species, the upper surface has vanished altogether and the leaf is truly circular in section with a cavity in the centre. The central cavity in one such group of species is full of pith, while in a second it is divided by transverse partitions (and sometimes also by longitudinal ones).

Widespread species Toad rush is probably our commonest rush, found almost anywhere that is wet during the growing season, and where competition is minimal. Its habitat ranges from muddy pond and stream sides to roadside ditches, trampled fields, paths, tracks, wheel ruts and gardens.

WIDESPREAD RESILIENT RUSHES

Although wet places are not inhabited exclusively by rushes, there is scarcely a pond or stream side, wet meadow, marsh, fen, bog, or muddy seashore where one or more of Britain's thirty species of rushes cannot be found.

Above: Soft rush (*Juncus effusus*) in flower. It favours marshy habitats where it may grow to heights of 1.5m (5ft), while bulbous rush (*Juncus bulbosus*), opposite, rarely reaches a height of more than 20cm (8in).

Grasses, sedges and rushes tend to share the same kinds of habitats and often look much alike, but only the rushes have a recognisable flower. This is wind-pollinated and looks very much like a tiny version of the flower of members of the lily family – such as ramsons – although the families are only distantly related.

Above: Common rush (*Juncus conglomeratus*) is found throughout the British Isles, particularly on acid soils. It is very similar in appearance to the soft rush, but with small, compact inflorescences. The best way to distinguish between the two species when not in flower is to feel the stems. The stem of common rush is ridged, while that of soft rush feels quite smooth.

A rush or not?

Despite its name, the flowering rush, noticeable for its attractive pink blooms, is not a rush at all. In fact, it is the only species in its genus.

Flowering rush (*Butomus umbellatus*). Flowers July-Sept by water. Ht to 1.5m (5ft).

It is a small species with a very loose and open inflorescence and widely spaced flowers. The leaves are simple, but in some individuals they may be almost circular with a groove along the top.

Heath rush is fairly widespread in the British Isles on moors, bogs and damp heaths. It has the same kind of leaf as the toad rush—almost circular in section, but deeply channelled along the upper surface. The leaves are, however, much stiffer and thicker than those of the toad rush and grow in a manner unusual among rushes, being confined to a basal tuft lying almost flat on the ground. A characteristic of heath rush is that in the autumn the entire tuft of leaves is detached easily from the roots, and these brown, dry tufts are often seen scattered among the heather and tussock grasses.

Rushes of acid soils The small, rather grass-like bulbous rush is common throughout the country, but favours more acidic soils. It is rather variable in appearance and may be erect and densely tufted, or procumbent and rooting at intervals along the stem, or even floating in water and profusely branched.

Bulbous rush derives its name from its habit of producing small bulbous-based shoots instead of flowers, which means it is not always immediately recognisable as a

rush. It can, however, be distinguished from grasses and sedges by its leaves. These are the most advanced type of leaf, being cylindrical, hollow and with transverse internal divisions known as septa.

Jointed rush is another rather variable species, common on acid soils and particularly abundant in meadows or moors subject to grazing. Like bulbous rush, it has hollow leaves with numerous internal septa, but instead of being circular in section, the leaves are quite distinctly flattened. The inflorescence is loosely formed, bearing tight clusters of four to eight flowers.

Meadow and marsh rushes Three species—common, soft and hard rush—are most usually associated with damp meadows and marshes. They are all tall, reaching up to 1.5m (5ft) in height, and form dense tufts of straight, apparently leafless stems. The inflorescences, instead of being at the top of the stem, seem to project from one side of it about four-fifths of the way up. This unusual appearance is due entirely to the strange nature of the leaves. The base of the stem is clothed in brown scales which are the sheathing bases of leaves which have no blades. The only true leaf present is one that begins below the inflorescence and is almost identical to the stem in appearance. This makes it appear as if the stem continues beyond the inflorescence, whereas in fact the inflorescence is at the top of the stem, not some way up it at the side.

Right: **Jointed rush** (*Juncus articulatus*). Flowers July-Sept. Ht to 80cm (32in).

Right: **Heath rush** (*Juncus squarrosus*). Flowers June-July. Ht to 50cm (20in).

Left: **Toad rush** (*Juncus bufonius*). Flowers May-Sept. Ht to 15cm (6in).

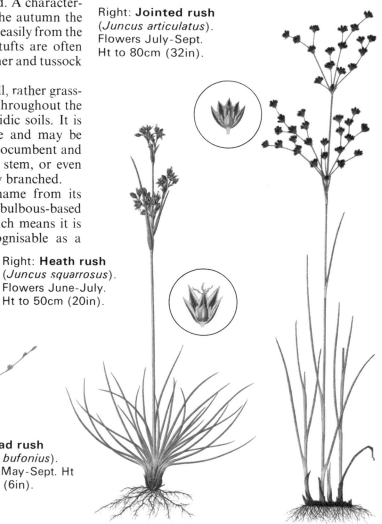

Insects of lake, pond and marsh

The surface of a pond or lake may at first sight look quiet and devoid of animal life, but in fact any unpolluted body of water, especially if it is well-vegetated, is a veritable paradise for insects. Almost all groups of insects have at least some members which have adapted to aquatic life, while in some other groups all the members are completely dependent on water. The dragonflies and damselflies are such a group.

Insects are more complicated than other animals or plants in that their life-cycle goes through a number of quite distinct phases – egg, larva or caterpillar, pupa or chrysalis, and adult (though some groups do not have a chrysalis phase). Quite different circumstances may be needed for each of these stages to survive. Many insects make use of water for their feeding and growing phase – the larva – while the adult insect is winged and independent of water and therefore able to disperse to find new sites. Dragonflies, for example, all have aquatic predatory larvae which spend up to several years in water, emerging eventually as winged insects that may live for only a few weeks. So, although the insect that we think of as the dragonfly seems to be terrestrial, water is essential to its survival. The same applies to caddisflies, midges, mosquitoes, mayflies and some hoverflies.

Other insects have adapted wholly to water, and spend their entire life-cycle there, including the adult phase. Some, like the water scorpion, have lost the powers of flight altogether, while others, like the backswimmers or water boatmen, spend most of their lives under water but may emerge and fly to new sites when the need arises.

Among all these insects, from so many different groups, there are voracious predators – the larvae of diving beetles, dragonflies and damselflies for example; herbivores – such as the larvae of some reed-beetles and the China mark moths; and all-purpose scavengers such as the surface-dwelling pond skaters and water crickets – all interacting together, feeding and being fed upon in a complex, seasonally variable web of underwater life.

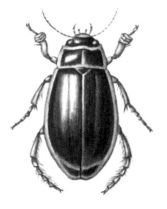

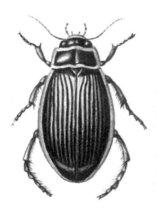

Left: Male and female great diving water beetles. The male has smooth wing cases, the female grooved ones. These insects, common in ponds, lakes and other still waters, are highly carnivorous and feed on other insects, molluscs, tadpoles and fish fry.

CHECKLIST

*This checklist is a guide to some of the insects you can find in and around lakes, ponds and marshes. Although you will not see them all in the same place, you should be able to spot many of them throughout the changing seasons. The species listed in **bold** type are described in detail.*

Alderflies
Anopheline mosquitoes
Backswimmer bugs
Biting midges
Black darter dragonfly
**Broad-bodied libellula
  dragonfly**
Caddisflies
**Common darter
  dragonfly**
**Common hawker
  dragonfly**
**Corixid water boatmen
  bugs**
Culicine mosquitoes
Damselflies
Great diving water beetle
Great silvery water beetle
**Highland darter
  dragonfly**
Hoverfly larvae
Mayflies
Non-biting midges
Pond skater
Saucer bug
Screech beetle
**Southern hawker
  dragonfly**
Stoneflies
Water cricket
Water measurer
Water scorpion
Water stick-insect
Whirligig beetle

Left: You can see the broad-bodied libellula dragonfly hunting by day along slow-moving and stagnant water. It often chooses to breed in garden ponds. The female has a brownish-yellow abdomen while the male is powder blue.

PONDS: A PARADISE FOR INSECTS

The lush vegetation around the edges, the open water, the numerous submerged and floating weeds and the muddy floor make ponds a haven for many insects—and for amateur naturalists, provided they know a few tricks of the trade.

Ponds are packed with insects, the various species occurring in many different zones—around the water's edge, among the submerged plants, in the open water and on the muddy floor of the pond. The best ponds for finding insects have sloping sides and shallow edges with flourishing marginal vegetation. A

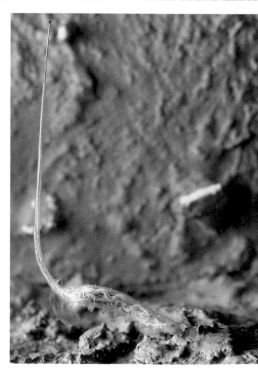

Above: An ideal pond in which to find insects.

Right: Rat-tailed maggots—dronefly larvae—live on the muddy bottoms of foul ponds, using their long 'tails' to breathe.

ord of warning however. Be careful where ou tread and try not to damage the vegetation. Probe with a stick before walking on uspect ground.

Equipment for pond hunting A water net is bviously essential if you are going to examine he insects closely, and so is a butterfly net for atching dragonflies, mayflies, caddisflies and ther flying insects associated with water. You lso need a few shallow pie dishes and a couple f clear plastic jars with screw-on lids, to ransport specimens home for close examination—and for returning them to the pond gain. Never fill a jar more than half full of ater, as the creatures must be able to breathe xygen.

Also useful is a small sieve or tea strainer nd an old kitchen spoon. Don't forget a agnifying glass, a notebook, a pen and an ld towel. Binoculars can be useful for ooking at dragonflies which have settled on eds far out in the centre of large ponds.

Marginal vegetation Around the edges of onds you are likely to find a number of sects which are only associated with water r part of their lives. Many are brightly oloured, such as the darter dragonflies which n be seen catching smaller insects such as ddisflies, mayflies and mosquitoes.

As you look at a pond you will notice that me plants grow around the edge in clumps omposed of one or two species only. Common reed is one such species often extending t into the shallow water. Various species of sh (*Juncus*), with rounded stems, and sedges *Carex*), with triangular stems, also occur by ost ponds. Search among these plants and u may come across the greenish-blue or red-auve *Donacia* beetles. If there is a clump of ater mint, unmistakable by its smell, there e also likely to be a few brilliant green mint etles, about 11mm long, lurking among the

A simple pond net . . .

To make a simple pond net, bend a wire coat hanger into a loop and wind the ends around a wooden pole. Secure the wire to the wooden pole with string. Then find a length of stocking, about 25cm (10in) long, and sew one end around the coat hanger. Sew the other end together to make a pond net (**stage 1**), or attach it to a small jar by tying string around the rim—thus making a simple diatom net (**stage 2**).

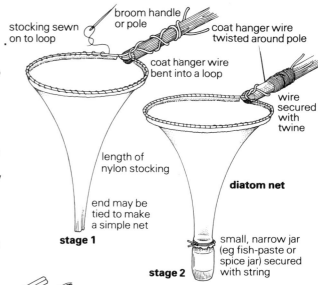

stocking sewn on to loop — broom handle or pole — coat hanger wire twisted around pole — coat hanger wire bent into a loop — wire secured with twine — length of nylon stocking — end may be tied to make a simple net — **stage 1** — **diatom net** — small, narrow jar (eg fish-paste or spice jar) secured with string — **stage 2**

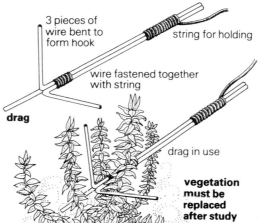

3 pieces of wire bent to form hook — string for holding — wire fastened together with string — **drag** — drag in use — **vegetation must be replaced after study**

. . .and a drag

If you wish to examine the insect life on aquatic plants, a drag is useful. To make one, find three stout pieces of wire of the same length, and bend them at one end. Fasten the wires together with string—leaving enough string at the unbent end to hold. Throw the drag among a stretch of weed, and then pull it out and examine your catch. In the interests of conservation, do not pull out too much vegetation.

Below: Banded agrion damselflies roosting on aquatic vegetation. The adults are seen fluttering over water between May and August, but the nymphs live at the bottom of slow streams and ponds among the plant roots.

leaves. Also examine the nettle-like leaves of gypsywort, which has small white flowers from July onwards, and you may find the very flat, green tortoise beetle sitting on the upper surface of the leaves.

The stems and roots which creep along the mud at the water's edge are the homes of such insects as the larvae of the rush wainscot

Life in the depths

surface film

mid-water

Surface-film dwellers

Best known of the surface dwellers are pond skaters (**1**), whirligig beetles (**2**), which travel at great speed, and water measurers (**3**) with their long legs. Gnat larvae (**4**) can be seen hanging down from the surface film.

Mid-water dwellers

Insects found in the free water zone include backswimmers (**5**), which (as their name implies) swim on their backs, great diving water beetles (**6**) and corixid water boatmen (**7**). Saucer bugs (**8**), which are oval, and phantom midge fly larvae (**9**), which are transparent, also occur here.

Plant dwellers

Among the weeds in a pond you may come across *Aeshna* dragonfly nymphs (**10**), water scorpions (**11**) with their curious 'snorkels', green *Lestes* damselfly nymphs (**12**), great silvery water beetles (**13**), *Cloeon dipterum* mayfly larvae (**14**) and the spectacular water stick insects (**15**).

submerged plant zone

Mud dwellers

Species which thrive in the muddy bottoms of ponds are larvae of the caddisfly *Phryganea grandis* (**16**), which construct their own shelters, and bloodworms (**17**), the larvae of *Chironomus* midges.

bottom

moth, and larvae of the *Donacia* beetle. The latter bores into stems below water level with the two short spikes which protrude from its rear; these spikes are breathing tubes and air is drawn through them from the plants and into the larvae.

Surface dwellers Several species live on the pond's surface, so just by sitting quietly and watching, you should be able to see some activity. The long-legged pond skaters of the genus *Gerris* move jerkily around picking up small insects, such as aphids, which have fallen or been blown on to the water. The extremely thin water measurer steps sedately over the surface film with its long legs and body well clear of the water. Try picking it up –carefully–and it may feign death. You may also see a group of small black whirligig beetles charging about on the surface at great speed, yet miraculously never bumping into one another.

With a pie dish or strainer try and obtain a sample of the floating egg rafts of mosquitoes (*Culex*), and their larvae and pupae from the water surface. The eggs float on the surface but the larvae and pupae hang under the surface film – the gnat larva at an angle from the surface, and the mosquito larva (*Anopheles*) parallel to the surface.

Open water swimmers The next area in which to look for insects is the open water. Dip your net in the water and draw it backwards and forwards four or five times, sweeping through any submerged vegetation on which the swimmers may be resting. (Do not scrape the bottom at this stage.)

Your catch is best sorted out in a pie dish with clear water. The active swimmers are obvious at once–large or small stream-lined water beetles such as the great diving beetle and backswimmers of the genus *Notonecta* which, as their name implies, swim on their backs. Some insects, such as backswimmers, carry down a bubble of air which they use for breathing, coming up to the water surface to renew the bubble from time to time; this often gives them a silvery appearance on the undersurface.

The smaller, lesser waterboatmen (*Corixa* species) are often very common in ponds; they swim the right way up and occur in pondweed, water crowfoot and on the undersurface of such plants as water lilies. The oval, greenish saucer bug, a particularly good swimmer, is about 15mm ($\frac{1}{2}$in) long and has strong piercing mouthparts, capable of giving the human thumb a sharp prick.

Submerged plant home If you fish some of the plant material out of the water with a drag (see diagram) and float it in a pie dish, a number of insects may appear. Some will be true swimmers while others are species which clamber about the plants after crawling up from the bottom in search of food.

One fascinating larva, quite common in ponds, is that of the phantom midge fly. About 10mm long when fully grown, it xtremely difficult to see since it is as ransparent as glass. You can best spot it by its lack eyes and two air sacs, one at each end, vhich help to balance it in water. When a mall animal like a water flea comes within each the phantom larva grabs it–not with its :gs, for it has none, but with its antennae.

Found among plants near the bottom of a ond, the conspicuous water stick insect *Ranatra linearis*) is a thin brown creature bout 6-7cm (2½in) long. Its front legs are nuch shorter than the middle and hind pairs nd are used for grabbing prey. A close relation, lthough physically dissimilar, is the more ommon water scorpion (*Nepa cinerea*), a attened oval creature, brownish in colour. oth have a long tail about one third of their ody length, which is actually a breathing ube on the snorkel principle. This allows iem to take in water without exposing iemselves to the dangers of predators above ie water surface.

The muddy floor The bottom of the pond, vhich is the home of crawlers and mud-wellers, can be scraped with the net to obtain

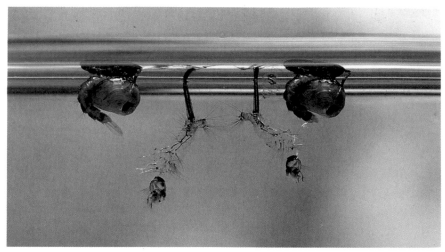

Above: Where there is stagnant water you can be sure there are mosquitoes. Here you can see their empty larval cases–in the centre–and their pupae. The round, bulky part of the pupa contains the mosquito's head, thorax and abdomen.

Above: The insect population of ponds is greatly reduced by the feeding habits of such birds as coots.

Left: Pond skaters are surface insects, moving jerkily across the water as they feed. If you manage to catch one, examine it carefully with a lens, and you can see that the claw on the foot is situated before the tip so that it does not penetrate the surface film, and hinder the insect's movement.

specimens. In shallow water an old kitchen spoon attached to a long handle can be used to bring up samples of mud or sand for examination in a pie dish.

You are almost certain to find some fearsome dragonfly nymphs, especially those of the darter flies. A particularly rewarding sight is when the nymph crawls out of the water and on to a stem where it becomes transformed into a mature dragonfly–all in a matter of an hour. Also interesting to watch is the dragonfly nymph's feeding habits. Its mouthparts can suddenly shoot out to grab prey such as a worm, or even another dragonfly nymph. If the intended meal is not near enough to be grasped the nymph jet-propels itself forward by a sudden expulsion of water from its rear end. This action is best seen by placing a small amount of mud or sand in the bottom of the pie dish so you can see the jet of water.

A good sample of mud from the bottom of a pond may well contain some bright red, wriggly 'bloodworms'–larvae of *Chironomus* midges. Their red colour is due to the presence of haemoglobin, a substance which absorbs oxygen, so helping the larvae to breathe in rather stagnant ponds. These bloodworms can be mistaken for the little red *Tubifex* worms which usually live in clearer water and are true worms. The *Tubifex* worms have about 30 segments in their bodies, however, as opposed to 12 in midge larvae.

Caddisfly larvae are well known for the curious shelter houses which many of them construct from pieces of plants, sand or small stones. They creep about the bottom and mainly inhabit the better aerated ponds. *Phryganea*, a genus with several common species, has larvae which build cases of root, reed or other pieces of plants in the form of a neat spiral cylinder.

Amateur research The food web in a pond is complex, and not easy to follow. Besides birds, fishes take a heavy toll of aquatic insects, but there is still much work to be done to find out exactly who eats what. Much of this is well within the scope of amateur naturalists who can make a real contribution to science in this area.

WATER SURFACE INSECTS

The thin film on the surface of water is a kind of mini habitat, supporting lightweight creatures that scoot about on top and feed on insects which fall on the water.

In spring the first aquatic insects to appear are pond skaters, bugs which belong to the Gerridae family. These seem to turn up suddenly on the surface of still waters everywhere; there are ten British species and you'll find one or another of them in most parts of the country. Strangely enough, the first thing you might notice are the shadows of the insects reflected on the bottom of the shallower parts of the water; these look like clusters of dark spots with light edges and show the ends of the legs resting in shallow depressions on the surface of the water.

Pond skaters, and some other insects, have successfully exploited a most unusual habitat which is intermediate between land and water – the surface film. This layer, although not chemically different from the rest of the water, is in a peculiar physical state of tension and acts rather like an elastic skin which can support small objects both above and below it. The pond skater is a small insect, up to 15mm ($\frac{5}{8}$in) long, but its extraordinarily long legs make it seem larger and spread the slight weight of the insect over a wide area. At the end of each leg there is a pad of bristles which depresses the surface film into dimples and prevents the legs from breaking through the water. Using a kind of rowing motion of their long middle legs, the insects can glide over the water as confidently as an experienced ice skater.

The surface film has two great advantages as a habitat for pond skaters: relative freedom from predators and a superabundance of food in the form of innumerable small aerial insects that fall on to the water and cannot get off again. The struggles of potential prey alert the pond skater which glides rapidly towards its victim and seizes it with the short front pair of legs. Using its sharp rostrum or beak, the pond skater then sucks out the body fluids of its victim. There are both winged and wingless pond skaters.

Pond skaters lay eggs in about March or April and attach them in small groups to submerged or surface plants depending on the species. The emerging young, as in all bugs, resemble their parents in everything but size and develop through several moults.

Other surface skaters Water crickets (family Veliidae) and water measurers (Hydrometridae) are relatives of the pond skater and are equally well adapted to life on the surface of the water.

The two species of water crickets, both of them rather smaller than pond skaters and with shorter legs, often inhabit slow rivers as well as still waters, even in winter. In fact, they are not crickets at all and don't make the cricket's characteristic chirping sound. They are only about 7mm ($\frac{1}{4}$in) long when adult and you need a lens to see their handsome orange-red back markings and orange undersides. Water crickets support their weight mainly on their front and hind legs and

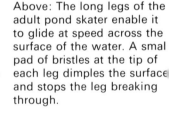

Above: The long legs of the adult pond skater enable it to glide at speed across the surface of the water. A small pad of bristles at the tip of each leg dimples the surface and stops the leg breaking through.

Left: The pond skater relies for its food on the numerous small creatures which fall on to the water and cannot get off. This species, *Gerris gibbifer,* one of ten British pond skaters, is feeding on a fly trapped on the surface layer.

move their middle pair of legs alternately, not simultaneously as pond skaters do.

The commoner of our two species of water measurer, *Hydrometra stagnorum*, is about 12mm (½in) long and is found in most parts of Britain. *Hydrometra gracilenta*, slightly smaller, is restricted to a few localities in the Norfolk Broads and the New Forest. Water measurers are extremely hard to see, partly because they have such remarkably slender bodies and partly because they tend to stay among vegetation at the edge of still and flowing water. Whereas water crickets are quick in their movements, water measurers move very slowly and the apparent pacing out of distances accounts for their common name of measurer. Both groups of insects feed on small creatures trapped on the surface film, but the water measurer can also catch small animals such as water fleas and mosquito larvae just below the surface. Both crickets and measurers attach their eggs, laid in May and June, to waterside plants.

Whirligig beetles Twelve species of whirligig beetle, of the family Gyrinidae, live on the surface film of the water. *Gyrinus natator* is one of the commonest species and is found throughout Britain. This tiny black beetle, only 5-6mm (¼in) long, lives in schools on open still or slow-running water, performing endless gyrations at great speed as it searches for prey floating on the surface. It is beautifully adapted for this mode of life, with a smooth, shiny, streamlined body and curiously modified middle and hind pairs of legs, each segment of which is flattened and fringed with hairs to increase the surface area. On the backward swimming stroke the plate-like sections of the legs present their broad surface to the water, but on the return stroke they fold up and offer little resistance. When alarmed, the beetle dives rapidly down into the water. The front pair of legs is used for grasping prey. The beetle has curious eyes, specially adapted for its way of life; they are divided into two parts, the upper able to see above and along the surface of the water, the lower part positioned to look below the surface.

Whirligig beetles lay their eggs from March to May on submerged vegetation. The larvae, which take about a year to develop, are long and narrow and have long tracheal gills on each segment of the abdomen which enable them to absorb dissolved oxygen from the water for respiration. They creep out of the water at the beginning of August and make a greyish pupal cocoon some distance up a plant stem. Although there must be great numbers of these cocoons about, they are so well hidden as to be very rarely seen. The adult beetle emerges from the pupa towards the end of August. During severe spells of winter weather, the beetles may bury themselves in the mud at the bottom of the water, but in mild spells they come up to hunt for food.

Spider predator In certain areas in most parts of the country you may find a large, strikingly marked spider sitting at the water's edge with its front legs resting on the water surface. This unmistakable spider, known as the raft spider, with brown body and pale stripes is our largest species; females can be up to 20mm (¾in) long and males about 12mm (½in). It too walks on the water surface. Ripples caused by any disturbance on the water, such as the movements of the surface-dwelling insects or the struggles of other creatures which have fallen on the water, are detected by the spider's front legs. As soon as a likely victim is located, it darts across the surface of the water to catch it.

Above: There's no mistaking this raft spider for any other species – the pale markings down the sides are very conspicuous. This spider catches flies and damselflies on the water surface. By vibrating the water surface with its front legs, it is reputed to attract and catch tiny fishes.

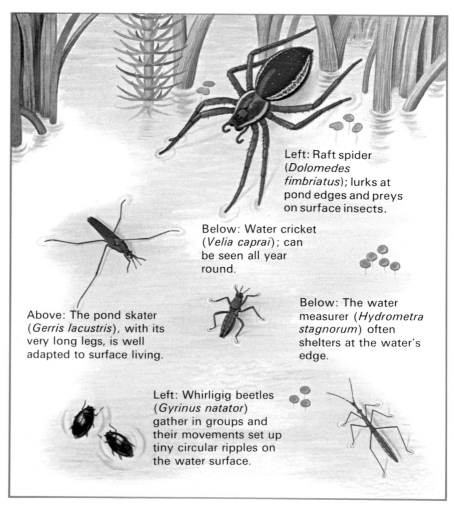

Left: Raft spider (*Dolomedes fimbriatus*); lurks at pond edges and preys on surface insects.

Below: Water cricket (*Velia caprai*); can be seen all year round.

Above: The pond skater (*Gerris lacustris*), with its very long legs, is well adapted to surface living.

Below: The water measurer (*Hydrometra stagnorum*) often shelters at the water's edge.

Left: Whirligig beetles (*Gyrinus natator*) gather in groups and their movements set up tiny circular ripples on the water surface.

THE GREAT SILVERY WATER BEETLE

One of Britain's largest and bulkiest beetles, the great silvery water beetle belongs to the family Hydrophilidae–a family renowned for their vegetarian nature and the fact that, despite their aquatic existence, they are neither fast nor efficient swimmers.

The largest insect found in ponds and weedy ditches is the great silvery water beetle (*Hydrophilus piceus*), the bulkiest British beetle apart from the male stag beetle. It was comparatively common at one time but sadly it now only occurs locally in England south of Yorkshire. Here it is found in ponds and dykes, feeding mainly on aquatic plants, although water snails occasionally add a little variation to its otherwise vegetarian diet.

Silver swimmer If you examine one of these beetles carefully you can see that its antennae are short, clubbed and held back under the eyes. The other organs you could easily mistake for antennae are in fact the palpi, which have taken over the sensory duties of the antennae.

The beetle's underparts are covered with short yellowish-brown hairs which are water-repellent. These hairs trap a thin film of air giving the beetle a silvery appearance underneath when it is below the water. The beetle is actually a blackish-olive colour.

The male's front feet are enlarged in a triangular shape to form claspers although

they lack the suckers which are found on the great diving water beetle. The middle and front legs on both sexes are fringed with hairs and used for swimming. The beetles fly from pond to pond at night and they are equipped with well developed wings which are folded beneath the wing cases.

Water crawler When you watch the great silvery water beetle in a pond the differences between it and the great diving water beetle soon become apparent. Unlike the latter, it is a poor swimmer, moving its legs alternately– as if walking. It lacks the strong rowing movements of most other aquatic insects and gives the impression of crawling rather than swimming through the water.

Its respiratory system is also quite different from that of the great diving water beetle. When it needs to replenish its air supply, it rises to the water surface, positioning itself not tail upwards but nearly horizontal and inclined to one side, with its head uppermost. The inclination of the body automatically brings one of the antennae to the water surface. As the antenna's club is covered with

Breathing systems

Below: *Dytiscus marginalis* replenishes its air supply at the surface by raising its elytra so the spiracles can take in air directly.

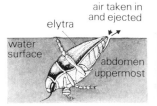

a) beetle rises to surface

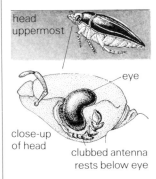

b) antenna brought forward

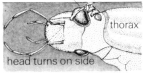

c) antenna breaks surface

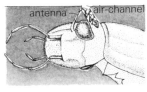

Above: *Hydrophilus piceus* positions itself almost horizontally below the water surface (a). In this way only the antennae break the surface, their hairy tips forming a 'funnel' down which the air passes to air retaining tracts, finally reaching the spiracles (b,c).

Above left: The great silvery water beetle's name comes from its appearance under water–its underneath glistens from a thin film of air trapped between the ventral hairs. It is a poor swimmer (top right), preferring to creep among the pond vegetation.

Hydrobius fuscipes.
Length 6-7mm ($\frac{1}{4}$in).
Black with metallic
reflections.

**Great silvery water
beetle** (*Hydrophilus
piceus*). Length 4cm
($1\frac{5}{8}$in). Black/olive.

water-repellent hairs a funnel-shaped channel
is formed which links the beetle's air-retaining
tracts to the atmospheric air. Situated within
these air-retaining tracts are the spiracles (air-
vents) through which air enters the body.
Fresh air is taken in and stale air ejected by
rhythmical pumping movements of the abdomen. Sometimes the beetles breathe in too
much air and become over-buoyant, making it
necessary to dislodge some of the air before
they are able to move freely.

Floating cocoon Mating between great silvery water beetles takes place in spring, and
afterwards the females can be seen searching
for floating leaves. A most unusual process,
for beetles, then occurs. On finding some
suitable pond weed, the female lies under the
leaf, holding on with her legs, and proceeds to
push in and out two small tubes at the end of
her abdomen. These together make a spin-
neret – a spinning organ – enabling her to spin
a silken cocoon around the end of her body.

When the cocoon is half completed the
female neatly lays her eggs, wrapping each
one in silken thread and placing them side by
side in the upper half of the cocoon. She then
builds the second half of the cocoon, with-
draws her abdomen, and finishes it off with a
'mast' which projects upwards. Finally she
fills the cocoon, which is about 2.4cm (1in)
long, with air from her own store. The
cocoon is waterproof and floats, remaining
attached to a leaf or similar object. One adult
female may complete two to three cocoons in
her lifetime.

Sluggish larva The eggs hatch after a
month and the tiny larvae swallow the air in
the cocoons, making themselves buoyant.
After about twelve hours they make a hole in
the top of the cocoon and escape into the
water. They are not unlike the larvae of the
great diving water beetle, although they are
fatter and more sluggish.

A pair of powerful jaws betrays the larva's
carnivorous nature, although it is not as
fierce as the great diving water beetle's larva.
It feeds mainly on water snails. The larva
seizes the snail with its mandibles and then
rises to the surface where it pushes its tail up
into the air, clasping a leaf or a twig for sup-

port. It then bends backwards and rests the
snail upon its back, puncturing the unfortunate victim to allow its juices to escape.
These are then sucked in by the larva.

When fully grown, in July or August, the
larva leaves the water and makes a pupal cell
in the damp soil by the edge of the pond. The
pupa has two prominent hooked spines on
its head and one on its tail which support it
on a tripod, away from the damp soil.

The adult beetle emerges from the pupa
after a few weeks, but spends the winter
hibernating in the cell. Only in the spring
does it finally come out of the ground.

Common hydrobe There are about 90 other
British species belonging to the family Hydrophilidae, but many are terrestrial. One common aquatic species is the common hydrobe
(*Hydrobius fuscipes*), frequently found in
shallow grassy ponds where it looks like a
smaller version of *Hydrophilus piceus* with its
silvery underneath. They are easy to tell apart,
however as *H. fuscipes* is about a sixth of the
length of *H. piceus*.

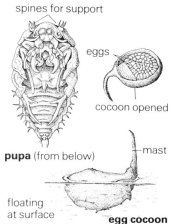

spines for support

eggs

cocoon opened

pupa (from below)

mast

floating
at surface

egg cocoon

Above: The great silvery
water beetle lays its eggs in
a floating cocoon; the larva
(below) is carnivorous.
After a short pupal stage the
adult emerges, but
overwinters within its
pupal cell.

CARNIVOROUS WATER BEETLES

The great diving water beetle is a surprisingly savage insect. Besides possessing a lethal defensive mechanism which is capable of killing a frog, it is also a fierce predator, feeding on any small water animals from insects to fishes.

It is not difficult to distinguish the sexes—the male has smooth elytra and expanded front tarsi, while the female has deeply grooved elytra and normal front tarsi. On the male's front tarsi the first three segments are enlarged to form a conspicuous circular disc fringed with stiff hairs. On the underside of the disc there are rows of small, close-set suckers which, when moistened with a sticky fluid, become adhesive. These organs are capable of supporting more than 13 times the beetle's own weight, and are chiefly used to hold the female during mating. The two final segments of the tarsi are normal and end in the usual pair of claws.

Rowing and flying In common with many water-dwelling insects the great diving water beetle's hind legs are highly adapted for swimming. The tibiae and tarsi are fringed with long stiff hairs which spread out during the swimming stroke, so maximising the 'pull', and become flattened during the return stroke, thus minimising resistance to the water.

This 'feathering', as rowers would call it, is brought about by a slight but automatic rotation of the tarsus as it moves through the water, so that its broad face is presented during the swimming stroke and its edge during the return. The two hind legs work together and are most efficient rowing organs.

These beetles are not entirely restricted to an underwater existence. They fly readily from pond to pond, usually at night, and often turn up in garden ponds. Sometimes they are confused by the reflection of moon light and land on greenhouses and glass frames. Their membranous flying wings are folded flat on top of the abdomen and covered by the elytra.

Carnivorous feeders Great diving water beetles do not hibernate, but swim about and feed in all but the coldest weather. They are extremely rapacious and feed on any small

Above: Great diving water beetles keep a store of air under their elytra which makes them extremely light. To remain under water they must either swim or hold on to aquatic plants.

Opposite: When the larva of the great diving water beetle feeds on a tadpole it injects digestive juices into the victim, liquefying it within a matter of minutes. The predator then draws back the liquid and discards the tadpole's empty skin.

Anyone interested in pond-life is sure to have come across the great diving water beetle (*Dytiscus marginalis*) – probably the best known and studied of all water beetles. This species is a common insect in ponds and slow rivers, but can also be kept easily in aquariums where it may survive for two or three years.

Water beetle anatomy The oval body of the great diving water beetle is dark greenish-brown above and yellow around the margins of the thorax and the elytra (wing cases), and underneath. The eyes, large and each possessing about 9000 facets, are situated at the sides of the head so they can see easily above and below. The antennae are thread-like and not particularly conspicuous.

Anatomy for an aquatic life

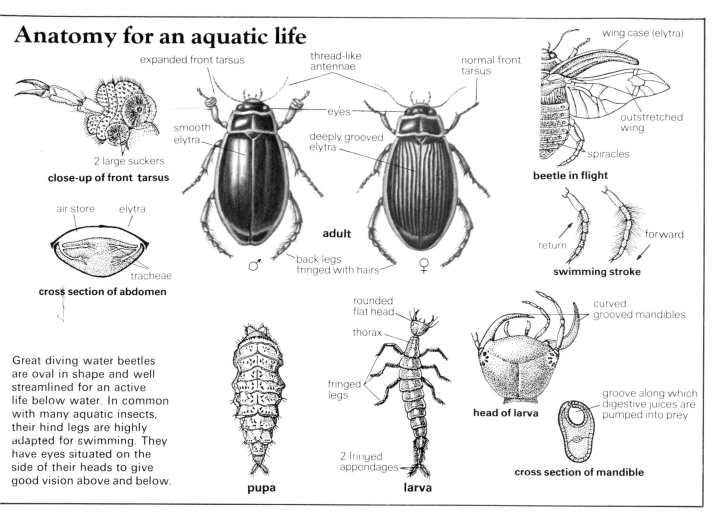

close-up of front tarsus
- expanded front tarsus
- 2 large suckers

cross section of abdomen
- air store
- elytra
- tracheae

- thread-like antennae
- smooth elytra
- eyes
- back legs fringed with hairs
- **adult** ♂

- normal front tarsus
- deeply grooved elytra
- ♀

- wing case (elytra)
- outstretched wing
- spiracles
- **beetle in flight**

swimming stroke
- return
- forward

Great diving water beetles are oval in shape and well streamlined for an active life below water. In common with many aquatic insects, their hind legs are highly adapted for swimming. They have eyes situated on the side of their heads to give good vision above and below.

pupa

larva
- rounded flat head
- thorax
- fringed legs
- 2 fringed appendages

head of larva
- curved grooved mandibles

cross section of mandible
- groove along which digestive juices are pumped into prey

reatures they can catch—insects, molluscs, adpoles and even small fish. They tear the rey up with their strong biting jaws and wallow the pieces, finally digesting them in heir stomachs.

If you keep these beetles in an aquarium ou will find they feed readily on pieces of neat or worms, but make sure you do not ive them too much food. The surplus will ecay and cause the water to turn foul.

Breathing and defence You can tell if a pond ontains great diving water beetles by sitting uietly and waiting for them to come up for ir. They have an extremely efficient breathng system comprising two rows of spiracles air vents) arranged along the sides of the bdomen. The last two pairs of spiracles are nuch larger than the rest; when at the water urface the beetles raise their elytra slightly so hat these large spiracles can take in air irectly. The other spiracles use the air which s stored under the elytra.

The defensive powers of the great diving vater beetle are no less impressive than its reathing system. In addition to a pair of harp spikes on the beetle's underside, it can roduce an unpleasant-smelling nerve poison vhich is sufficiently lethal to kill a frog. This eadly fluid emanates from glands on the horax.

If you catch any water beetles try not to ouch them. They are best tipped straight rom the net into a jar of water or into a box

filled with wet water weed.

Life cycle In March and April the females lay their eggs singly in slits which they cut in water plant stems with ovipositors equipped with extremely sharp blades. Individual adult females lay eggs at the same time each year. The eggs are rather large–up to 7mm (¼in) long–and hatch in about three weeks.

The larva is quite unlike the adult beetle except that it is even more rapacious, feeding

Below: Great diving water beetle viewed from the underside. Should you catch one of these in a pond net, handle it carefully—not because of its jaws, which it seldom uses, but because of the sharp spikes on its underside, clearly visible in this picture.

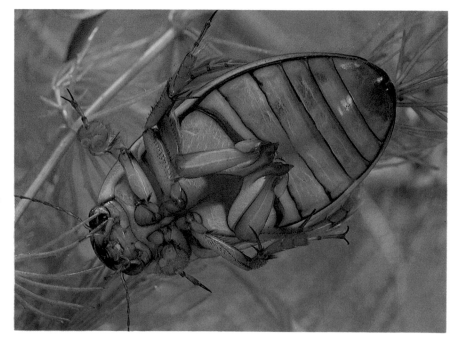

Above: A good view of the small diving water beetle, (*Acilius sulcatus*) with an air bubble at the rear of its abdomen. This species is commonly found in ponds, particularly sandy or gravelly ones, although it is only active from March to November. In many ways it is similar to the great diving water beetle, but it is hardly more than half its size, at 16-18mm ($\frac{5}{8}$-$\frac{3}{4}$in) long, and rather paler in colour. While the male has smooth elytra (wing cases) and enlarged front tarsi, the female has strongly ridged elytra and normal front tarsi. The larva is just as rapacious as that of *Dytiscus marginalis,* feeding on small aquatic creatures throughout summer. When fully grown it is smaller than *D. marginalis* with a narrow thorax, long neck and small head—almost shrimp-like in form. The fully grown larva builds cells in mud at the water's edge where it pupates, emerging as an adult before the winter sets in.

on any living thing it can catch, including its own brethren. It is elongated with a rounded flat head carrying slender, pointed mandibles. Its three pairs of legs are long and fringed with hairs, so that they work efficiently as oars, enabling the larva to move slowly through the water. It can also make a sudden spring by active, snake-like body movements.

The end of the larva's abdomen narrows and has two small hair-fringed appendages. As the larva is lighter than water it rises, tail first, if it is not holding on to any vegetation. This occurs when the larva's air stores need replenishing—the tail appendages break the surface film so the two larger spiracles at the tail end can take in fresh air while the larva hangs from the surface. These two spiracles, the only open ones it possesses, communicate with two longitudinal air tubes in its body, which are unusually wide to allow for air storage.

Rapacious larva One of the larva's most interesting features is its jaws, which have a fine, almost closed groove along the inner edge. When the larva seizes the prey with its jaws it injects digestive juices along the grooves into the victim. The prey's tissues are then rapidly digested, and the larva draws in the resulting fluid using a pump in its throat. Only the victim's empty skin remains.

In about six to eight weeks the larva is fully fed. At this stage it leaves the water and burrows into damp soil near the water's edge,

making a roundish cell to pupate in.

In summer the adult beetle emerges from its pupa after only two to three weeks, but if the larva does not pupate until autumn, it will not emerge as an adult until spring.

Other species Six species of *Dytiscus* are found in Britain, but only *Dytiscus marginalis* is common everywhere. Of the remainder *Dytiscus semisculatus*, a smaller species is not uncommon, but is more restricted to running water. *Dytiscus circumflexus* is much the same size as *D. marginalis* but has black markings on a yellow underside.

There are more than 100 other carnivorous water beetles in Britain—two of the more common species are worth mentioning. *Colymbetes fuscus* 17mm ($\frac{5}{8}$in) long and yellowish brown in colour, is found in almost any pond with a muddy bottom. Its larvae are similar to those of *D. marginalis* except that the mandibles are shorter and the thorax broader. This species overwinters as a larva and does not pupate until spring.

Hygrobia hermanni is known commonly as the screech beetle because of the way it stridulates when picked up. It does this by rubbing the tip of its abdomen against a file on the underside of the elytra. The adult is reddish yellow in colour and can be found in southern England and Ireland.

Unlike other species its larva does not come to the water surface; it breathes by means of gills along the lower side of the abdomen.

Left: *Dytiscus semisculatus*. 2.5-3cm (1-1$\frac{1}{4}$in) long. Common in running water.

Right: *Dytiscus circumflexus*. 3.8cm (1$\frac{1}{2}$in) long. Uncommon, ponds and canals.

Left: *Colymbetes fuscus*. 17mm ($\frac{5}{8}$in) long. Common in ponds with muddy bottoms.

Right: **Screech beetle** (*Hygrobia hermanni*). 8-10mm ($\frac{3}{8}$in) long. Ditches and ponds.

WATER BUGS COMING UP FOR AIR

Water bugs such as saucer bugs and water boatmen, being insects, must all breathe air. The ways they have of doing this under the water are diverse and fascinating.

Bugs are distinguished by having mouthparts in the form of a piercing and sucking beak through which they can take only liquid food, such as the sap of plants or the body fluids of animals. They are found in great variety on the land, but a much smaller number of species inhabit fresh water. Some of the truly aquatic underwater bugs are predators, while others feed on algae and particles of organic matter and, with one exception, are adapted to breathe atmospheric air and must visit the surface to obtain it.

Backswimmers The most familiar water bugs are the backswimmers, sometimes also called water boatmen. You can see them on almost any fairly clean weedy pond or ditch,

floating just under the surface or swimming down as you approach. If you come close to the water and keep quite still, they soon reappear and float again, with tails just projecting through the surface film.

Both when floating and when swimming these insects look remarkably like tiny boats propelled by a single pair of oars. These 'oars' are the hindmost pair of legs, and are long and fringed with hair–two adaptations that make swimming easier. The two front pairs of legs are short and form a cluster just behind the head. They appear to be on top of the body, but this is an illusion produced by the fact that the insect always floats and swims upside down. An unusual discovery has been made about this upside down swimming. It seems to be controlled by the insect's sense of sight rather than by any appreciation of gravity. If a backswimmer is put into a glass tank lit from below, it swims with the back uppermost.

There are several species of backswimmer, the most common one being *Notonecta glauca*, which is about 15mm ($\frac{1}{2}$in) long. These insects are fierce predators, taking insects, tadpoles and even little fish under the water and also drowning flies at the surface. They kill their prey by holding it with the four front legs and piercing it with their sharp beaks. A combined poison and digestive fluid is injected and the contents of the prey are liquefied and sucked back. If you catch a

Above: A pair of corixas, or water boatmen. The forelegs of the male are used for producing a high-pitched courtship song, made by stroking the legs against the margin of the head. The insects that sing, or stridulate, often have sound-producing apparatus that, examined with a microscope, gives a reliable means of identifying the species. The males of the numerous kinds of corixas have rows of tiny pegs on the forelegs, the number and disposition of which differs very consistently in the different species. The male of each species sings a particular 'signature tune' which is recognised by females of his own kind.

backswimmer, be very careful in handling it; a jab from the beak is extremely painful.

Backswimmers take in air at the surface through their hind ends. When the insect dives it carries with it an air supply in a bubble held mainly by the hairs along the ventral (underside) surface of the body, but also between the wings and the body. The bubble is in contact with the spiracles (breathing tubes) on the thorax. The air makes the insect buoyant when it is submerged and it has to swim vigorously when diving, and cling to some underwater object in order to stay down. The backswimmer's eggs are laid in the spring, embedded in the stems of plants, and the nymphs take about two months to reach adulthood.

Corixid water boatmen If you fish about in water weeds with a dip net you can often find smaller insects that look like backswimmers and swim in the same way, by rowing with the hindmost legs. They differ from *Notonecta* in being flatter, with a more rounded outline, and in swimming the right

Below: The water stick-insect (*Ranatra linearis*) is about 6-7cm (2½in) long. It uses its front legs to catch food – mainly small prey such as water fleas and a variety of other animals. It is not a good swimmer, preferring to crawl about among the water weeds. Water stick-insects have special receptors that enable them to maintain themselves at the right depth of water for their breathing siphons.

way up, that is with the dorsal (top) side upwards. There are quite a number of species but the largest and one of the commonest is the common corixa (*Corixa punctata*), which is about 12mm (½in) long.

The corixas are not closely related to the backswimmers and are not predators, but feed by sieving the water through hairs on the front legs and straining out fine organic particles and algae, which are then sucked in by the short beak. The main air supply is carried as a bubble between the back and the wings and is captured at the surface by the head and thorax (and not via the tail end as in *Notonecta*). Corixas lay eggs from January to March, fixing them to the leaves and stems of aquatic plants.

The hind legs of both types of water boatman are beautifully adapted for rowing. On the propulsive back stroke the hairs that fringe the legs towards their tips spread out and resist the water, but fold up and offer no effective resistance on the recovery stroke.

The saucer bug is found only in the southern half of Britain, but within its range it is often common in muddy and weedy ponds and ditches, living on the bottom and surfacing to breathe at fairly long intervals. Its air supply is carried between wings and body. It is 12-16mm (½in) long, broad-bodied and flat and rather beetle-like in appearance. A curious feature is that it has well-developed wings, but muscles so reduced that it cannot fly. The bugs probably colonize new water by creeping over the land; the legs are less modified for swimming than those of corixas and backswimmers. The saucer bug is a fierce predator and kills its prey just as backswimmers do; its bite is also equally painful.

Another broad-bodied predatory bug is the uncommon and seldom-seen *Aphelocheirus aestivalis*. Its distribution is based on old established river systems, including the Thames and the Severn. The most interesting feature of this insect is its remarkable respiratory system. The body is largely covered by microscopic hairs, so minute as to number two million to the square millimetre. This hair covering is unwettable, and carries a film of air into which oxygen continually diffuses from the water. This so-called 'plastron' is developed only in the adult bug; in the nymph respiration takes place through the skin. It is also present in some kinds of water beetle, and is really a type of gill since it extracts oxygen from water.

Water scorpions There are two British bugs belonging to the Nepidae or water scorpion family. Their chief peculiarity is their breathing apparatus, which has the form of a tube or 'snorkel' at the tip of the tail. It looks like a sting, and may alarm people unfamiliar with the creature's habits. Of the two species *Nepa cinerea* is the more common, living in shallow weedy ponds.

The water scorpion's movements are slug

Right: Water scorpion (*Nepa cinerea*) resting on reeds underwater. It is a dark brown flattened insect, about 19mm ($\frac{3}{4}$in) long, with a 'tail' over half as long again. The whole insect looks very much like a decayed leaf. The forelegs are sharply angled and used for grasping prey, and they do have a rather remote resemblance to the claws of a scorpion. The victim is despatched and its body contents extracted by the poison-injecting and sucking beak.

Below: The underwater-dwelling water bugs have various different methods of breathing. (Note that you would not find all these different bugs in the same stretch of water.)
1. **Water scorpion** *(Nepa cinerea).*
2. **Water stick insect** *(Ranatra linearis).*
3. **Backswimmer, or water boatman** *(Notonecta glauca).*
4. **Saucer bug** *(Ilyocoris cimicoides).*
5. **Water bug** *(Aphelocheirus aestivalis).*

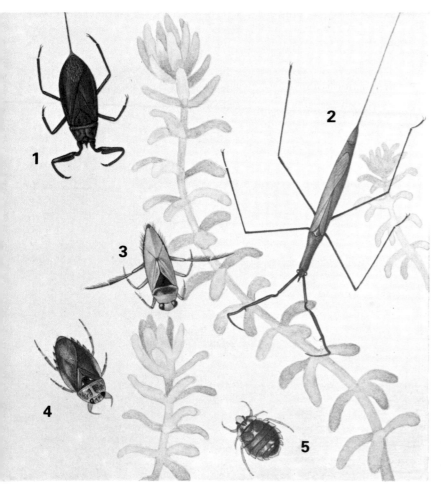

gish and mainly confined to walking on the bottom of the pond, although it can swim rather awkwardly to reach the surface and extrude the tip of its breathing tube; normally it does this by climbing up water plants.

If you lift the wing cases (really the forewings) you can see the brightly coloured pink and red hind wings. There is some uncertainty about the water scorpion's ability to fly. In most specimens the wing muscles are so weakly developed that flight is impossible, but some individuals have been seen to fly so this must be a variable feature.

The water stick insect is considerably larger than the water scorpion; its English name describes it very well. The forelegs are adapted for seizing prey, like those of the water scorpion, but are longer and more slender. The breathing tube is only a little shorter than the body. Water stick insects are able to fly and use this means of escape from pools that threaten to dry up. The species is restricted to the southern half of Britain, and frequents fairly deep pools with water plants growing around their margins.

The eggs are laid in rows in the stems of water plants, and each egg has two thread-like appendages at one end. The nymphs have a fairly short tail and when they are small they hang down from the surface film of the water by their legs, with the breathing tube just breaking the film. Adults can remain below for 30 minutes or so.

DRAGONFLY: HAWKERS & DARTERS

Dragonflies – brilliantly coloured sun-loving insects – are fast-flying hunters that spend the summer darting over ponds in search of prey.

Dragonflies, together with their close relatives the damselflies, belong to an order known as the Odonata. All of them are predators throughout their lives and have aquatic larvae, frequently called nymphs, and they are regarded as being among the most primitive of winged insects.

Dragonflies can be distinguished from damselflies by their more robust build and usually larger size, and by the way in which they hold their wings when at rest. In dragonflies the wings are extended horizontally on each side; damselflies hold their wings together over their backs just as butterflies do.

The two pairs of wings are usually colourless and transparent, their membranes supported by a fine network of 'veins' quite unlike those of any other insects. This is one of the characteristics regarded as primitive. Another is the direct and simple way in which the muscles of the thorax move the wings up and down; they are attached on each side of a pivot at the base of the wing, so that the outside muscles pull the wing down and those inside the pivot pull it up. The higher insects, such as the bees, flies and butterflies, have mechanisms that are far more complicated.

Dragonflies also have an immensely long geological history. At the time when our coal was formed, about 300 million years ago, their evolutionary ancestors were already flying in the great swampy jungles; some species had a wingspan of nearly 70cm (27in) and were the largest insects known to us.

Above: A male hawker dragonfly, *Brachytron pratense*, of the Aeshnidae family. Members of this family have a wingspan of up to 10cm (4in) and are generally out and about in summer. The female hawker dragonfly lays its eggs in the stems of water plants or in moss beside ponds or streams. The larvae, which are large, have elongated, torpedo-shaped bodies. Any clear, fairly still water with plenty of water weeds provides breeding quarters for hawker dragonflies, and most of them have a life cycle lasting two or more years.

Adult dragonflies have the lifestyle of falcons, hunting and catching other insects on the wing. To do this they must be fast, active flyers – which they are, despite the archaic design of their wings. The legs of dragonflies are arranged so that, when spread out, they form a forward-directed basket or net which is used in capturing flying prey. A dragonfly can rest by clinging on to a twig or grass stem with its feet, but can walk only in a slow and awkward manner.

Dragonfly larvae, or nymphs, also capture prey. Most insects have a segmented organ, called the labium, below the mouth. In dragonfly larvae this is elongated and hinged so that it can be extended in front of the head, and it bears a pair of pincer-like claws near the tip. It is sometimes referred to as a 'mask'. A hunting larva stalks its prey to within a centimetre or less, then shoots out the labium and seizes the prey with its claws. The victims are mostly water insects, but large, well-grown larvae kill small fish, and are most unwelcome in trout hatcheries.

The larva's breathing mechanism is rather peculiar. It has gills inside the rectum and water is drawn in and out to aerate them. The water can be forcibly expelled, causing the larva to shoot forward if threatened by danger. This combination of breathing and jet propulsion is a feature shared by the marine squids and cuttlefish.

The dragonfly larva's life is usually long. Some libellulid species may complete their life cycle in a year, but most of the other dragonflies spend at least two years in the water, and some spend as many as five years.

Darters and hawkers There are 27 species of dragonfly in the British Isles, most belonging either to the Aeshnidae (hawker) family or to the Libellulidae (darter) family. The names 'darter' and 'hawker' come from the different habits of flight of the two families of dragonflies. Darters fly quickly out from a perch in waterside vegetation, returning to it again just as rapidly, while hawkers have a stronger, sustained flight.

The most frequently seen are probably the darters of the genus *Sympetrum*. The most abundant of these is the common darter

(*Sympetrum striolatum*). It is a moderate-sized species with a wingspan of 5.5-6cm (over 2in). The wings are yellow right at the base, but otherwise clear, and the body is slender, red in the male but reddish-brown in the female. This is the dragonfly that you can often see in middle and late summer sitting on the handle of a spade or on a bare patch of earth in the sun. If you scare it away it soon comes back to the same spot. It remains on the wing later than any other species, sometimes even into late November.

It is common in southern England, but absent from most parts of Scotland, where its place is taken by the very similar Highland darter (*Sympetrum nigrescens*). Large pale

Below: Dragonfly larva of the species *Libellula depressa*. This larva is a mud-dweller and is commonest in southern England. Most adult *Libellula* males have a powder-blue hind-body, while that of the females is always brown. These dragonflies seldom go far from the marshes and pools where they breed. Their continued existence depends on the preservation of suitable breeding sites.

Right: Ruddy sympetrum dragonfly (*Sympetrum sanguineum*), one of the darters (so-called from their habit of darting out from a perch). Residents occur in south and east England; migrants coming from the Continent may be seen in other areas as well. *Sympetrum* dragonflies breed in clean ponds, canals, and ditches. The larvae are broad-bodied and short with long legs and wide heads.

Mating and laying eggs

Before mating the male common hawker (right) transfers his sperm from the end of his abdomen to an 'accessory' organ on his underside. He pursues a flying female, lands on her back and seizes her head with a pair of claspers at the tip of his tail. The female brings her abdomen up so that its tip touches the male organ, and sperm is transferred to her.
Egg-laying varies between species. Some insert the eggs in water-plant stems or in moss at the water's edge, others fly over the water and drop the eggs, while some dip the abdomen into the water to wash the eggs off the tip.

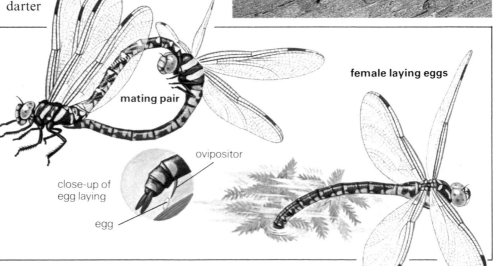

mating pair

female laying eggs

ovipositor

close-up of
egg laying

egg

Below: Brown aeshna dragonfly *Aeshna grandis*. Both males and females of this hawker species have a dark brown body; they are common in south and south-east England. You can see this species from June to October, often in towns and well away from water. The female lays her eggs in ponds, lakes, rivers and canals and the larvae take anything from two to five years to reach adulthood.

specimens of the common darter seen near the south coast are likely to be migrants that have flown over from the Continent. Some of our other darter dragonflies are also regular migrants, including the black darter (*Sympetrum scoticum*). This species is common in marshy places on heather moors and is widespread in the British Isles in suitable localities (not confined to Scotland as its specific name suggests). The body is black in the male and dark brown in the female.

The other familiar and conspicuous group of dragonflies in the British Isles are the hawkers, of the genus *Aeshna*. These are much larger than the darters, with wingspans of up to 10cm (4in), and most of them are boldly marked with green, blue and black. You can generally see them in summer, flying up and down over a definite beat, often but not always over a stream, and they spend less time sitting at rest than darters do. In the southern and midland counties of England the southern hawker (*Aeshna cyanea*) is the species most often seen. It flies from July to September and both sexes have a black body spotted with green, the male with some blue spots near the end of the tail. It frequently breeds in garden ponds.

The common hawker (*Aeshna juncea*) is hardly less common, and much more widely distributed, its range extending from the south coast to Ireland and northern Scotland. It is commonest on heaths and moor lands. The male is dark brown with blue spots, while the female has green spots. The presence in both sexes of *A. cyanea* of a conspicuous yellow triangle in the centre line just where the abdomen joins the thorax, and its absence in *A. juncea*, is a good distinguishing mark if you can observe the insects closely enough to see their body colouring.

One of the largest and most striking of our hawkers is the emperor dragonfly (*Anax imperator*) which has a wingspan of nearly 10cm (4in) and has a bright blue and black abdomen. It is common in south-east England but does not occur in Scotland. This species is thought to be the largest hawker dragonfly in the British Isles.

Scotland has its special *Aeshna* dragonfly, the beautiful azure hawker (*Aeshna caerulea*) in which both sexes have a body spotted with bright blue. It is widespread in Scotland but by no means common.

Threat from pollution All wild life is threatened by pollution, but animals that live and breathe in fresh waters are especially endangered. There is little doubt that recent reductions in the numbers and ranges of our dragonflies are due to this hazard, and also to mechanical dredging of canals and ditches in low-lying areas. Unless action is taken to control these destructive agencies, our dragonflies, and much else that is interesting and beautiful, will disappear from the countryside of Britain.

The eyes have it—vision in dragonflies

Dragonfly eyesight needs to be good for the insects' mode of hunting. Their eyes are among the most highly-developed of all insects. Each eye occupies the whole of one side of the head. Their eyes, like those of most adult insects, are of the type known as compound—made up of minute units called ommatidia, each of which is rather like a tiny telescope. In each eye there may be as many as 20,000 of these, packed together in a precisely radiating bundle, the outer end of each appearing as a hexagonal facet on the surface of the eye. The radial arrangement covers a wide visual field—a dragonfly can spot a victim or enemy 12m (40ft) away in almost any direction. A result of their dependence on eyesight for hunting, finding mates and escaping enemies, is that the antennae—used in other insects for smell and touch—are degenerate and tiny.

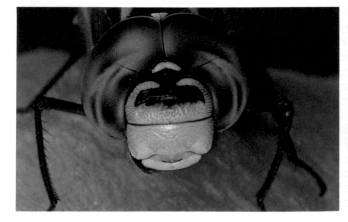

MYRIADS OF MIDGES

Almost any small gnat-like creature is popularly called a midge, and is thought to bite. However, the name should really be reserved for two related kinds of flies – biting midges and non-biting midges.

n the British Isles there are about 450 species f non-biting midge (family Chironomidae) nd 150 species of biting midge (family Ceratopogonidae). They are Diptera (true ies). In spite of the existence of all these pecies, many of the 'dancing' flies you see in ardens are not in fact midges at all but are mall species of craneflies.

Dancing swarms The way you are most kely to see midges is in swarms. The males f both kinds form dancing swarms, usually n the afternoon or around dusk, the insects onstantly flying up and down. Swarms may ontain only a few individuals, but often onsist of hundreds or even thousands. They lways dance over a conspicuous marker –

a bush, a cow, a rock, an outstanding leaf, or perhaps the margin of a lake, according to the habits of the different species.

The swarms of biting midges tend to be rather inconspicuous as they are small insects and their markers may be fern leaves or low boughs. Those of non-biting midges are much more conspicuous; some species regularly swarm high up over trees or tall buildings, often resembling a column of smoke.

The antennae of male midges have long hairs which give them a bushy, feathery appearance. This is much more conspicuous in non-biting midges, because once their hairs are erected they can never be lowered; those of biting midges are more mobile.

Above: A female *Chironomus* midge laying her eggs. The larvae of this and other species of midge are abundant in ponds, lakes and rivers; there are frequently many thousands to the square metre. They form an important part of the diet of fish and the adults are eaten in large numbers by such birds as swallows and swifts.

Below: *Chironomus* larvae, after their first moult, turn red and are then known as blood-worms.

Above: *Chironomus* pupa emerging from its larval skin. The pupa overwinters in mud at the bottom of the pond, breathing by means of tufts of respiratory filaments on its thorax. You can see these tufts at the front end of this emerging pupa.

Non-biting midges The Chironomidae harmless to man, slightly resemble mosquitoes but can easily be distinguished by the complete absence of a long biting proboscis Their front legs are often very long and are held in a raised position. When at rest their wings are either parted slightly or held roof like along the sides of the abdomen. Neither male nor female takes food of any kind, and they live for only a few days.

The vast majority of non-biting midges lay their eggs in water. Different species prefer differing levels of acidity, alkalinity and organic content, so many kinds of water are chosen. A small number breed below the high tide mark on the seashore, and the males can often be seen in dancing swarms over patches of seaweed exposed by the retreating tide. A few have even abandoned their aquatic habitat and lay their eggs in decaying vegetation or dung.

A typical life cycle A typical non-biting midge, such as *Chironomus dorsalis*, lays eggs in ponds or garden rainwater butts. The female embeds her eggs, several hundred in number, in sinuous rows in a gelatinous material. This swells in the water to form a mucilaginous rope, about 20mm (¾in) long which is moored to the side of the butt or pond by a thread secreted by the female. The eggs hatch within a week into tiny greenish larvae equipped at both ends with a pair of false legs carrying hooks. The larvae feed on decaying vegetable matter, making small protective tubes from a salivary secretion and particles of mud and leaves.

After their first moult the larvae become red in colour, due to the presence of haemoglobin (a red, oxygen-carrying substance in their blood. They are then popularly known as blood-worms. Haemoglobin is unusual in insects, but is often found in those that live in places deficient in oxygen, such as the mud at the bottom of a pond, since haemoglobin is a more efficient oxygen carrier than the other blood pigments usually

The antennae act as a directional hearing organ and are used to detect females. The hairs vibrate in response to the sounds made by the wing beats of the females, which produce a slightly different tone from the wing beats of the males.

The females are attracted to the swarms, where they are seized by the males for mating. This may take place quickly in the air, but the pair usually fall out of the swarm and complete mating on the ground or among vegetation.

Left: *Chironomus* midges— they are the non-biting kind —are often much larger than biting midges. Some species can reach a length of 9-12mm (½in). There are about 450 species of non-biting midge in the British Isles. They are completely harmless to man in Britain, except that they are a nuisance when present in large numbers, near reservoirs for instance. On the Continent a few small species can cause an asthma-like reaction in some people.

Culicoides nubeculosus, one of the largest man-biting species at 4mm long, can be troublesome around farms, especially if horses are present. It feeds readily on blood from these mammals. Its larvae live in the liquid running from manure heaps.

Not all biting midges attack vertebrates. Another group, of which the genus *Forcipomyia* is an example, take their blood meal from other insects. They have been recorded sucking blood from caterpillars and from the wings of butterflies, dragonflies and lacewings.

Meat-eaters Some biting midges, the best known genera being *Palpomyia* and *Bezzia*, do not suck blood but are actively carnivorous. The females seize other small flies, especially the males of non-biting midges and mayflies. They usually have modified legs, either spiny or with long claws, for grasping prey. They normally enter swarms of males and seize one of about their own size. The two insects sink to the ground where the predator pierces its prey in the head or thorax and injects saliva to reduce the body contents to liquid, which is then sucked in. The females have been seen congregating over likely markers, waiting for swarms of males to form. When their own males form dancing swarms, the females enter the swarms and, as the males grasp them for mating, the females seize the males for prey. The females end up doubly satisfied – fertilised and fed.

Anatomy of a biting midge

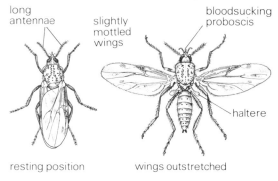

resting position   wings outstretched

Above: Chironomid midges caught in a spider's web. Many common species are greenish in colour, and the males have very bushy antennae. Notice the iridescent wings.

Right: Female biting midge *Culicoides nubeculosus*, in resting position with wings folded, and with wings outstretched. It is one of the largest man-biting species, at 4mm long, and has a painful bite. The black spots on its thorax and wings readily identify it.

Below: Pupae of the biting midge *Forcipomyia* under the bark of a tree. The adults of this species suck blood, not from mammals but from other insects, including caterpillars and butterflies, dragonflies and lacewings.

...und in insects. The haemoglobin is not ...ntained in corpuscles, as in a vertebrate, ...t is free in the blood.

The blood-worm lives concealed in its tube ...burrow in the mud, keeping up an un-...latory movement which maintains a flow ...water for respiratory purposes. It does not ...ed to come to the surface for breathing, ...ough it may leave its tube occasionally.

More than one generation appears each ...ar, but autumn larvae do not change to ...pae until the spring. The pupa stays half ...ried in the mud, breathing by means of ...fts of respiratory filaments on its thorax. At ...e end of the pupa's body are fin-like flaps ...at enable it to swim to the surface after a ...eek or so. At the surface the perfect insect ...nerges.

Biting midges: the bloodsuckers All biting ...idges are tiny, at no more than 1-4mm long. ...e man-biting ones appear, frequently in ...ge numbers, on warm summer afternoons ...d evenings to take a meal of blood from ...yone out-of-doors. Fortunately, not all ...ecies attack man; some feed on the blood ...other mammals such as horses, sheep and ...bbits, and probably on birds as well. Forty-...e species in Britain take vertebrate blood ...d each has its own preferred hosts. Most ...ople have been attacked at one time or ...other by these bloodthirsty creatures. Only ...e female midge bites; she is equipped with ...arp, piercing mouth appendages and needs ...meal of blood for her eggs to mature. The ...ales feed on nectar from flowers.

A look at some species The female ...licoides obsoletus lays her eggs, about 100 ...number, in damp soil where the larvae ...ed on decaying plant tissue. There are two ...aks of adult activity, the first in May-June ...d the second in September; this suggests ...at there are two generations a year. These ...dges overwinter as larvae.

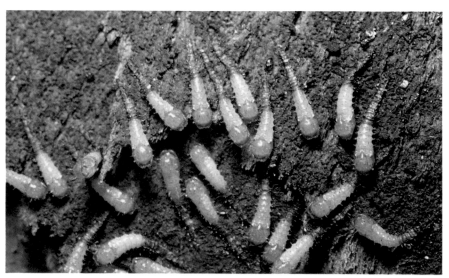

Left: A female of the species *Culiseta annulata*, one of the Culicines, attempting to bite through cloth. These mosquitoes are common around houses and can be recognised by their size (up to 8mm/⅜in), black spotted wings and white banded legs. They bite man readily, but do not transmit malaria or ague. The familiar itching lumps that appear on the victim's skin when bitten are due to an allergic reaction to the saliva of the mosquito.

How a mosquito bite

The mosquito's proboscis is not the piercing organ itself, but a hollow half-tube, holding the fine, sharp stylets and sucking tube proper. The sucking tube is the elongated upper lip and floor of the mouth, closely fitted together.

When a mosquito bites, the sharp stylets make the initial puncture, into which the sucking tube is then pushed. The hollow, sheathing half-tube then loops away so that it does not enter, but acts as a support and guide for the stylets. The mosquito uses a muscular pump in its throat to pump up blood, at the same time injecting saliva, which acts as an anti-coagulant and lubricant, into the wound through a duct in the sucking tube.

before penetration

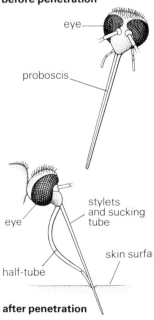

eye

proboscis

stylets and sucking tube

eye

half-tube

skin surfa

after penetration

MOSQUITOES –MIGHTY BITERS

More than 30 species of mosquito are found in the British Isles, but although most bite man, few cause more than minor irritation.

There are two different sorts of mosquitoes, Anophelines and Culicines, a distinction which is important medically as Anophelines transmit human malaria while Culicines transmit bird malaria and, in warmer countries, yellow fever, other viruses and parasitic worms.

Although everyone knows more or less what a mosquito looks like, there are many other similar insects that do not bite and which are regularly confused with them.

Mosquito characteristics The average body length of a mosquito is about 6mm (¼in) and with its long legs and two wings it resembles a small crane-fly or a non-biting midge. However, two aids to identification are the long proboscis, which projects out from the head, and the wings which are held in a flat, folded position when the mosquito is at rest.

The larvae and pupae of all mosquitoes are aquatic, so the adults tend to be found in damp places. Only the females suck blood and although some will fly for several miles in search of a blood-meal, 1.5-3km (1-2 miles) is a more usual distance. Male mosquitoes also have a proboscis but they feed only on nectar and fruit juices, which are also taken by the female in addition to blood. A blood-meal seems to be a necessity for the females of most species to ensure the laying of a larger number of eggs.

Male mosquitoes have large bushy antennae, making them easily recognisable. They form swarms at dusk over prominent objects, just as midges do, and the females are attracted to these swarms for mating. The males pick up the slightly differing wing-beat frequency of the females with their antennae and coupling takes place in the air, with mating usually completed on the ground.

Life-cycle The life history of a mosquito is well illustrated by that of a common Culicine, *Culex pipiens*, the house mosquito which is abundant everywhere. It breeds in water butts, ditches and other small collections of water, clean, foul or brackish, found around houses or elsewhere. The female feeds on the blood of frogs and birds, including cage birds left uncovered overnight.

Mosquito life-styles

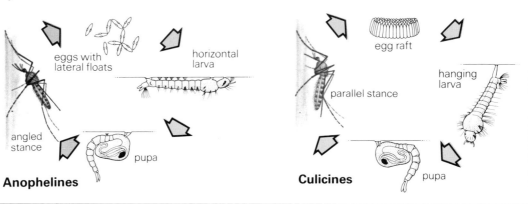

Anophelines differ from Culicines in several ways. Their eggs have lateral floats and their larvae, lacking breathing siphons, float horizontally below the surface instead of hanging down. The adults also have different stances—Anophelines hold their bodies at an angle to the surface, while Culicines adopt a more parallel position.

Anophelines

eggs with lateral floats

horizontal larva

angled stance

pupa

Culicines

egg raft

parallel stance

hanging larva

pupa

After mating, the female finds suitable water and stands on the surface, crossing her hind legs to make a V-shaped mould. Into this she lays 150-350 spindle-shaped eggs, which adhere to form a tiny egg-raft, floating on the water. She may lay five or six such rafts in her lifespan of a few weeks in summer.

The eggs hatch after a few days into larvae which have a swollen thorax and a cylindrical abdomen ending in a respiratory tube or siphon. They normally hang by this siphon from the surface water film and feed by sweeping minute organic particles into their mouths with a pair of moustache-like 'brushes'. If disturbed, the larvae swim down with vigorous jerking movements, but soon rise to the surface again. They moult three times before changing to pupae after a week or ten days.

The pupae are normally described as 'comma-shaped', the large head and thorax making the dot of the comma and the flexible abdomen forming its tail. The pupae also hang from the surface film, but the right way up, and not head downwards like the larvae. They breathe through two respiratory trumpets on the top of the thorax. A large air cavity in the centre of the thorax helps to keep the pupae buoyant. The pupal stage lasts only three to five days, then the adult emerges by splitting the dorsal skin and drawing itself out. The newly emerged mosquito rests for a brief period before flying off.

Man-biters There are five species of Anophelines in Britain, all of which bite man and large domestic animals. Two species, *Anopheles messeae* and *Anopheles atroparvus* are important because, although almost identical in appearance, they differ in habits, the latter being the main European malaria carrier. Although they are common where they occur, in practice you are less likely to see an *Anopheles* than a *Culex* or *Aedes* (another common genus).

Anopheles atroparvus lays its eggs on the water's surface, normally in brackish coastal ditches and pools. There are two or three broods a year and the females often used to be found indoors, where they bit man freely. They do not go into complete hibernation, but continue feeding throughout the winter in warm houses and animal sheds, choosing dark, cobwebby corners for resting. *Anopheles messeae*, on the other hand, lays its eggs in fresh water and the females go into complete hibernation in cold buildings. They seem to prefer the blood of domestic animals to that of man.

Disease carriers Malaria or ague used to be common among people living near the fens and marshy coastal areas, particularly in East Anglia and Kent. Malaria is caused by a protozoan which attacks the red blood corpuscles. Mosquitoes pick it up when they bite an infected person. The malaria parasites make large cysts on the mosquito's stomach, before arriving in its saliva, ready to be injected into another person as the mosquito bites. The infected mosquitoes have a reduced egg output.

It has been estimated that as many as 150 million people worldwide may suffer from malaria each year. However, during the last 150 years, the malaria-carrying *Anopheles atroparvus* has virtually disappeared from houses in Britain.

Below: A male *Aedes cantans* exhibiting large, bushy antennae. Our commonest and most troublesome biting species belong to the genus *Aedes*, the largest group of Culicines. The females will fly for more than a mile in search of a blood-meal. They lay their eggs singly in dry hollows that are liable to flooding. The eggs have hard shells and can withstand long periods—even years—of desiccation. They hatch when flooded, usually in autumn or winter, the adults appearing in spring and summer. There may be several generations in wet seasons, the adults breeding in temporary pools in shady places. In or near woods, they are persistent biters of man, but they do not fly far or enter houses.

Cold-blooded creatures of lake, pond and marsh

Apart from the teeming mass of insects in the aquatic habitat, there is also a whole world of other animals that spend all or part of their lives in water. Leaving aside mammals and birds, these include the fishes, the amphibians (frogs, newts and toads), and smaller invertebrates like snails, leeches and spiders.

Perhaps the most important and obvious, however, are the fishes. Although dependent both on the plant and all the other animal life, they dominate most still waters by their presence. Still water fishes range from tiny minnows or sticklebacks with their fascinating courtship displays through to huge pike and carp, with some of the latter weighing over 20kg (45lb). Most fishes eat any small animal matter they can find, including snails, small crustaceans and many of the aquatic insects such as damselfly larvae. Some feed among the bottom mud while others search among the weeds. Most of these fishes also eat plants at some time or another, especially algae, and a few are wholly vegetarian. There are also the real predators of the fish world, of which the ferocious pike is the best example – it eats anything living, including other fishes, frogs and toads, and even birds pulled from the surface.

Less obvious, but just as much a part of the aquatic web of life, are all the small invertebrates. Snails and others feed mainly on plants, especially algae; leeches are either parasites on other pond animals or predators on any small creatures that they can catch. Others, such as some of the crustaceans, are detritus feeders, sifting or filtering the pond water constantly to remove edible matter. There is even one spider – the water spider – that is wholly aquatic and a predator like all spiders.

Amphibians are rather different. They use ponds and lakes mainly as breeding grounds, returning each spring either to regular 'ancestral' breeding sites or to new ones. There they mate and the females lay eggs. The young stages (the tadpoles) are wholly aquatic, at first as plant eaters but later as carnivores – as well as being, themselves, food for anything that can catch them.

Left: The rudd, easily identified by its colourful markings, lives in lakes, gravel pits and canals.

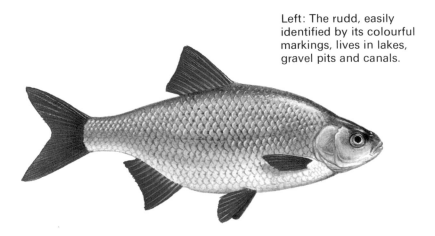

114

This checklist is a guide to some of the invertebrates, amphibians and fish you can find in and around lakes, ponds and marshes. Although you will not see them all in the same place, you should be able to spot many of them throughout the changing seasons. The species listed in **bold** *type are described in detail.*

LEECHES
Fish leech
Horse leech
Medicinal leech
Worm leech

SNAILS
Dwarf pond snail
Glutinous snail
Great pond snail
Great ramshorn snail
Marsh snail
Moss bladder snail
Ramshorn snail
Wandering snail

SPIDERS
Pirate wolf spider
Raft spider
Swamp spider
Water spider

FISH
Bitterling
Bream
Carp
Eel
Leather carp
Mirror carp
Pike
Roach
Rudd
Tench

AMPHIBIANS
Common frog
Common toad
Crested newt
Natterjack toad
Palmate newt
Smooth newt

Left: The common frog must return to water for breeding and hibernation, but it otherwise lives on the land. The frog chooses a pond or canal for spawning but is likely to retreat to a ditch or other damp spot for hibernation in winter.

TENACIOUS LEECHES

Not all leeches are blood-suckers–many are predators, feeding on invertebrates such as snails and worms. Although parasitic leeches live on the blood of larger animals, only the medicinal leech attacks man.

Leeches belong to the same group of animals as earthworms and, like them, have a segmented body with a thin, flexible outer skin. They differ, however, in the ways that they are adapted to their predatory and parasitic ways of life.

Earthworms continue adding segments to their bodies throughout their lives, while leeches have a constant number of segments (33), which are often difficult to see, being obscured by the large number of 'annuli' or rings on the outer surface of the animal. The shorter body tends to make the leech more agile, allowing it to swim or move rapidly to its host or prey, often with the aid of its suckers.

Light-sensitive leeches To locate prey, leeches have highly developed sensory organs. Some have as many as three pairs of eyes; others, such as *Theromyzon tessulatum*, a parasite of water birds, may be phototactic (in other words, they can sense light). When hungry, this species moves towards the light, changing its body colour as it does so, so that it matches its surroundings on reaching the surface, where it waits for its host. Other species respond to changes in temperature, such as the passing of a warm-blooded mammal, or to vibrations. The fish leech, for example, responds to any disturbance in the water by swimming towards it.

Clinging on A leech has two quite obvious suckers, used for feeding, locomotion and

Above: The medicinal leech (*Hirudo medicinalis*) is the largest British leech, measuring up to 12cm (4¾in). Its population suffered in the 19th century, due to the collection of vast numbers for bloodletting, and for its valuable anti-coagulant, hirudin.

Below: A gorged specimen of *Theromyzon tessulatum*. A parasite of water birds, it can cause the death of the young. It enters the nostrils of its host and sucks blood from the nasal cavities.

attaching itself to its host or to the substrate. The anterior sucker around the mouth is usually smaller than the posterior one, but size really depends on the mode of life of the leech. Fish leeches tend to have large, powerful suckers, enabling them to remain attached to their fast-swimming hosts. Carnivorous species such as the worm leech may have suckers that are no more conspicuous than the mouth of an earthworm.

Parasitic leeches do not feed on one species alone, but their range tends to be restricted to either fish, amphibians or mammals. They are extremely adept at removing considerable quantities of blood from their host without being noticed. To do this, they are equipped with precise cutting equipment, and even an anaesthetic substance which they inject into the wound. Leeches also produce an anti-coagulant which prevents the host's blood from clotting and allows the leech to suck freely. It is this substance that causes leech wounds to bleed so profusely even after the leech has dropped off.

Carnivorous or predatory species, such as the horse leech, catch their prey and devour whole, using either strong jaws or, in the case of the worm leech, a muscular pharynx. Leeches are even able to survive by using the materials of their own bodies for energy, and as a result may decrease to a fraction of their original size during long periods when there is no host available.

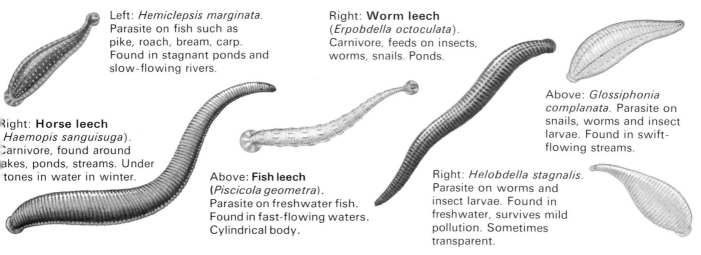

Left: *Hemiclepsis marginata*. Parasite on fish such as pike, roach, bream, carp. Found in stagnant ponds and slow-flowing rivers.

Right: **Worm leech** (*Erpobdella octoculata*). Carnivore, feeds on insects, worms, snails. Ponds.

Above: *Glossiphonia complanata*. Parasite on snails, worms and insect larvae. Found in swift-flowing streams.

Right: **Horse leech** (*Haemopis sanguisuga*). Carnivore, found around lakes, ponds, streams. Under stones in water in winter.

Above: **Fish leech** (*Piscicola geometra*). Parasite on freshwater fish. Found in fast-flowing waters. Cylindrical body.

Right: *Helobdella stagnalis*. Parasite on worms and insect larvae. Found in freshwater, survives mild pollution. Sometimes transparent.

Looking for leeches There are about 16 species of freshwater leeches in Britain, and a number of marine species are known as parasites of various fishes living around our coasts. The freshwater species occur in lakes, ponds, canals, marshes, streams, rivers and drainage ditches. Away from their hosts, they are usually found under stones or in aquatic vegetation. Their main requirement is a solid substrate so they can hang on with their suckers, and vegetation to protect them from predators such as fish or water birds. Most species prefer slow-flowing or standing water in which they can easily maintain a firm hold.

Some species have an ability to survive where oxygen is limited, which means they can live in mildly polluted water. *Glossiphonia complanata* and *Helobdella stagnalis*, both predators, can reach high densities in water with a high organic content, either as a result of natural conditions, or through pollution from sewage or organic fertilisers. This is probably because their main food source—small crustaceans–thrive under the same conditions. However, in heavily polluted water, leeches disappear along with most other forms of life.

Spring breeding Like earthworms, leeches are hermaphrodites, all individuals having both male and female reproductive organs. The breeding season is probably triggered by the temperature of the water, and for freshwater leeches it is usually spring or early summer. Some of the segments near the middle of the body become modified to form a saddle-like clitellum which secretes a cocoon in which the eggs develop. Species such as the medicinal leech leave the water to deposit their cocoons in damp places a little above the water-line. Others, such as the fish leech, cement them to stones under water, while *Glossiphonia complanata* holds the cocoon under its body until the young hatch.

Species of leeches The medicinal leech is probably the most well-known British freshwater leech, but other species are quite common. The mis-named horse leech does not live on horses, but feeds on worms, snails, insects, tadpoles and small fish. It is common on the shores of lakes or ponds where it seeks its prey, particularly at night. The name 'horse' is used simply in the sense of 'large'.

One leech, the fish leech, is a serious pest in fishponds where it is a parasite on trout, salmon, charr, bream, perch, pike and sticklebacks. It is unusual among leeches in preferring fast-flowing streams with a high oxygen content.

Very little is known about marine leeches since specimens are difficult to obtain. *Placobdella muricata* is a species which feeds off the blood of rays, skates, and other cartilaginous fish and it may carry parasites from fish to fish. While waiting for its prey, it rests in a coiled position on the sea bed, attached by its posterior sucker.

Above: The teeth and jaws of the medicinal leech are contained in one of the suckers (below). Through the Y-shaped incision it makes in its host, the leech can pump out up to 5 times its own weight of blood in a single meal. This can support it for a whole year.

SNAILS OF POND AND STREAM

Freshwater snails are perfectly adapted to their underwater existence. They spend most of their lives creeping around plants and stones in ponds and streams, but some species can be spotted coming up to the surface for air.

Above: The great pond snail, as its name suggests, is one of the largest freshwater snails, reaching up to 6cm (2½in) in shell height. Here, a great ram's horn snail is hitching a ride on its back.

There are about 36 species of freshwater snails in our waters, of which around 20 are pond dwellers while the rest are found in slow-flowing rivers, fast-flowing streams or in the turbulent margins of windswept lakes. The group as a whole is sub-divided into two – the lung-breathers (pulmonates) and the gill-breathers (operculates).

The gill-breathers can be recognised by the plate known as an operculum that is attached to their foot, and which they use to close their shells. (Hence their other name operculates.) These snails need to live in oxygen-rich water at all times, and hence are often found in running fresh water, rather than in ponds.

Pond water is far more likely to suffer from lower oxygen levels than running water, and so pulmonate pond snails have a distinct advantage in being able to breathe air from the atmosphere. Some species can absorb all the dissolved air they need from the water. Others absorb only a limited amount, taking the rest from the atmosphere. They can often be seen crawling under the surface film of the water and rising to breathe oxygen. A bubble retained in the snail's lung aids buoyancy, but when it is expelled, the snail sinks like a stone and quickly disappears from view.

The pulmonate ram's horn snails are further adapted for dealing with low levels of dissolved oxygen in pond water. Their blood contains the red iron-based pigment haemo globin, an unusual feature in molluscs. The majority of snails have the less efficient oxygen carrier haemocyanin.

Aids to identification When identifying a snail it is best to establish first which of several natural groups it belongs to. If it is an operculate snail, it will probably be found in running water and it is recognisable by its disc-shaped operculum. When the snail is active, this disc can be seen on top of the rear portion of the exposed body.

A snail shell has its opening on either the left or right hand side of the shell. This can be checked by holding the shell with the pointed tip uppermost and the opening facing you. If the opening is to the right, the shell is said to be dextral; if the opening is to the left, then the shell is sinistral.

Bladder snails of the family Physidae have sinistral shells, although in dextral species, sinistral shells sometimes occur. The moss bladder snail (*Aplexa hypnorum*) is the only bladder snail truly at home in fresh water. It lives in ponds and ditches throughout the British Isles, but it is absent in many areas.

Ram's horn snails also have sinistral shells, but as these are more or less flat they are not easily confused with other pond species, most of which have shells with spires (that is, an upward twist). There are several varieties of ram's horn snails living in ponds, including the ram's horn (*Planorbis planorbis*) and the great ram's horn (*Planorbarius corneus*). There is also a sub-division within the family, producing a distinct group called *Segmentina*. These are small snails whose flat, shiny shells expand rapidly from the centre in a characteristic way that is easy to recognise.

Another method of identification is to look at the tentacles: all the ram's horn snails have long, thin tentacles, while species such as the wandering snail (*Lymnaea peregra*), and the great pond snail (*Lymnaea stagnalis*) have triangular tentacles.

Feeding habits It is often assumed that pond snails feed on living water plants, but this is largely untrue. Pond weed provides a large surface area on which a thin layer of micro-organisms such as algae can grow, and it is these micro-organisms that probably form the major part of their diet. Decayed remains of pond weed are also an important food item, but healthy plants are seldom eaten. Some snails are not totally herbivorous; the great pond snail, for example, will eat small, dead fish and soft-bodied invertebrates.

The way in which snails feed can be seen clearly by watching them in aquaria. A snail crawling across the glass sides often turns its head from side to side, leaving a zig-zag line where the glass has been cleared of algae. The mouth, with its tiny jaws and tongue-like protrusion, can be seen to work away vigorously at the algal film. However, the scrapers that remove the algae are too small to be seen with the naked eye. They are

attached in rows across the tongue-like organ, and under a microscope this appears as a mat with hundreds of tiny teeth attached. This is called the radula and it is a very efficient scourer.

Reproduction All pulmonate snails are hermaphrodites, each animal possessing male and female reproductive organs, whereas most species of operculates have separate sexes.

Although hermaphrodite, pulmonate snails reproduce by exchanging sperm, thus fertilising each other's eggs. However, if the snail is unable to find a mate (for example, if it is the first to colonize a pond), then it is quite possible for it to fertilise its own eggs.

Most species of pond snail reach maturity and reproduce within a year. Some, such as the common wandering snail, may have two generations in one season. Such short-lived species usually die after egg laying and, if the eggs are laid late in the season, only the newly hatched young will overwinter. Even the great pond snail does not usually live for

Above: Great pond snails on the surface film of a pond. The film is used by the snails to move around the pond and to search for food. As they are pulmonate snails, they obtain their main supply of air at the surface, taking it into their lungs through a round cavity on the right-hand side of their shells.

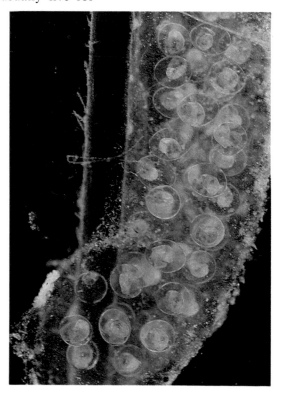

Right: The pond snail lays its eggs in a mass of jelly, usually on plants or hard surfaces. Snails kept in aquaria often lay their eggs on the glass sides. Through the clear, gelatinous mass, tiny snails can be seen as they develop. The jelly protects the eggs from predators and fish can often be seen vainly endeavouring to nibble at the developing snails. However, newly hatched snails are very vulnerable, and their thin shells offer little protection from their many predators. Adult snails have fewer enemies, but may be eaten by ducks, herons, otters and trout.

Above: The wandering snail, Britain's most common species, is very variable in appearance.

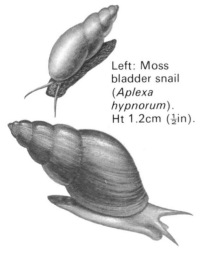

Left: Valve snail (*Valvata piscinalis*). Ht 6mm ($\frac{1}{4}$in).

Right: Dwarf pond snail (*Lymnaea truncatula*). Ht 1.2cm ($\frac{1}{2}$in).

Left: Moss bladder snail (*Aplexa hypnorum*). Ht 1.2cm ($\frac{1}{2}$in).

Above: Marsh snail (*Lymnaea palustris*). Ht 2cm ($\frac{3}{4}$in).

more than a year in this country, but in parts of Central Europe where the winters are long and severe, they are said to need two or even three years to reach maturity. However, the great ram's horn snail lives and grows for two or three years in ponds in this country, and breeds regularly throughout. In the sheltered conditions of captivity it may grow to over 3cm (1$\frac{1}{5}$in) across the shell, and live for six years or more.

Looking for new homes Since the majority of pond snails cannot survive for long out of water, it is very difficult for them to move from pond to pond. They are mainly restricted to the water in which they were born, which can cause problems if the pond becomes polluted or overcrowded.

It seems that many pond snails are inadvertently transported by water birds carrying young snails or snails' eggs on their feet or feathers. Certainly, some species of pond snail seem to have little difficulty in colonizing isolated bodies of water. However, this does not apply to all species. The great ram's horn

snail, although living happily in the smallest of ponds, seems unable to move from one isolated pond to another, unless introduced by man.

In wet weather, some species of snail will crawl out of the pond and lead an amphibious existence, travelling quite large distances over land. One such species is the marsh snail (*Lymnaea palustris*). However, the majority of species seem never to travel far overland and isolated ponds are rarely colonized by this means.

Some species of snail have almost deserted the water altogether in favour of a life on the land. The dwarf pond snail (*Lymnaea truncatula*), for example, can hardly be considered a pond inhabitant at all. It lives in the muddy margins of ponds, in small wet depressions such as hoofprints and in damp meadows, and can even withstand dry conditions. The dwarf pond snail is the intermediate host for the sheep liver fluke which lives in the snail shell, leaving it to climb out into the damp grass where it is eaten by sheep.

The freshwater valve or operculate snails are normally only found in ponds if they are fed by a stream, which is their normal habitat. These snails are related to the familiar sea snails such as winkles and whelks, and being gill-breathers, they are more dependent on water than pulmonate snails such as the ram's horn snail.

One species of snail which is rapidly becoming rarer is the glutinous snail (*Myxas glutinosa*) which disappears from areas where it was once relatively abundant, and may just as mysteriously reappear. Once known at over 30 sites in England and Wales it is now found at only one site in England – in the Lake District – and one in North Wales. Several sites are known in Ireland, but the future of this species seems bleak.

The primary cause of the decline of these endangered species is disappearing habitats. Agriculture and development mean that many ponds have to be drained. Those that remain are either polluted or vulnerable to pollution. As a result, the diversity of Britain's pond snail species is becoming impoverished.

Left: The glutinous snail is a rare species with unusual features. Its shiny shell is extremely thin and fragile, but a film of tissue folds out from inside the shell and spreads over the surface, usually leaving only a tiny space exposed. The tissue is believed to provide a surface through which the snail breathes, but as it is so rarely found, this has been difficult to prove.

AQUATIC SPIDERS: HAIRY HUNTERS

Of the more than 600 species of spider in the British Isles, only a very few live in or near water. One species is, indeed, unique, being the only spider in the world that lives mostly under water and swims freely without holding on to plant stems for support.

Above: The water spider (*Argyroneta aquatica*) is about 13mm (½in) long, excluding the legs which are noticeably hairy. Unusually for spiders, the males are bigger than the females. The chelicerae (fangs) are fairly large.

The water spider, the raft spider and the pirate wolf spiders are not closely related to each other (they belong to three different families) but they all have in common the fact that they dwell in or near water. Typically, they frequent woodland ponds and marshy, swampy areas. Whether they are adapted to life in the water or on its surface, however, these spiders essentially remain dry because of their covering of hydrophobic (water-repellent) hairs.

Free-swimming spider The unique water spider (family Agelenidae) is distributed throughout temperate Europe and Asia. So far, it is the only spider in the world, of the thousands of existing species, ever to have been discovered living mostly underwater.

Like all spiders, it obtains its oxygen by absorbing air through respiratory openings on the underside of its abdomen. Underwater, however, it breathes by means of a jacket or bubble of air that adheres to its body. The lightness that results from this air bubble demands a very energetic swimming action on the part of the spider and it flails its legs wildly as it swims in its characteristic upside-down position. This spider lives under water for most of its life in specially constructed 'diving bells' stocked with air.

Out of the water the water spider has an undistinguished appearance, with both abdomen and cephalothorax pale brown and lacking in any pattern. It has the reputation,

Building an underwater home

To collect air the water spider swims to the surface, raises its abdomen briefly, then dives again bearing a silvery bubble of air (**1**). To build and stock its 'diving bell', in which it spends most of its life, the spider uses larger air bubbles, obtained by raising its last pair of legs above the surface as well as its abdomen. The construction of the diving bell is begun as a platform of fine silk threads (**2**) secured among the water plants. The spider delivers bubbles of air, shed by crossing its last pair of legs, to the underside of the platform (**3**). These accumulate, buoying the structure upwards into a dome (below). The area around the underwater lair becomes criss-crossed with silk threads which, while not actually a snare, probably help in the detection of prey. The water spider lies in the bell, front legs extended into the water, waiting to pounce on prey. Food is not swallowed in pieces, but liquefied while held in the jaws. The spider must return to the air bubble or climb on dry land to eat its victim.

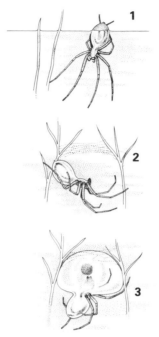

atmosphere below the surface, the water spider can not only continue all normal functions under water (feeding, moulting, reproducing) but can also exploit a plentiful food source that is not available to other spiders. It preys on any creature up to the size of a tadpole that comes within its reach.

However, instead of the usual spider enemies, such as birds, centipedes and parasitic wasps, the water spider contends with a formidable range of underwater foes—fish, frogs, dragonfly larvae, water boatmen and water scorpions, for example. Nevertheless, these predators have not prevented water spiders from becoming abundant. They frequent still waters in more than half of the counties in the British Isles. In particular, there are many thriving populations in the unpolluted dykes of the Norfolk Broads.

Handsome surface hunter By contrast with the water spider, the raft spider (*Dolomedes fimbriatus*) lives and hunts mostly on the surface of the water. It is also considerably bigger—it has the distinction of being Britain's largest spider at a body length of 2.5cm (1in)—and is rather handsomely marked, being dark brown with a broad white, yellow or orange band running down each side of its body. It has a wide but local distribution in this country, being found in still or slow moving waters that are clean and well vegetated. It seems to prefer sunny places in swampy woodland where the pools do not dry up. The species has a very extensive range throughout much of Europe and Asia; the genus *Dolomedes* (fishing spiders), to which it belongs, is worldwide in its distribution.

When the raft spider is waiting for prey it uses the water surface as if it were a web. Typically, it stands at the edge of a floating leaf with its front legs extended on to the water. A struggling insect, such as a mayfly that has fallen on to the water surface signals its size and location by vibrations. If the spider runs out to intercept the prey it extends a line of silk (a drag-line) from the leaf. The spider returns to the leaf whether the hunt has been successful or not.

Although it finds it difficult to penetrate

given to few British spiders, of being capable of biting humans with its large fangs (though of course it is not difficult to avoid being bitten).

Adults of both sexes are active throughout the year. Mating begins in the spring. A mature male may build a diving bell next to the home of the female of his choice, connect the two dwellings with an air tunnel, then bite his way through the wall of her bell. Courtship is very brief. The peak months for egg laying are May and July, when the female encloses 50 to 100 eggs in the upper part of her bell. She stays below the water surface to defend the eggs.

The eggs hatch in about 20 days and the spiderlings stay in their mother's bell for a further two to three weeks before leaving to set up their own little diving bells. Individuals may live for up to two years. They survive adverse conditions, such as winter and the the drying up of ponds, by enclosing themselves in silken cells and remaining inactive.

By securing for itself a small portion of the

Below: The raft spider (*Dolomedes fimbriatus*) is kept afloat by hydrophobic (water-repellent) hairs and cannot easily penetrate the surface tension. Here you can see the dimples made in the surface by its feet.

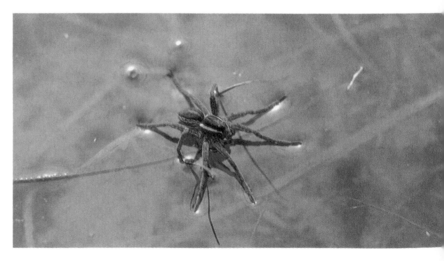

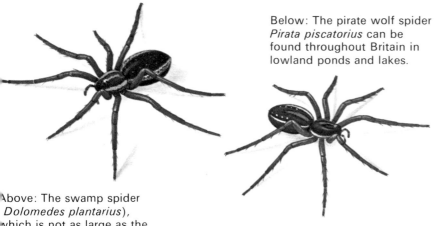

Above: The swamp spider
Dolomedes plantarius),
which is not as large as the
raft spider, lives in East Anglia.

Below: The pirate wolf spider
Pirata piscatorius can be
found throughout Britain in
lowland ponds and lakes.

Below: A female pirate wolf
spider with her egg sac
which she produces in late
summer and carries in her
spinnerets. These spiders
hunt prey both on the water
surface and in emergent
vegetation. Like land spiders,
they respond to man-made
vibrations, mistaking them for
the struggles of potential
prey. Researchers have found
that *Pirata* spiders will
attempt to bite a tuning fork
touching the water surface
near them in just the same
way that web spiders attack
a tuning fork used to vibrate
their webs.

the surface tension, the raft spider, if threatened by predators, can climb down a plant
and, breathing air adhering to its body, is
able to remain submerged for up to half an
hour. Sometimes it catches prey such as
tadpoles under water and, although reports
of the spider riding on the back of large fish
are fanciful, a close relative, *Dolomedes
triton*, is known to have caused considerable
damage in American fish hatcheries. This
American species has been seen to raise some
of its legs vertically to assist its locomotion in
a form of rudimentary 'wind surfing'. *D.
imbriatus* is reputed to catch small fish, but
there are no certain records of it actually
doing so. It is, unfortunately, a myth that
the raft spider actually binds leaves together
to make a floating raft.

The life cycle of the raft spider takes about
15 months; the winter is passed in an immature stage and adults can be found from
May to September. The approach of the
male in courtship is extremely circumspect,
but he is less likely to be repulsed if the
female happens to be eating an insect at the
time.

The first eggs are laid in early summer and
the large globular egg sac is carried about in
the female's jaws for two to three weeks. She
may climb on to plants to sun the eggs or dip
them into water to avoid desiccation. When it
is time for the eggs to hatch she fastens the
cocoon to a plant and spins silk around it in
the form of a small protective tent. The
spiderlings disperse when they are just a few
days old.

Rare swamp dweller The much rarer swamp
spider is similar to, but not as large as,
the raft spider. It inhabits two adjacent fens
in East Anglia where water levels have
become critical and is now the subject of a
conservation project started by the World
Wildlife Fund. The swamp spider is distinguished from the raft spider by a reduction
in, or complete absence of, the pale bands
down the sides of its body.

Piratical predators The pirate wolf spiders
owe their name to their habit of living near
water and hunting prey on the surface. All
have a c-shaped dark mark on the cephalo-

thorax and a velvety brown abdomen with
two rows of small white spots on it. There are
six species in this country, belonging to the
family Lycosidae, and many more world-
wide. Possibly because of their smaller size
they are less well known than either the water
spider or the raft spider, but they are often
abundant in wet habitats throughout Britain.

The largest species, and the one which
lives closest to the water's edge, in lowland
ponds and lakes, is *Pirata piscatorius* which
has a body length of 10mm ($\frac{1}{3}$in). This spider
builds a silken tube approximately 15-20cm
(6-8in) long and 2cm ($\frac{3}{4}$in) wide among grass
tussocks or Sphagnum moss. From an open-
ing at the top of this tube the spider hunts
passing insects, but if danger looms it
descends the tube which leads below the
water surface. Submerged, but covered by
bubbles of air, it may rest for some time.

Salt water survivor The wolf spider *Pardosa
purbeckensis* deserves mention because it
lives in the intertidal marshy zone among salt
tolerant plants and is able to withstand long
periods of immersion in the sea during high
tides. The great arachnologist W. S. Bristowe
has observed that on salt marshes the sea's
advance is often so fast that any spider has
difficulty running before it. The ability of this
species to hold on to plant stems while the
tide washes over it enables it to live in an
environment where there is very little competition from other spiders.

NEWTS: AGILE AMPHIBIANS

During the breeding season male newts are notable for their gaudy colours and elaborate courtship dance. Newt tadpoles can be found in freshwaters in the summer.

Newts are slim, tailed amphibians that spend most of their life on land, but usually within striking distance of ponds–on which they converge annually around February-March for a 2-4 month breeding season lasting into late summer.

The most common of our three native species is the smooth newt which is found in lowland Britain; it is the only species in Ireland. A recent survey of the chalk uplands in south-east England revealed it was widespread in densely vegetated ponds bordered by gorse scrub. Its close, but slightly smaller, relative the palmate newt is more numerous in mountainous areas up to 900m (3000ft), but can also be found at sea level.

The spectacular crested, or warty, newt is by far the rarest. It inhabits those lowland regions with slightly deeper ponds, and more open water, again with a scrub surround.

Mass migration Newts migrate to breeding ponds–often en masse–under cover of darkness and ideally when it is wet. Newts are expert climbers, surmounting most obstacles with ease, so there is little to impede them.

Taking the plunge after their long stay on land is a tentative business, but once in the water newts quickly adapt to the novel diet of aquatic insect larvae, small crustaceans and molluscs. The abundant food in the water will restore the animal's vigour after egg-laying, and help the young to grow quickly.

Egg-laying After a successful conclusion to

Opposite page: The smooth newt (*Triturus vulgaris*) is 10cm (4in) long, including the tail. As its name implies, it is smooth skinned. Outside the breeding season it is olive green in colour. It is the most widely distributed newt in the British Isles. It tolerates all sorts of conditions, including peaty Scottish tarns, stagnant flooded quarries and even brackish water.

The courtship dance

1

2

cloaca

spermatophore

When the male encounters a female at the breeding pond, he sets about wooing her with a cat-and-mouse display of surprising complexity for an amphibian. Though the mating ritual varies with the three newt species, the basic elements are similar.

First the male approaches the female and 'sniffs' her; this may tell him if she is in breeding condition. To gain her undivided attention, the male newt endeavours to keep just ahead of her, blocking her path with his body. He then proceeds to wave and lash his tail–sometimes violently enough to wash the female backwards. At other times a mere quiver of his tail gently fans the water–and his own stimulating skin odour–towards her snout (**1** above). The shallow groove at the base of the ridge on the male's back helps to channel and direct the current through her lateral line system–a row of sense organs appearing as pores along the sides of both male and female newts.

As the display reaches its climax, the male creeps forward,

gently quivering his tail which the female softly nudges with her snout. On this signal, the male folds and lifts his tail, depositing his whitish sperm on the bottom of the pond. He then bodily manoeuvres the female right over the sperm, which is contained in a jelly-like capsule (spermatophore) 2-3mm ($\frac{1}{8}$in) long.

Unlike frogs and toads, fertilisation in newts is internal, so the male must ensure that he entices the female into a position (**2** above) where she can take the spermatophore up into her sexual opening (cloaca). As he does this, a fluid-filled sac at the base of the spermatophore expands quickly, and lifts the whole structure upwards at the female's cloaca. This sac does not guarantee successful interception, and it may miss its mark in up to half the transfer attempts. However, the courting couple may repeat the ritual–sometimes up to seven times. The male takes several other mates during the breeding season and produces more spermatophores to accommodate them.

125

Above: The crested, or warty, newt (*Triturus cristatus*) is up to 18cm (7in) long. Its rough, moist skin is brownish with darker spots above, contrasted with an orange belly with black spots.

the newts' colourful courtship sequence, the male's sperm mass is stored in a special, pocketed chamber inside the female, till her eggs are just ripe for fertilisation. The male is not ensured outright of parenthood, however, because a sexually mature female may court with a number of males over a short period; which male newt's sperm ultimately fertilises the eggs is anybody's guess.

Once fertilised, however, the female newt begins within a few days to lay 100-300 jelly-coated eggs—each wrapped individually in an underwater leaf to conceal it from predators.

The female carefully inspects several sites before choosing one on which she will lay her eggs. Mounting a chosen leaf, she grasps the

In spring, male newts, including the crested newt (left), acquire a flamboyant nuptial dress—oranges, yellows and reds with black spots, appear on the wrinkled crest, skin flaps on the hind toes and tail fin (a glandular ridge down the back).

edges with her hind feet and, drawing her leg together, makes a fold in which to deposit th oval egg. The natural stickiness of the egg coating is enough to keep the crease till th egg hatches. The female prefers broadleave plants, but may use any available vegetation even floating algae. Laying and hiding up t 300 separate eggs is a most laborious process and the female may take up to a week t complete the task.

Tadpoles Developing newt tadpoles ea their way out of their egg capsules after 3- weeks; they are equipped with stubby gil for breathing. At first tadpoles are withou limbs and have only a random ability t orientate themselves, with the aid of a pair c stalked adhesive organs. Mounted behind th chin, these stick readily on to any firm objec the wriggling animal encounters.

In a few days, however, the tadpole be comes more co-ordinated, and absorbs it adhesive organs once they have outlived thei usefulness. In the days that follow the fore limbs grow and sprout fingers, while the gil also branch, taking on a feathery, ruff-lik appearance. The fast-growing tadpole ha minute teeth; these are used efficiently to tak the small aquatic organisms which form it staple diet. In time the tadpole tries out large prey, including other tadpoles.

After about six weeks, the hind limb emerge, and tadpoles can crawl on the pon floor or among plant stems. This provides th est cover from enemies. Dragonfly larvae, with their diabolical jaw apparatus, are voracious predators, as are the larvae of various diving beetles; fish like sticklebacks also take a heavy toll, as do frogs and toads. Stalking herons relish newts and in dry summers, when the water level drops, other wading birds also prey on them.

Once the tadpole has absorbed the gills and tail fin, metamorphosis is complete. The whole process takes about 10 weeks for eggs laid in mid-summer. After that it takes several more months for the newt to reach full adult proportions, and develop the lungs and a thickening of the skin, which equip it fully for life ashore.

Back to the land After leaving the pond, the young newts live exclusively on land, subsisting (like adults) on insects, small snails, slugs and worms till they reach sexual maturity – in 2-3 years in the case of smooth newts, up to 4 for the crested newt. As summer draws to an end, the water temperature cools and slows the tadpoles' development, so that the latest-hatched have to overwinter in the pond, completing their aquatic phase when temperatures pick up the following year. Palmate newts living in high altitude, chilly ponds may take up to a year to metamorphose fully.

Once the breeding season is over, a few adults may overwinter in the pond, but most seek a retreat ashore – usually a damp, dark crevice. Sometimes a specially favoured spot will harbour several newts of various ages. Not only must the sites be damp, or the newts risk dying from loss of moisture, but they must also be well-concealed. Any vertebrate that hunts at ground level – a hedgehog snuffling through wet leaves, or grass snake patrolling the pond in or out of the water – will snap up newts.

Defence systems The crested newt has a unique defence against would-be predators. It keeps its warty skin moist all year round, which enables skin glands to secrete a highly noxious substance when it is threatened. It is highly irritating to the skin – any crested newt unwittingly seized is likely to be dropped quickly; probably few predators even tackle them. Household cats, perhaps more naive about the wiles of would-be prey, have been reported foaming at the mouth and showing evident distress when they grab a crested newt. However, these newts are not actually venomous and the effects, though unpleasant, are short-lived. Only the occasional grass snake seems able to make a meal out of them without ill effects.

Although both the smooth and the palmate newt turn dry and velvety after the breeding season, and therefore have no defence mechanism like the crested newts, they feed mostly at night and so escape many predators. In water all newts can, to some extent, change their skin colour to match the surroundings, and so effect a certain degree of

camouflage. They regularly shed their skin, sometimes at intervals of only a few days, and this process maintains colour intensity, both for courtship and camouflage.

Even if newts are seized by predators – all is not lost. Sometimes a newt utters a high-pitched squeak when picked up. Although it is not piercing, it may surprise a predator momentarily, and enable the newt to make its getaway. As a last resort the newt has one very special talent; should a predator bite off a limb, the newt survives simply by growing another.

Newts that avoid all these hazards have the potential to live for 20 years, though few probably live longer than half a dozen.

Above: The palmate newt (*Triturus helveticus*) is 9cm (3½in) long. Its skin texture and colour is similar to the smooth newt's, but its throat is not spotted, and the hind feet are noticeably webbed.

As befits her more passive role in courtship, the female newt is relatively drab throughout the year. She produces only one batch of eggs per season, and wraps each one separately in an underwater leaf (shown below).

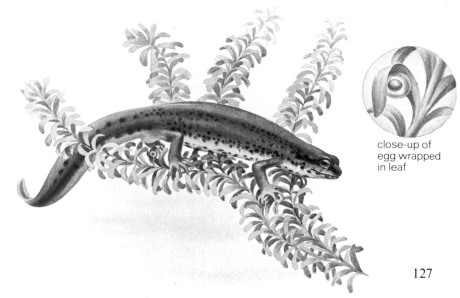

close-up of egg wrapped in leaf

TOADS' SPRINGTIME SPAWNING

Spring is the time when toads stir from their winter hibernation and make unerringly for suitable water in which to spawn. The one you are most likely to see is the mottled, earthy brown common toad, although you may be lucky enough to spot the rarer, smaller, greenish-hued natterjack toad.

Above: The common toad emerges from hibernation in spring. It is unfortunate that as common toads converge on their spawning ponds and streams, many are killed by vehicles as they try to cross roads.

Below: The common toad is distributed throughout England and Scotland and in parts of Wales and Ireland, while the natterjack is found mainly on the Mersey Coast

The common toad, widespread throughout the British Isles, is easily recognisable by its warty skin and mottled brown colour. The natterjack toad, on the other hand, is much rarer. Once widespread in Britain, its numbers have dwindled with the disappearance or modification of its favourite haunts, especially the dry heaths. Absent from the West Country and highly localised in Ireland, it now has a scattered distribution in England, being found mainly on the Mersey Coast, where a population of some 10,000 animals are living in sand dune systems in the area. It can still be found locally in the south and east of England, but in much smaller numbers.

Both species, although perfectly able to swim, spend most of their lives on land, returning to water only to breed. The natterjack is smaller than the common toad and is an altogether trimmer animal, being capable of running fairly fast—at least in comparison with the somewhat shambling gait of the ponderous common toad.

By day both species live in holes in hedgerows or among tree roots, only coming out at dusk to feed. Their diet consists of worms and snails and a wide range of insects, including beetles, ants and caterpillars.

Springtime travels Toads come out of hibernation in spring and make straight for suitable water in which to spawn.

The common toad is the first to emerge,

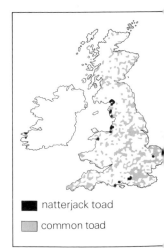

■ natterjack toad
▨ common toad

Above: Natterjack toad with throat distended in the act of croaking. The male natterjack's croak is much louder, and more rattling in tone than that of the common toad. Note here the natterjack's distinctive yellow back stripe.

Below: A cluster of male common toads competing for the chance to mate with a female. The female is the one upside down in the picture.

appearing at the end of March or the beginning of April. It is more exacting in its requirements than the natterjack, favouring deep water – in all probability the pond or ditch in which it was born. To reach the right site, the common toad shows great persistence, travelling by day and night and ignoring apparently suitable alternative sites along the way. The natterjack delays its appearance until late April; being less fussy about its choice of spawning site, it may have to make only a short journey to reach water, which can be quite a shallow pool or even a puddle.

Finding a mate The male toad's priority is to find a female with whom he can mate.

Although male common toads generally set out for ponds a few days in advance of the females, animals of both sexes finally converge on the pond together; and most females are waylaid before they ever get to water. On intercepting a female, the male attaches himself, limpet-like, to her back, girdling her under the arms in an embrace called amplexus. So strong is the male's instinct to clasp in this way that he will readily accept an offered finger, or the toe of a boot, as a substitute.

With the male aboard, the female finds her way to the pond. A male has no permanent right to a female, however, and several other suitors may attempt to unseat him. The incumbent male kicks out at his rivals; but if he fails to deter them, the female may eventually find herself embroiled in a heaving mass of ardent males. Nobody wins when, on rare occasions, the female is smothered to death in the mêlée.

Just what determines who does win has recently been discovered by two Oxford zoologists. It turns out that size, and thus brute force, determines the outcome of most encounters. Small males that grasp females en route to the pond have usually been usurped by bigger rivals by the time the female reaches water. If two contenders for a female are about the same size, battles can be prolonged – up to 12 hours – and extremely strength-sapping.

Croaking is the clue When time to find and seize a female is a precious commodity, a male toad has much to lose by challenging an opponent who will eventually outclass him. Fortunately, evolution has provided a signalling system that allows the likely outcome of any battle to be gauged in advance.

During a fight there is much croaking; the bigger the male, the deeper and more resonant his croak will be. Because of this, each contestant can immediately tell the other's size by his voice – a useful clue in the dark. A male who assesses his opponent to be much larger than himself seldom presses home his attack for long, knowing that defeat is inevitable.

Since only male toads croak, voice also conveniently resolves the numerous incidents of mistaken identity when one male, in his eagerness, clasps another male. Croaking when clasped is an automatic response on the part of the male and it announces his sex unequivocally.

Research into the raucous croak of the male natterjack has identified it as a mating call. Less vocal males often wait beside a 'crooner' and intercept females answering his invitation.

The business of competing and fighting would be less vital if there were unlimited females but the opposite is, in fact, the case. Male common toads greatly outnumber the females. Moreover, the females stay in the pond for only the few days it takes to find a suitable spawning site and lay eggs. The males, on the other hand, give themselves every

Telling toads apart

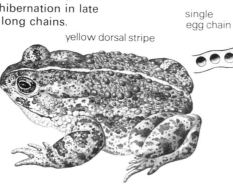

Below: **Natterjack toad** (*Bufo calamita*) ranges in colour from yellow-green to olive-grey, with a yellow line down the back; 7cm (2½in) long. Comes out of hibernation in late April. Its spawn appears in long chains.

yellow dorsal stripe

Left: This Gloucestershire pond is an ideal, secluded spot for toads to spawn in. It is likely that they try to find the place where they themselves were born.

single egg chain

double-braided egg chain

Above: **Common toad** (*Bufo bufo*) muddy brown, olive or grey in colour; female 10cm (4in) long, male 7cm (2½in). Emerges from hibernation late March/early April. Its ropes of spawn appear in long, double-braided, strands.

chance of several successful matings by remaining in the pond for the full two or three-week duration of the mating period.

Spawning When she is ready to lay, the female, with the male in amplexus, slowly extrudes her jelly-coated eggs in a long string or rope which can reach 2-3m (6-10ft) in length. She entwines it carefully among the stems of water plants. As the eggs are shed, the male expels his milky sperm and so fertilises them. It is a monumental feat of production for the female, involving up to 7000 eggs. It is little wonder that when her load is jettisoned she leaves without further delay. The male, however, may then seek other females, leaving the first eggs he sired to their fate.

Natterjack toads lay shorter strings of eggs, but even so they may contain up to 4000 eggs. Sometimes the two species spawn in the same pond; you can tell which eggs belong to which toad by their differing structure. Natterjack strings are single, while the common toad's often appear to be double-braided. (Remember that natterjacks are protected by law; it is an offence to keep them in captivity at any stage of their life cycle, including spawn and tadpoles.)

Tadpole development A week after fertilisation, the common toad's eggs change shape from round to oval. Shortly after this the young tadpoles begin to develop and the first faint traces of head, body and tail appear. In two weeks they wriggle free of the jelly. This contrasts with the faster development of the natterjack tadpoles which emerge from the egg five to ten days after fertilisation. Since, however, natterjacks breed later than common toads, the tadpoles of the latter are often more advanced in ponds shared by the two species. The older, larger tadpoles happily devour natterjack spawn, while the eggs of both kinds are, in turn, likely to be eaten by frog tadpoles, which have a month's start on the toads. Other dangers for tadpoles, particularly for natterjacks in shallow pools, include the drying out of the water in hot summers. With the various hazards they face, only a few tadpoles from any one batch of eggs finally develop into adult toads.

Toad tadpoles

The female common toad extrudes her jelly-coated eggs in a long string; they are immediately fertilised by the male.
A week after fertilisation, the eggs change shape from round to oval (above).
Shortly afterwards the young tadpoles begin to develop. They wriggle free in another two weeks. The little tadpoles (top right) feed on algae at first, but later progress to animal food.
Toad tadpoles are poisonous to newts and fishes and therefore escape being eaten themselves. An egg takes anything from 9-15 weeks to develop into an adult toad.
When they finally lose their tadpole shape, the young toads (bottom right) leave the water for life on land.

CUNNING CARP

The carp, an introduced fish, is found mainly in the warm, sunlit lowland waters of the British Isles. Once purely a food fish, this cunning fighter has become an exciting challenge for anglers everywhere.

Above: The mirror carp is irregularly covered with large scales.

No one knows exactly when the carp was introduced to Britain, but it was certainly long before people kept records of fish they caught. Carp bones have been found in Greece and along the Danube in very early prehistoric settlements and were clearly native to these areas. The original distribution of the carp was in the basins of the Black and Caspian Seas. From the Black Sea, it travelled westwards along the Danube into Austria and Germany, spreading into the Rhine and the Elbe, and from there throughout western Europe. Its spread was assisted by its tenacity. Out of water, the carp is very passive and it will survive for many hours in baskets or sacks packed with wet straw, allowing it to be transported quite freely.

Introduced carp The point at which the carp arrived in England has often been discussed. The doggerel lines 'hops and turkeys, carps and beer, came into England, all in one year' although interesting, unfortunately do not provide a firm date for the carp's introduction, as none of the other items can be accurately dated. Other evidence is fragmentary and often conflicting. In 1279, the feast prepared to celebrate the enthronement of the Archbishop of Canterbury is said to have included 100 carp, which seems to indicate that it was present in fair numbers by that date. On the other hand, William More, Prior of Worcester from 1518 to 1536, who kept careful records of the fishes introduced into his stockponds, did not stock carp until 1531, and then only

The wild carp

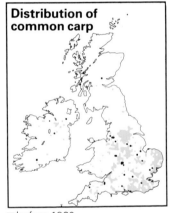

Distribution of common carp

■ before 1960
□ after 1960

Below: The slender wild carp (*Cyprinus carpio*). Pond-bred or cultivated carp tend to have deeper bodies and higher backs.

on a small scale. The evidence, although rather confused, does seem to indicate that until the 1600s carp were stocked as a food fish in the fish ponds of monasteries and landowners, but were uncommon elsewhere.

The range of carp in Britain today is heavily dependent on where it was stocked in previous centuries as a food fish, and in the 19th and 20th centuries for angling purposes or as an ornamental fish. It is widely distributed in the British Isles but is common only in lowland England. It is virtually absent from Scotland, apart from a few lakes in the lowlands.

Typically an inhabitant of still waters, the carp is usually found in ponds and lakes, but substantial numbers live in slow-flowing lowland rivers with muddy bottoms and plenty of vegetation. These river carp tend to be more slender, athletic-looking fishes than their pond-dwelling cousins, bearing more resemblance to the wild carp of the Danube and other Black Sea rivers. Paradoxically, the race of wild carp of the great rivers of Europe and Asia has become almost extinct being overtaken by the mass of selectively bred carp from fish farms in all the inland countries.

Temperamental reproduction An important natural factor which has affected the carp's success in our country is temperature. A warm water fish, it requires temperatures of 18 to 20°C (64-68°F) in which to spawn. Relatively few lakes in Britain attain temperatures as high as this in late spring, the carp's spawning time, and as a result it breeds successfully each year in only a few waters. However, the carp is a relatively hardy fish and can live in ponds with an average summer temperature of between 15 and 18°C (59-64°F), although it will not spawn at these levels.

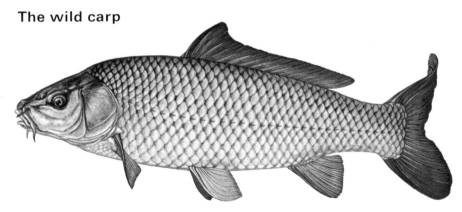

When the temperature is high enough for spawning to take place, the eggs are shed on plants such as *Potamogeton* and *Myriophyllum* in shallow water, and sometimes on the stems of reeds at the water's edge. The eggs are very small and yellowish in colour. They hatch in three to eight days, depending on the temperature. This is best expressed as about 100 day-degrees Centigrade, for example five days are needed at 20°C (68°F). The newly hatched larvae have a yolk-sac and attach themselves to the plants on which they hatched. Two or three days after hatching, they rise to the surface and fill their swim-bladders with air. After this, they become more active, feeding on microscopic algae, rotifers and small water-fleas. The carp also crossbreeds with the crucian carp, which is actually a different species, producing hybrids which are hardy, but sterile.

Foraging fish As the carp grows, it extends the range of its diet, taking bottom-living animals such as the blood-red midge larvae, snails, insect larvae generally, and plants. During summer it forages in mid-water and near the surface, eating considerable quantities of plant material. In winter, it retreats to deep water where it feeds much less. If the water temperature falls below 5°C (41°F) it stops feeding altogether. In cold winters it hibernates in deeper water.

Growth is very variable and again depends very much on temperature; below 13°C

The leather carp

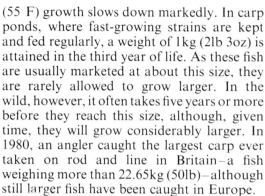

Above: The body of the leather carp is usually scaleless, but it sometimes has one or two scales close to the dorsal fin.

Below: The ideal conditions in a carp pond are shallow water, a muddy bottom, not too much shade from trees and plenty of sun. The lily pads provide hiding places for the fishes.

(55 F) growth slows down markedly. In carp ponds, where fast-growing strains are kept and fed regularly, a weight of 1kg (2lb 3oz) is attained in the third year of life. As these fish are usually marketed at about this size, they are rarely allowed to grow larger. In the wild, however, it often takes five years or more before they reach this size, although, given time, they will grow considerably larger. In 1980, an angler caught the largest carp ever taken on rod and line in Britain—a fish weighing more than 22.65kg (50lb)—although still larger fish have been caught in Europe.

Many of the waters which contain carp only do so because they have been stocked by angling clubs and individual anglers. Perseverance is required to catch carp, and they are popular because of the fight they put up when hooked. These fish—especially the large specimens—are actually rather difficult to tempt with bait. As a result of this, anglers tend to put large quantities of ground bait into the water to attract the fish to the vicinity, ensuring a plentiful supply of food for carp in the popular waters.

Selection of species The carp's history of semi-domestication goes back at least a thousand years. More than any other fish it has been modified by selective breeding in carp ponds. Over the years fish farmers have produced many varieties, bred from the slender-bodied, fully scaled carp of the rivers of the Black Sea basin. The fully scaled carp are usually known as king carp or wild carp (although they are deeper-bodied than the true wild carp). Mirror carp have a row of scales along the back and large scales scattered along their sides, the rest of the body being naked, like the leather carp.

All these varieties were bred originally as food fishes, their scale patterns cultivated to appeal to regional taste.

The koi carp—not to be mistaken for a goldfish which is an entirely different species—has been bred for other reasons. It is purely an ornamental fish with patches of colour varying from reddish-gold to blue-black, yet still retains features in common with the wild carp, such as the four barbels around the mouth.

probably why the tench is now an inhabitant of lakes, gravel pits and ponds.

Sleep by day – feed by night During daylight hours, especially in sunny weather, the tench seeks the shade and scarcely moves. The fish appears to favour the warmth of the sun, since it is most often found near the surface. As evening falls it becomes more active, and begins to move around the lake, searching for food in small schools numbering between five and forty fish. Although you can often see tench feeding in the shallows among water plants, they appear to eat very little vegetation.

The adult fish's main food comprises bottom-living animals, or those which live among the plant fronds. The most important of these for the tench include the various kinds of pond snails that inhabit the water plants; but the tench also eats bottom-dwelling water slaters and dragonfly/damselfly larvae in large numbers. Over muddy bottoms the tench feeds heavily on the red, blood-worm larvae of midges, stirring up clouds of mud in the process, and giving its position away by the bubbles rising to the surface.

The young tench also feeds heavily on midge larvae and smaller pond snails, but much of its food consists of small crustaceans, particularly water fleas and copepods. It also eats a variety of aquatic insect larvae and, unlike the older fish often has some plant matter in its gut. It is likely that the fish does not deliberately eat this, but rather ingests it accidentally, along with animal food. It seems that the tench, like most other fish, cannot actually digest plant food.

Crushing teeth Like all the members of the carp family the tench has no teeth in its jaws. However, as much of its prey is hard-shelled or chitin-covered, the tench requires an effective means of crushing food to make it digestible. The throat, or pharyngeal, teeth do this job. These are positioned on a pair of bones one each side, and lie just under the pectoral fins' supporting bones.

In the tench these teeth are in a single row of four or five teeth on each pharyngeal bone. The innermost tooth on each side is bluntly pointed but the remainder have a flat surface

SLIMY SKINNED TENCH

The tench is a fascinating fish: the slime coating its body is reputed to have healing qualities, both for other fish and for man. This has earned it the name 'doctor' fish.

The tench is moderately large, varying from 20 to 50cm (8-20in). Large fish can grow to a maximum weight of about 8kg (18lb), but rarely reach 1.8kg (4lb) in the British Isles. This discrepancy arises because in Europe the tench is farmed as food, and in the near perfect conditions of the farm pool growth is rapid. In Britain, fish of 1.8kg may be 8 or 9 years old, and growth is slow. The young lad (above) is holding a large tench, and you can see the slimy skin.

The tench, a thickset, heavy fish of still waters, thrives best in lakes and reservoirs, but is also common in small ponds, since it can survive the low supplies of oxygen and tolerate extremes of warmth and cold. Those in ponds rarely grow to any great size however.

The tench also occurs in rivers, but only in the lowland reaches, where flow is slow. Here it seeks out any shelter offered by backwaters or bends, where the current is not so noticeable. Unfortunately, few lowland rivers in Britain have escaped having their course straightened, bed deepened, and banks built up. So there are now fewer suitable river habitats for the tench, and other fish like it which choose to live in backwaters. This is

Slime in fish

Most fish are slimy and the tench has a particularly heavy covering of mucus. However, there are even more slimy fish; a single hagfish—sometimes called the slime-eel or glutinous hag—is reported to be able to produce a pail-full of slime.

The mucus comes from special gland cells in the fish's skin and has several functions. It provides an outer coating to the skin which can be sloughed off without damage to the fish, and which carries away with it potentially harmful micro-organisms. It is also slightly alkaline, and may act as a mild antiseptic against infections.

Fish mucus also serves to lubricate the fish's movements. Burrowers, like the eel, have particularly slimy skins. Active swimmers, such as the roach or cod, can slide through the water—the diluted slime on their outer surfaces reduces friction.

Some tropical fish produce toxic mucus—the boxfish's can kill other fish in an aquarium—and this slime protects them against predators.

Slow-flow feeder

The tench is designed for catching food in a slow methodical way. Its heavy shape is not the build of a sprinter such as the pike. But its mouth, with one barbel at each corner, is perfectly placed for picking up small items of food among vegetation. The barbels especially have many taste cells in the skin, so that the fish knows long before it takes a morsel if it is edible and, presumably, what it tastes like.

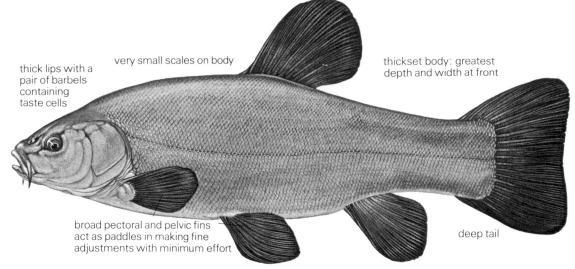

thick lips with a pair of barbels containing taste cells

very small scales on body

thickset body: greatest depth and width at front

broad pectoral and pelvic fins act as paddles in making fine adjustments with minimum effort

deep tail

They crush food against a tough, horny pad on the roof of the mouth which is hard up against the base of the skull. This efficient mill cracks and crushes prey in a thorough manner – so thoroughly that biologists often cannot establish what the fish has eaten.

Sex and spawning The tench is one of the few members of the carp family to show an external difference between the sexes (sexual dimorphism). The males have a much thickened outer ray on each pelvic fin, developing when they become sexually mature; and the skin on the ray becomes 'puffy' just before spawning.

The tench spawns from late spring to mid-summer, usually in late May in the south of England, and June or July in the north, depending on the temperature of the water. The adult fish come together in a large school and mass over a specially selected weed bed. The eggs, pale green in colour when shed, and about a millimetre in diameter, become firmly stuck on to plant leaves. The eggs take from six to eight days to hatch at a temperature of 18°C (64°F), and longer if it is cooler.

Doctor fish The copious slime on the tench's skin is reputed to have healing qualities, and there is an old belief that a wounded fish would seek out a tench and rub its wound along the tench's body so that the slime would seal and heal the wound. Hence the tench's title of 'doctor' fish. As an extension of this tale, it was believed that the pike – an ever present eater of smaller fish – would not attack a tench out of gratitude for its healing powers.

It is quite true that the tench is rarely found in pikes' stomachs; but the tench's relative immunity is more likely explained by its habit of lying low in the weeds and being active mainly at night (while pike feed mostly in daylight). The tench is also a slow swimmer, usually keeping near the bottom, and as such is not likely to attract a feeding pike's attention.

Certainly, a reputable naturalist at the turn of the century, Dr Bowdler Sharpe, observed individuals of a school of another predatory species, the perch, swimming in towards a large tench and rubbing themselves against it.

Could it be that there is some attractive quality for other fish in the tench's skin? Or is it possible that the tench is a parasite picker for other fish, nipping parasites off their skin? Such behaviour is reported in many marine fish and even in some freshwater species such as the stickleback. But the slimy seduction of the tench remains a mystery.

Folk-lore The belief in the tench's healing powers may have gained currency because this fish figures in ancient folk medicine. A tench applied to the palms of the hands or the soles of the feet was said to absorb the heat from a fevered patient, or if hung round the neck would cure sore eyes. So the tench was believed to benefit man as well as fish.

Below: If you stand by a lake or gravel pit, such as this one in Nottinghamshire, on a hot summer's day, you may spot a stream of bubbles breaking at the surface. These often come from a tench searching for food among submerged water plants.

STILL-WATER BITTERLING

Until a few years ago a bitterling could only be seen in aquariums in Britain, for it is not native here. Now however, this fish, although uncommon, occurs in many British waters.

Superficially, the bitterling is shaped like a crucian carp, the head being relatively small, the body deep, and the dorsal fin moderately long and high. Its scales are rather large with between 34 and 40 rows between the head and the tail fin. It is, however, unique among our carp family fishes in that its lateral line – the series of open pores leading to sensory cells under the scales – has openings on only the first five or six scales from the head. This possibly gives a clue to its relationships within the carp family, for other European and Asiatic fishes have similar short lateral lines, and similar breeding biology.

Breeding dress Outside the breeding season the bitterling is a very modestly coloured fish,

the back being grey-green, and the sides and belly bright silver, while along the mid-side from the level of the dorsal fin to the root of the tail there is a shining grey-green stripe. The dorsal fin is dark greenish, but the other fins are a delicate yellowish brown. In the breeding season, however, the male in particular is transformed. His back becomes distinctly green, the sides iridescent and the stripe along the side steel blue with rainbow tinges showing at the edges as the fish turns. The dorsal and anal fins are reddish with a black edge, and the throat and belly become dull red. Large white spawning tubercles develop on the front of the head.

The female bitterling is less brilliantly coloured, but nevertheless her coloration is brighter when spawning. The most striking change in the female is that she has a long – up to 5cm (2in) – coral pink egg-laying tube which projects from the front of her anal fin.

Undoubtedly it was the brilliant coloration of the male fish, and the quiet beauty of the female, that made them popular as cold water aquarium fishes from the 1920s onwards. At that time, it was possible to purchase them from a number of dealers in pond-life, most of whom obtained much of their stock from mainland Europe. Inevitably, fishes escaped when garden ponds flooded, and aquarium fish were released into ponds and rivers when their owners tired of them.

Escapee population The earliest established

Above: The bitterling (*Rhodeus sericeus*) is a member of the carp family and, like all members of that family, has a scaly body but no scales on the head. Neither the single dorsal fin nor any of the other fins bear spines. Its jaws are toothless but all carps have a pair of curved bones, set in the back of the throat, on which there are fixed numbers of broad teeth which crush their food against a pad in the roof of the pharynx. These are called the pharyngeal teeth and the bitterling has five strong flattened teeth on each side. Now that this fish has been introduced to British waters, there is always the possibility that anyone pond-dipping for water life, or an angler, will come across new localities, for it has proved to be a very successful fish in English fresh waters and will continue to spread, with man's help.

populations of bitterling in Britain were found round St Helens in Lancashire before World War II, in two or three waters known as lashes. Then, soon after the war, they were reported from about a dozen waters in the area. Local naturalists, and possibly children, helped their spread, and anglers were reported to have used them as live bait, releasing some unharmed in other waters. Soon their range increased to parts of Cheshire. Subsequently they have been found in several Midlands canals and lakes, including one at Stoke-on-Trent, and in Hertfordshire and Surrey in southern England.

The bitterling is not a large fish–it grows to 9cm (3½in) at the most–and it does not appear to be a serious predator on our native fauna, nor a competitor with our native fishes. Its food is comprised of a mixture of plants (mainly algae growing on other plants, but also the new growths of aquatic plants), small crustaceans and insect larvae.

Swan mussel nurseries Probably the most fascinating feature of the bitterling is its interesting and complicated breeding behaviour. For successful reproduction it depends on the presence of swan mussels (*Anodonta* spp.). The long egg-laying tube developed by the female bitterling at the beginning of the spawning season in April and May allows her to lay her eggs inside the valve of the mussel, on its gills. But before egg-laying the fish conditions the mussel to her presence by nudging it with her snout, which ensures that the mussel does not react to the insertion of the ovipositor by clamping shut on the female fish. After the first eggs are laid the male bitterling comes close to the mussel and ejects a small quantity of sperm, which is pumped into the mussel's gills as it respires; the eggs are thus fertilised. Usually only two

Seasonal colours

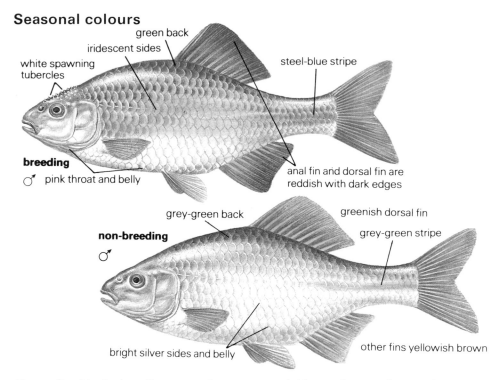

breeding ♂ — white spawning tubercles — iridescent sides — green back — steel-blue stripe — pink throat and belly — anal fin and dorsal fin are reddish with dark edges

non-breeding ♂ — grey-green back — greenish dorsal fin — grey-green stripe — bright silver sides and belly — other fins yellowish brown

Above: Outside the breeding season the bitterling is not particularly bright in colour, but in spring the male is transformed, developing iridescent sides and pink/red dorsal and anal fins, throat and belly.

Below: The bitterling prefers to live in still waters, especially among dense weeds in the shallows at the edges of ponds and lakes, in the backwaters of rivers and in slow-flowing rivers (although it avoids strong currents).

or three eggs are laid at a time, and spawning is repeated by the pair of fish until all the female's 40-100 eggs are laid. Several mussels are used as nurseries.

The eggs are about 3mm in diameter–large eggs for such a small fish–and remain wedged in the mussel's gills for up to four weeks, although in warm seasons they may hatch in 21 days. They leave the mussel within two or three days of hatching, once their supply of egg yolk is used up.

This fascinating use of another animal to act as a nurse to the eggs is clearly very successful. Compared with many of their relatives of similar size, the bitterlings lay very few eggs, in itself evidence that their system works well. The eggs, of course, are placed in a highly suitable position to develop in the oxygen-rich surroundings of the mussel's breathing current, an important consideration in the shallow, still waters in which they live. Moreover, if there is a drought, or conditions in the water become unfavourable for its own survival, the mussel closes its shell, or moves through the muddy lake or canal bottom to a more suitable area, taking the bitterling's eggs with it. In addition, the eggs and early fry are well protected from predators inside the mussel's hard valves at the bottom of the lake or pond.

The only price the bitterling has to pay for its use of the mussel is that when it comes close to the mollusc it frequently becomes host to the minute, parasitic, glochidium larvae of the mussel. The larva, attached by a long sticky thread, is taken in tow by the fish until its toothed shells take hold of a fin, when they clamp shut, later to become encysted in the fish's skin. This causes little damage to the fish but aids in the dispersal of the swan mussel, a classic case of one good turn deserving another.

Above: The roach (*Rutilus rutilus*) rarely grows longer than 45cm (15in) or weighs more than 1kg (2lb). It has a dark, rounded back, silvery-white sides and reddish eyes.

Roach distribution

☐ 1990

☐ early Roman times

The map above shows how the distribution of the roach is thought to have increased from Roman times to the present day.

RESILIENT ROACH

The roach survives and flourishes in more varied conditions than probably any other freshwater fish in Britain, so much so that the species has spread dramatically throughout Ireland in just 40 years.

The roach is a member of the carp family, which makes up the major group of British freshwater fish. One of the notable features of this group is that they have no teeth in their jaws. Consequently their food consists mostly of small invertebrates and plants; they are never aggressive fish-eating predators. Yet somehow the roach has come virtually to dominate the rivers and lakes of Britain (but not of Scotland), and is possibly our most common fish.

Invading Ireland Roach are not native to Ireland, and the story of their spread there is symptomatic of their resourceful nature. Imported probably in the 1950s, roach were stocked in a lake in County Tyrone. At that

time the nearby river Foyle flooded and som fish escaped from the lake into the river. B 1957 the roach in the Foyle were attractin the attention of anglers because the fish wer both numerous and fine specimens. Durin the 1960s and 1970s roach spread through th Foyle river system, into the Erne and th Shannon, and are now commonly found i many waters of Ireland.

Survival skills It seems that once it ha become established in a river, the roach wi spread far and fast. This is just as true i England and Wales. One of its qualities is it adaptability. It inhabits both lakes and rivers although it is not well-suited to the fastes streams. It can withstand the relatively hig water temperatures of ponds in summer, an also in rivers where the water has been use for industrial cooling, which raises the rive temperature. The roach is well known for it tolerance of moderately polluted waters.

The roach can also survive on relativel small amounts of dissolved oxygen, whic means it is capable of thriving in small pond and stagnant backwaters where oxygen leve are often low in warm weather. It can adap equally well to low levels of dissolved oxyge in extremely severe winters, when the water ice-covered for weeks. These conditior usually kill off other fish.

Abundant food The roach eats a wide rang of animals, helping it thrive in unfamilia waters. The young roach feeds on micro

copic aquatic animals such as rotifers, di-
toms, small copepod crustaceans (relatives
of the water flea) and water fleas themselves.
As it grows it eats more insects, including
large numbers of mayflies in all their developing stages, caddis and midge larvae,
also waterboatmen and water beetle larvae.
Roach also eat water snails and freshwater
shrimps together with other crustaceans.

The roach eats a certain amount of algae,
especially during spring and summer, but
some of this may be accidentally swallowed
while feeding on animals that live on water
plants, or on the river or lake bed. Few fresh
waters do not contain such a mixture of
animal life, so the roach usually has plenty of
suitable food for its wide-ranging diet.

Spawning success Another factor in the
roach's success story is that each female
produces a very large number of eggs. Asses-
sed as so many thousands of eggs per kilogram of fish, the roach comes high on the
scale at around 50,000 eggs per kilogram.
This is not as high as the tench, which produces about twice that figure. However,
tench may fail to spawn in a cold spring,
whereas the roach can spawn at temperatures
of 14-15°C (58-60°F), usually from April to
May. The roach try therefore get off to an
early start and are ready to take advantage of
any boom in the food supply that may occur.

Roach are curiously aggressive when
spawning. They frequently mingle with

spawning rudd and bream (their nearest
relatives in Britain) and produce hybrids.
These are sterile or have only low fertility,
and so fail to dominate the waterways. Rudd
and bream do not seem to return this intru-
sion, and the roach are therefore left alone to
their own prolific spawning.

Man's influence The most potent of all the
influences in the roach's success is undoubtedly man. By altering so many rivers for
navigation, building canals, constructing
reservoirs and making gravel pits, man has
provided many new and highly suitable
habitats for the fish. As it is also a highly
popular angling fish, the roach has been
transported to many new areas.

Above: This slow-flowing
water leading into the River
Avon, near Bickton Mill in
Hampshire, is typical roach
territory. The roach tolerates
poorer quality waters, even
those with moderate
pollution, and so spreads
rapidly – much to the delight
of anglers.

The roach: a member of the cyprinid family

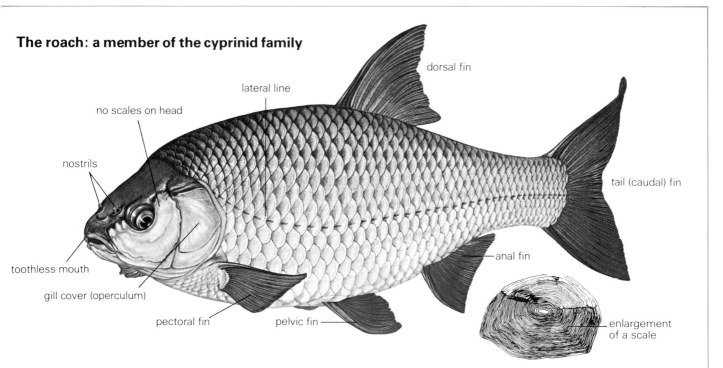

dorsal fin

lateral line

no scales on head

nostrils

tail (caudal) fin

toothless mouth

anal fin

gill cover (operculum)

enlargement
of a scale

pectoral fin

pelvic fin

Members of the carp family, known as cyprinids, include
the carp, tench, chub, gudgeon, bream and minnow, as
well as the roach. They form the major fish fauna of
British fresh waters. Typical features are fins without a
series of spines in them, a single dorsal fin and no teeth in
their jaws, compensated for by a set of teeth on paired
bones in the back of the throat to help them crush their
food. The scales of cyprinids cover the body but not the

head, and have no toothed edge (magnified above); they
are called cycloid scales.
Like most other fish the roach swims by side-to-side
sweeps of its tail, the caudal fin acting like a sculling oar.
Both the dorsal and anal fins keep the body steady, while
the pectoral and pelvic fins help the moving fish to stay
level in the water – and also to make small correcting
movements when the fish is still.

Birds of lake, pond and marsh

Although there are no totally aquatic birds, an enormous variety of species are attracted to water at some time or other during the year. Birds make use of water in different ways. Some are completely dependent upon it, and spend the greater part of their lives on or by it. All the ducks, for example, and the unrelated but similar grebes, feed while on the water – either by diving or by dabbling near the surface. They also nest close to the water's edge. As soon as the young hatch they take to the water and rapidly learn to make use of its abundant resources by watching and learning from their parents.

Other birds spend most of their lives close to the water, but not usually on it; they are adapted to finding food in the soft, marshy ground or lush vegetation around still waters. Snipe, for instance, nest in wet places and spend the rest of the year close to water or wet areas. They feed in mud by probing for invertebrates with their long sensitive beaks. Many other wading birds may breed in the Arctic, but come to waters farther south in winter for just the same reason – the abundance of invertebrate food in wet areas.

Birds like the reed warbler, sedge warbler or the reed bunting nearly always nest near water, though they never actually venture on to the water itself. They build their nests among the marginal growth of reeds or other vegetation and feed themselves and their growing brood on the abundant supply of flying insects – mayflies, mosquitoes, damselflies, midges and many others. This food supply is probably more abundant and reliable near lakes, ponds and marshes than anywhere else. A few birds, like the reed bunting, have done so well in the wetland habitats that they are spreading into drier habitats, but most wetland birds are sadly in decline as marshes are drained, ponds filled in and waters polluted.

Left: The elusive water rail is a ground dweller, lurking for most of its life among reed thickets. It is extremely difficult to spot, but once seen it is unmistakable with its long red bill and slate grey underparts. It feeds on small aquatic animals, plant roots, tubers, seeds and berries.

CHECKLIST

This checklist is a guide to some of the birds you can find in and around lakes, ponds and marshes. Although you will not see them all in the same place, you should be able to spot many of them throughout the changing seasons. The species listed in **bold** *type are described in detail.*

Bearded tit
Bittern
Black-necked grebe
Black-throated diver
Common snipe
Coot
Gadwall
Goldeneye
Great crested grebe
Great northern diver
Grey heron
Grey wagtail
Jack snipe
Little grebe (dabchick)
Mallard
Mandarin duck
Marsh harrier
Marsh warbler
Moorhen
Mute swan
Pochard
Red-necked phalarope
Red-throated diver
Reed bunting
Reed warbler
Sedge warbler
Shoveler
Slavonian grebe
Teal
Tufted duck
Water rail
White-billed diver
Wigeon

Left: The reed warbler is a migrant, coming from southern and tropical Africa to Britain in April and returning again in October. It frequents reed and osier beds and other dense vegetation near water. It feeds on the plentiful supply of marshland insects.

SKILFUL DIVERS OF REMOTE LOCHS

A rare and thrilling sight on remote lochs and islands, divers–hardy, Arctic birds–are experts at diving and underwater swimming. At breeding time their wild, shrieking calls, uttered on water and in flight, ring out by day and night.

Below: A black-throated diver walks ashore to its nest. Divers sometimes build a substantial heap of waterweed and grass, but the simple type shown here –a grass-lined hollow–is more usual for all species.

All four of the world's species of divers are to be seen in Britain and Ireland, although one, the white-billed diver (which breeds in Arctic North America), occurs very infrequently, usually only one or two individuals being seen during a year. The two smaller species, the red-throated and black-throated divers, breed in the north and west, but travel south to spend the winter at sea around all our coasts, so that they can be found somewhere in Britain and Ireland at any time of the year.

The great northern The huge and spectacular great northern diver was made famous for many in Arthur Ransome's book for children *Great Northern*. In most years, some adults spend the summer on remote lochs in northern Scotland, and once every few years a pair attempts to breed. Only once in recent decades, in 1970, has breeding proved successful and resulted in a couple of youngsters.

Most great northern divers breed in northern North America, Greenland and Iceland. On the other side of the Atlantic they are called 'loons', a name which is often thought to derive from their song. Of all bird calls, that of the great northern diver must count as one of the most thrilling. Its weird cry, like a whooping, lunatic laugh, echoes wildly across the lochs between the mountains and forest of their breeding grounds.

Breeding areas of Britain's divers

The great northern and white-billed divers are too rare to be shown on our map. Black-throated divers are slightly more numerous, with 150 breeding pairs in Scotland; while only the red-throated divers are outside the class of rare birds, for there are about 1000 pairs of these in Scotland and Ireland. They are also the only ones that breed in Orkney and Shetland, for the lochans (small lochs) there are too small for the other divers, which need plenty of room for taking off and landing.

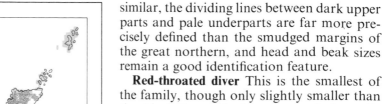

☐ black-throated diver

☐ red-throated diver

In full summer plumage, the bird is as spectacular as its song. Great northern divers are goose-sized, but with a short, thick neck and a powerful, dagger-like beak. The head is black with a greenish metallic sheen, and the back is black, but chequered with many brilliant white squares. On the side of the neck is a small black and white striped patch. In winter the plumage is much drabber: dark grey-brown above, shading to greyish white below.

Black-throated diver In summer, this bird could be mistaken for the great northern, as its plumage colours are an equally crisp combination of black and white. However, the black-throated diver is considerably smaller and slimmer, and has a less powerful looking neck and beak. The underparts are white and the back is black, with a chequerboard pattern of white blocks similar to that of its larger relative, but the head and nape of the neck are a plain dove-grey, while the throat, as the name suggests, carries a large, pure black 'bib'.

In winter, although the basic colours are

The calls of the black-throated (above) and red-throated diver (below) are similar – gruff, barking noises, and wailing calls interspersed with cackling or yodelling phrases – but less exciting to hear than the great northern diver.

similar, the dividing lines between dark upper parts and pale underparts are far more precisely defined than the smudged margins of the great northern, and head and beak sizes remain a good identification feature.

Red-throated diver This is the smallest of the family, though only slightly smaller than the black-throated. In summer it is easily recognisable because the upperparts are clearly brown, not black, and quite uniform rather than spotted. The head and neck are a finely streaked grey, and the 'bib' is a rich deep chestnut red, though at long range this may look black. An excellent identification feature at all times is the beak, which is slender and always seems to be tilted upwards.

In winter, the beak remains the best distinguishing feature separating red-throated from black-throated divers, but in addition the red-throated diver's back is brownish-grey and densely speckled with small white spots – a useful guide at close range.

Divers in flight The divers have a very characteristic flight silhouette, which helps (particularly in winter) to separate them from cormorants, shags, ducks, geese and grebes. The body is pencil slim, the wings slender and set well back, and the flight is straight and fast with powerful wingbeats. In the case of the black-throated, the wingbeats are conspicuously (and surprisingly) shallow. There are no interruptions for spells of gliding, as in the gannet or cormorant, for example. The tail and feet often seem to be held slightly depressed, and in the two smaller species the head and neck also droop a little, giving a hump-backed appearance.

The quiet of the loch All divers choose remote lochs for their British breeding grounds, the great northern and black-throated divers needing relatively large areas of water. The red-throated seems happy on the smallest of moorland pools, which explains why it is so widespread in the Orkney and Shetland Islands, where the lochans (small lochs) are tiny, and why the black-throated diver is absent there. Also, red-throated divers often fish far from their home pool, flying off to a larger loch or out to a sea-

Divers in summer plumage

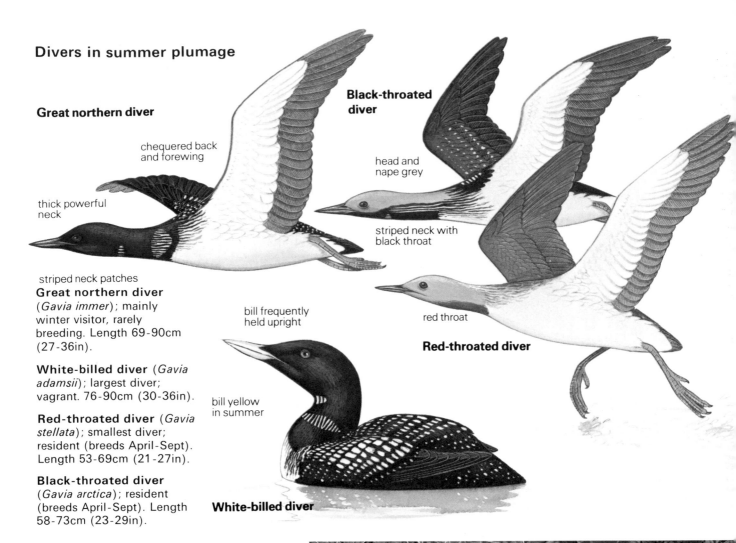

Great northern diver

chequered back
and forewing

thick powerful
neck

striped neck patches

**Black-throated
diver**

head and
nape grey

striped neck with
black throat

red throat

Red-throated diver

bill frequently
held upright

bill yellow
in summer

White-billed diver

Great northern diver
(*Gavia immer*); mainly
winter visitor, rarely
breeding. Length 69-90cm
(27-36in).

White-billed diver (*Gavia
adamsii*); largest diver;
vagrant. 76-90cm (30-36in).

Red-throated diver (*Gavia
stellata*); smallest diver;
resident (breeds April-Sept).
Length 53-69cm (21-27in).

Black-throated diver
(*Gavia arctica*); resident
(breeds April-Sept). Length
58-73cm (23-29in).

loch perhaps some miles away, and so can be
content with a small pool for nesting.

Winter on sea or reservoir Divers can be
seen in coastal waters during their spring and
autumn migrations. Many, probably including Scandinavian birds, spend all winter
around our coasts, often well out at sea but
coming closer inshore in bad weather. Many
large reservoirs, often well inland, have also
become regular places for seeing divers in
winter.

These reservoir birds offer by far the best
chance to watch the fishing technique (and
time the diving durations) of the various
species. The hunting diver patrols the surface,
often putting its head underwater to scan for
fish or other prey, including molluscs and
crustaceans, and even large insect larvae and
worms. If a likely food item is sighted, the
diver slips beneath the water surface, sinking
easily from view and hardly causing even a
ripple.

Once under the water, they are mobile and
speedy. The great northern and red-throated
divers regularly reach a depth of 10m (30ft),
and there are records of divers caught in
fishing nets 70m (230ft) under water – surely
a world record for diving birds.

Ancient species The earliest diver-like fos-
sils date from 100 million years ago, placing
the divers among the first recognisable fossil
bird groups. The continued presence of such
a seemingly 'primitive' line must surely testify

to the success of divers as underwater fishers.
The body is well streamlined for underwater
movement, being torpedo-shaped, and the
wings are relatively small in proportion to the
body, offering little resistance in the water.
The feet, set back near the tail, are highly
efficient in propelling the bird under water,
though rather ungainly on land.

Above: A great northern
diver incubating eggs on its
nest, a task that takes about
33-35 days. Fledging is slow
in this large species, taking
10-11 weeks. Both
processes are quicker in the
smaller species.

GALLANT GREBES

The great crested grebe, the largest member of its family in Britain, is a resident but the species often mistaken for it – the red-necked grebe – is a winter visitor here.

The great crested grebe has a slender body that sits rather low on the water, and a long thin neck that is generally held upright. In the breeding season this handsome water bird is readily identified by its black crest and prominent chestnut and black frills, usually called 'tippets', on either side of its head. The bill is dagger-like and brown, strongly tinged with red, in colour. The upperparts are grey-brown, while the face, neck and underparts are gleaming white. The tippets are shed in the autumn and the great crested grebe in winter is then an altogether duller bird, with a white face, dark crown and a thin white stripe over the eye. In this winter plumage it can sometimes be mistaken for our other large grebe species, the winter-visiting red-necked grebe.

Sad story with a happy ending The great crested grebe is a common breeding bird throughout the lowland areas of Britain and much of Ireland, being found on shallow lakes, reservoirs and gravel pits. It also breeds on some stretches of river. At the time of the last countrywide census in 1975, there were some 6500 pairs nesting in Britain.

This is very different from the bird's breeding status about 100 years ago, when the species was brought to the brink of extinction in this country. Up until about the middle of the last century, great crested grebes bred freely, though in comparatively small numbers, in some 13 counties of southern and central England. At about that time, however, the skins of grebes, with their thick layers of down feathers, became highly fashionable as articles of decorative wear. It is thought that as a result of being hunted for their skins there may have been as few as 32 pairs of great crested grebes left in the whole country.

Many efforts were made to protect the species, and gradually matters improved, with laws passed in the 1870s and 1880s to stop the exploitation. The number of pairs slowly increased, probably helped by immigration from the Continent. In 1931 a census taken throughout Britain revealed a total of just over 1200 pairs, nearly all of them in England and Wales. In the next few decades the num-

Above: A family party of great crested grebes. The adult male and female are very much alike in plumage, although the male is larger, with a heavier bill and larger crest and tippets. In the 19th century these handsome birds were ruthlessly hunted and shot in Britain for their exceptionally soft, silky feathers.

Grebe distribution

■ great crested (breeding)
■ red-necked (winter)

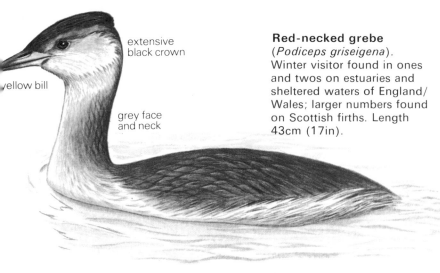

extensive
black crown

yellow bill

grey face
and neck

Red-necked grebe
(*Podiceps griseigena*).
Winter visitor found in ones
and twos on estuaries and
sheltered waters of England/
Wales; larger numbers found
on Scottish firths. Length
43cm (17in).

predators. Once the attractive, striped young have hatched, the parents take them straight on to the water. The brood often rides on the back of one parent while the other dives for food to bring them.

The young are fed on small insects at first, graduating to smaller and then larger fishes as they grow. After about four weeks, the brood may be split between the two parents, each adult taking some of the chicks to different areas of the nesting lake. After about two and a half months, the young fledge and become independent of their parents.

Elaborate courtship The displays of the great crested grebe, as in other birds, are a form of communication between the male and female. They are used first to establish a strong bond between them, forming a pair that can breed successfully and then be maintained through to copulation and egg-laying. Most of the courtship takes place on the water.

There are four different displays in the great crested grebe's courtship ritual: the 'head-shaking' ceremony, the 'discovery' ceremony, the 'retreat' ceremony and the 'weed' ceremony.

The commonest of the four displays is the head-shaking one. It is performed by both male and female birds, one starting off and the other soon joining in. The crest is raised into two shaggy ear-tufts rising from the back of the head, while the tippets are fanned out to the sides. Each bird slowly swings its head

...er increased, the grebes at the same time ...preading north into Scotland and west-...vards into Ireland.

Nesting and breeding The nests made by ...reat crested grebes are huge floating plat-...orms of waterweed, anchored to stands of ...eeds or rushes, or even an overhanging wil-...ow branch trailing in the water. The nest ...ften projects only a couple of inches above ...he surface, although there is usually a much ...nore substantial pile of waterweed lying ...nderneath.

Great crested grebes usually lay three or ...our whitish eggs. When the incubating bird ...eaves the nest it flicks a few pieces of weed ...ver the eggs to conceal them from passing

Above: In winter plumage the red-necked grebe, a winter visitor to Britain, lacks the white eye stripe of the great crested grebe, and has grey areas (not white) on the face and neck, a more extensive black crown, and a yellow (not red) tinged bill. In summer plumage the red-necked grebe's rich chestnut colour on the neck contrasts strongly with a white face and black crown. Very small ear tufts also develop, but are not nearly as obvious as the great crested grebe's crest.

Left: A great crested grebe on its egg-filled nest. The grebe suffers somewhat in very severe winters—a factor which may slow down its rate of increase in this country. In the past it also suffered from organo-chlorine residues in its fish diet. However, it is probably man's leisure activities—such as wind-surfing and water-skiing—that are the main causes of a grebe's failure to breed today.

Opposite page: A pair of courting great crested grebes – with their ear-tufts raised and cheek tippets fanned out.

Great crested grebe
(*Podiceps cristatus*). A resident bird on shallow lakes, reservoirs and gravel pits throughout lowland Britain and much of Ireland. Lays 3-4 blotchy white eggs any time from April-July. Length 48cm (19in)—our largest member of the grebe family. Winters on estuaries and on the sea, like the red-necked grebe.

Ceremonies of courtship

head-shaking

each bird shakes its head,
slowly or rapidly,
from side to side

discovery

one bird fluffs out
its feathers and crest

the other bird dives, then
re-emerges, rising on its tail
but with bill pointing down

one bird dashes away
then turns to face its mate

retreat

weed

the birds dive, emerge with waterweed
in their bills, then rise up in the water
breast to breast, shaking their heads

The great crested grebe has one of the most elaborate and distinctive courtship displays of any British breeding bird. When displaying, the pair are extremely intent on each other. At first the displays may appear to have little pattern, but close watching reveals that they occur in four parts or phases: the 'head-shaking' ceremony (**1**); the 'discovery' ceremony (**2**); the 'retreat' ceremony (**3**); and the 'weed' ceremony (**4**). In the picture (right) a display has been interrupted by an aggressive intruding male.

from side to side, sometimes with the bill pointing down, sometimes up, or even vertically to the sky. The pace of these movements varies from slow to fast, giving great variation to the character of each performance. Every so often one or other bird suddenly stops and bends its head down to preen among its scapulars (long feathers at the base of the wings). One bout of head-shaking may last for up to three minutes at a time.

In the head-shaking ceremony, both birds perform the same movements, but in the discovery ceremony they perform different movements, although either male or female can do both. If, while you are watching a pair of grebes which are some distance apart, one

Below: A male great crested grebe feeding its striped chick with fish. The grebe catches prey under water, submerging gracefully with little more than a ripple. Having located the prey by sight, the grebe pursues and captures it, swimming entirely with its feet and keeping its wings tightly folded to its sides. All but the smallest items of food are brought to the surface and eaten there. Fishes are turned in the bill until they can be swallowed head first.

of them dives, then watch its mate closely. I the birds are indulging in the discover ceremony, this bird will fluff out all its feather and raise its wings, crest and tippets. Th diving bird will be swimming straight for it mate, often leaving a tell-tale ripple on th surface. Then it abruptly emerges right besid its partner, rearing up on its tail but pointin its head and bill sharply downwards.

The head-shaking ceremony is often ende with the retreat ceremony. One of the pai suddenly ceases head-shaking, lowers itself i the water, and dashes away. At some distanc away, it turns and faces its mate again, per haps to come back and start the whol procedure once more.

The weed ceremony – the climax The clima to the displays is undoubtedly the weed cere mony, which has often been called the pen guin-dance ceremony. The birds start b moving together with their necks held bol upright, crests raised, then first one, followe by the other, dives. They emerge clutchin large pieces of soft waterweed in their bills.

At this stage the birds come together t perform the spectacular culmination, th weed-dance. The birds rise up out of th water, breast to breast, paddling vigorousl with their feet, at the same time swingin their heads, and loads of weed, from side t side. After as many as 40 such head swings the water churning under their feet and tails they subside, drop the weed, and finish quietly with a few shakes of the head. Eithe the male or the female can initiate any display but you can tell which is which because in th weed dance the male's head swings highe than the female's.

SMALLER GREBES OF SHELTERED WATERS

Our three smallest grebes – the little (also known as the dabchick), the Slavonian and the black-necked – spend almost all their time on or under water. They raise their families on floating nests in lakes and ponds, but from autumn throughout winter they are likely to frequent sheltered coastlines.

Besides the great crested grebe, there are three other species of grebe that breed in the freshwaters of Britain – the little grebe (or dabchick), Slavonian grebe and black-necked grebe. They are all smaller than the great crested grebe, being about half the length of the average duck. Although ducks tend to be more common on ponds, lakes and reservoirs, if you look carefully you may spot a grebe in such a habitat – perhaps in deep water but often near reed-ringed edges.

Grebes are not difficult to pick out because of their characteristic shape – a noticeable, rounded hump of a body without any tail feathers (by contrast, the duck's tail usually sticks up at an angle). The grebe's neck is longer than the duck's in proportion to the body, and grebes have a pointed bill quite unlike that of ducks.

Paddle-power Grebes may swim very low in the water, especially if alarmed, and when feeding they frequently dive. Like most swimming birds they paddle with their feet both on top of, and under, the water. Instead of having webbed feet like ducks and gulls, the long toes of all grebes have flaps of skin or lobes to make them into broad, efficient paddles. (The only other common bird with feet like this is the coot.) Grebes' wings are curved and lie closely against the streamlined body to ensure maximum speed.

Above: The male and female little grebe share the duty of incubating the eggs on their floating nest. The nest, consisting of a pile of waterweed loosely anchored to surrounding aquatic vegetation, is about 30cm (1ft) in diameter.

Little grebe (*Tachybaptus ruficollis*), 27cm (10½in) from beak to tip of tail. Sexes alike. Distribution most widespread of all grebes; partial migrant.

The little grebe, or dabchick, is the smallest European grebe and by far the most common. It is found throughout the whole of Britain but seems to prefer still lakes with dense vegetation at the edges. It also frequents small ponds, lochs and slow-moving streams. In the breeding season the little grebe stays hidden among the reeds (and is very difficult to spot), but in autumn and winter you may discover small flocks out in open water.

Dabchicks look very dumpy and blunt-ended at the back when they fluff out their feathers. In the summer, adults have blackish and dark brown body feathers, a black head and neck with chestnut cheeks and throat and, at the base of each side of the bill, a conspicuous pale yellow patch. (As with the other two grebe species, the plumage changes in winter.)

Dabchicks' head feathers are not as striking as other grebes' and their courtship displays are less dramatic, but you should listen for the distinctive call. Both sexes make a loud, drawn-out, whinnying trill, sometimes rising and falling in pitch. Occasionally they perform a duet.

Slavonian and black-necked grebes are very similar to each other (see illustration) but, as you might expect, the latter species has a black neck (though only in summer); the Slavonian's neck is chestnut. They also differ in the size and the positioning of their bright yellow 'ear tufts'–those of the Slavonian grebe sweep back from the eyes like horns (in America it is called the horned grebe), while those of the black-necked grebe radiate like tiny fans. The eyes of these small grebes are bright red, unlike the dabchick's which are black.

Winter plumage After breeding, the adults moult. They replace their body feathers just a few at a time, so the change to winter plumage is slow. However, all the flight feathers on the wings drop out together so the grebes are

flightless for up to a month while new feathers grow.

Most land birds need to retain the ability to fly so that they can escape from predators, but grebes rely on the safety of water and thick waterside vegetation to hide in. They even sleep on the water.

In their winter plumage little grebes are generally brown and white, and therefore fairly easily distinguished from the other species which are black, grey and white. If you see one of the three small grebe species flying–they all fly with neck outstretched and legs dangling behind–only black-necked and Slavonian grebes have white on the wings. In winter, the black-necked grebe has a dusky neck and the black of the crown extends below eye level. Its bill is also slightly uptilted. In

Above: Like all grebes, the little grebe's feet are set right at the back of the body to give good forward propulsion. This makes them clumsy on land so they rarely leave the water.

Opposite page: Slavonian grebe on its untidy waterside nest of dried reed.

Below: The Slavonian and the black-necked grebes shown here are both adults in their breeding plumage. Note the young chicks carried by the black-necked grebe.

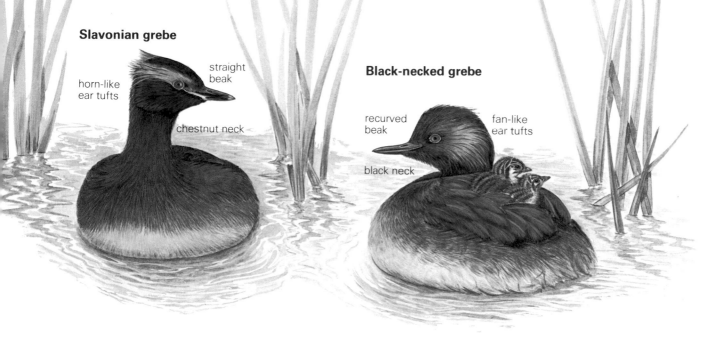

Slavonian grebe

horn-like ear tufts

straight beak

chestnut neck

Black-necked grebe

recurved beak

fan-like ear tufts

black neck

Weed-rush ceremony of Slavonian grebes

Grebes are well known for their amazing courtship displays, when they raise and fan their head feathers—showing off the colours to prospective mates. Complex rituals are performed in strict sequence. Perhaps the most dramatic display is the weed-rush ceremony exhibited by the Slavonian grebes.

Both male and female Slavonian grebe dive and then surface with some soft weed dangling from their bills. The courting pair approach each other and rise up breast to breast in a sort of dance. Then, in the same upright, penguin-like posture, they turn and dash across the water side by side (right) for several metres; this can be repeated up to 10 times.

Slavonian grebe
(*Podiceps auritus*), 33cm (13in) from beak to tip of tail. Sexes alike. Rare, partial migrant.

Below: On the central depression of her floating nest, the female little grebe lays 4-6 whitish eggs. The parents start incubation before the clutch is complete and, as a chick can swim within a few hours of hatching, it is not uncommon to see the mother feeding one while brooding the still unhatched eggs.

Black-necked grebe
(*Podiceps nigricollis*), 30cm (12in) from beak to tip of tail. Sexes alike. Rare, partial migrant.

Left: Although the adult little grebes take turns to incubate the eggs, one parent may leave the nest before the other is ready to return. In this case it carefully covers the eggs with weed to hide them from marauding crows.

contrast, the Slavonian grebe has a whitish neck and the black crown stops abruptly at eye level. It has a flatter forehead than the black-necked grebe, and a straight bill.

Floating nest Grebes make floating nests—a remarkable adaptation to a totally aquatic life. Little grebes often start several nests before choosing the best one to complete. The clutch of 4-6 eggs may be only 4cm (1½in) above the water. Passing boats are a dangerous threat because the waves they create can easily wash the eggs off the nesting platform. The eggs are initially chalky white, but they soon become stained brown by the rotting nest material.

The chicks hatch after about three weeks and are already covered in fluffy black and white down. They can swim within a few hours and dive after about ten days, but usually stay in the nest for the first week or so. They are often of slightly varying sizes because they hatch on different days—the first eggs to be laid hatch first because the parents start incubation before the clutch is complete.

Chicks hitch a ride The parents also have the fascinating habit of encouraging the brood to take rides. The chicks, while small, are particularly vulnerable to predatory fish such as pike, and they soon learn to climb onto the back of one of their parents and hide among the feathers while the other parent dives to catch food for them. Often all that can be seen is a tiny striped head poking up between the wings. It is a month or even longer before the chicks are fully independent.

Grebes' diet Small grebes rarely go more than 2m (6ft) down when they dive in search of food, although Slavonian grebes have been known to dive down to 25m (80ft). Grebes take insects and larvae, molluscs, tadpoles, small fish and crustaceans. They eat the smaller prey while submerged. Although dives usually only last 10 to 25 seconds, actively feeding birds spend more time under the water than above.

Sometimes they take food from the surface or swim with just their head below the water, and occasionally you may see one catching flying insects when they come within reach.

Secret sites Slavonian and black-necked grebes first nested in Britain early in this century. By 1930 there were hundreds of breeding black-necked grebes in a single colony in Ireland, but today both species are very rare. The breeding sites are usually shallow freshwater lochs in Scotland, but the exact locations are kept secret.

In winter, however, the British population is joined by continental birds which, like ours, fly from their summer territories to spend the winter in warmer waters. Sheltered bays, estuaries and reservoirs are favourite spots. Little grebes tend to remain in the same territories all the year round unless they are forced out by bad weather.

THE BOOMING BITTERN

The vast, flat, waving reedbeds of East Anglia are the home of the bittern – a secretive member of the heron family. Its fortunes in Britain have been mixed – driven to virtual extinction last century, it is now once more a breeding species here.

The bittern is a highly specialised bird, living its entire life in a reedbed sanctuary – feeding, roosting, breeding and wintering in the fastness of the strange, vertical world of swaying reeds.

Changing fortunes In the days before large areas of fenland were drained to form farmland, the bittern was a widespread and common species in lowland Britain. Nowadays, however, with the reduction of its reedbed habitat, the bird maintains a somewhat tenuous place on our list of breeding species.

Indeed, by the last quarter of the 19th century, the bittern had virtually disappeared from Britain, remaining lost to us as a breeding bird for several decades. The drainage of

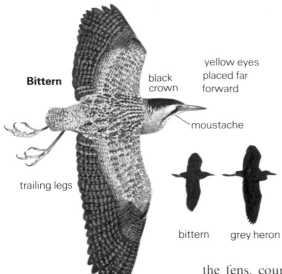

Bittern

yellow eyes placed far forward

black crown

moustache

trailing legs

Bittern (*Botaurus stellaris*). Resident in reedbeds, chiefly those in E Anglia and Norfolk. 76cm (30in).

Below: An adult male bittern in the typical hunched standing posture of members of the heron family. Note the strong, dagger-like bill and the disproportionately large feet.

Previous page: Bittern on its nest among the reeds.

Left: Bittern in flight— note the rounded, owl-like outline, and how it compares with the longer outline of the heron (also shown). In both birds the legs trail in flight.

bittern grey heron

Right: The streaky plumage and neck-stretched posture of the bittern are perfect adaptations for camouflage among old reeds.

the fens, coupled with shooting (for food), egg-stealing and general persecution by man all contributed to the extermination of breeding bitterns in Britain. The last nest was found in Norfolk in 1868.

By 1900, however, bitterns from the Continent started to recolonize the Norfolk reedbeds and, now protected by enlightened landowners, breeding was proved once more by 1911. Slowly pairs spread to such Broadland sites as Hickling, Horsey and Catfield, and by 1930 a small population had appeared in Suffolk. The steady period of build-up and expansion continued and by 1954 nesting was occurring in seven counties, with a total of just over 80 pairs. Leighton Moss, the RSPB

reserve near Morecambe in Lancashire, became a nucleus site in the north-west.

Throughout the past 20 years or so, however, a slow but steady decline has again taken place, the reasons for which are difficult to establish, although water pollution, the effect of hard winters, incidental disturbance through recreational activities and the local effect of reedbed grazing by excessive numbers of introduced coypu probably all played a part. At present the breeding population of bitterns is 20-25 pairs, almost all of them on RSPB or other reserves.

Skulker in the reeds The bittern is a somewhat stocky bird, notably thick-necked and with a heavy, powerful bill. It is generally golden-brown in colour, but mottled and barred with black and with a black crown and 'moustache'. The underparts are a pale creamy colour, striped with broken, rufous-brown lines. At any time it is a difficult bird to pick out against the reeds, even when it is in view, but the full effect of the cryptic patterning suddenly becomes apparent when the bird stretches upright, pointing vertically upward with its bill—the golden-brown markings merging perfectly with the moving background of reeds and the striping on the throat and breast matching perfectly the vertical columns of the reeds.

The bittern has other special adaptations too. Its feet, on shortish, sturdy green legs, are broad and strong and of disproportionately large size to enable the bird to move with maximum efficiency on the soggy mat of broken and submerged reeds. The yellow eyes have a malevolent and staring quality; they are placed unusually far forward on the

feeding and protecting the young. The fledging period is protracted and it is eight weeks before the young are on the wing.

At the end of the breeding season bittern families break up and the young disperse from their natal areas. Bitterns survive well in places where the water is open throughout the winter, but protracted freezes make feeding impossible; this is when the highest levels of mortality occur among our resident birds, which starve to death.

Feeding habits Within the constraints of the habitat within which it lives, the bittern is a catholic feeder, taking fish, amphibians, reptiles, insects and even small mammals—water voles are certainly vulnerable and often form a substantial part of the bittern's diet. Nestlings of smaller marshland birds also fall victim to the bittern.

Much of the bittern's hunting is carried out on the edge of the reedbed, often—if close to human activity—in the earliest part of the day when there is minimum risk of disturbance from people passing by.

ead, close to the base of the bill. This strange adaptation gives the bittern extremely good i-focal vision for hunting. The bird's amazng cross-eyed appearance can only be fully ppreciated if seen from the front.

Booming in the breeding season The bittern s secretive, elusive and a very difficult bird to ee, but it does have a uniquely distinctive call which heralds the breeding season. The eerie ound of the bittern's resonant 'booming' is ot unduly loud but it has great carrying ower and may be heard two miles or more cross the marshes on a still day in spring. he booming attracts the females and adverises the occupation of the territory and, in nild years, can be heard as early as mid-ebruary, lasting well into June.

Severe territorial battles can sometimes ake place in the breeding season, occasionally eading to the death of one of the combatants. uch extreme hostility is unusual among irds and may be related to the polygamous ehaviour of many male bitterns. Bittern ggression is not restricted just to others of its wn kind. Much has been written about the nutual antipathy shown between bitterns and narsh harriers; the appearance of an intrudng harrier over the bittern's nest site can ransform the bittern from a stealthy, secretve bird to a whirling fury, pursuing its dversary with lethal intent.

Mating and nesting As spring develops the ittern pair make short erratic courtship ights over the reedbeds, after which mating ormally takes place. The nesting pad is made p of matted reeds and other marsh plants, ntidily prepared and soon flattened through se. The four or five eggs are olive in colour, natt in texture and lightly speckled at the large nd. The male takes no part in the incubation nd in most pairings, particularly polygamous nes, the female is also left with the task of

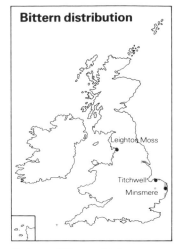

Bittern distribution

Leighton Moss
Titchwell
Minsmere

Below: Bittern chicks on the well-concealed nest. They take 8 weeks to fledge.

MALLARD: AT HOME EVERYWHERE

The mallard is a popular bird because it takes to many man-made surroundings, and tamely accepts food from the hand. In summer it moults its feathers and cannot fly.

The mallard is the most common, widespread and best-known duck in the British Isles. Although it is a water bird, the mallard has followed the example of other successful species—for instance starlings, pigeons and house sparrows—by adapting to man-made habitats.

Many water-birds have declined because pollution and the drainage of marshes have destroyed their natural environment. But the mallard has managed to outweigh such losses by colonizing the artificial lakes and ponds in many town and city centres, as well as taking to the smallest farm ponds. Even in the centre of London, you'll find mallard on the ponds in all the major parks. It is also invariably a mallard which features in press photographs of a policeman holding up the traffic to allow mother and brood to cross the road safely.

Courting You can see the courtship behaviour of the mallard on any mild winter's day, as the birds begin to form pairs ready for the summer breeding season. Ducks form a new pair in winter or spring, and then break up again after the breeding season. The female is actively courted by the males (drakes), often several at a time. From a group of displaying males the female eventually chooses her mate. She presumably selects the one which is displaying with greatest vigour, showing him-

Above: The dappled brown female mallard leads her downy nestlings to the water, almost as soon as they are hatched. They feed themselves without any parental help.

Right: The traditional mallard nest site in the wild is in thick vegetation—nettles, brambles, bracken and heather. Unusual sites, more associated with man, include water tanks, flower boxes and bridge supports. The female builds her nest using plant debris, grasses, and down feathers plucked from her own chest. She usually lays 7-11 pale bluish-green eggs, which she alone incubates. The young become independent at the same time they fledge—about six weeks after hatching.

Duck displays

There are a number of behavioural gestures, mostly associated with courting, which the male performs.

Grunt whistle is the most common display. The male tucks his head down to his chest, and lifts the front half of his body right out of the water. He then just flicks the surface with the tip of his bill, sending a little spray of water droplets up into the air. At the same time he lets out a low grunt, followed immediately by a clear whistle.

Head-up, tail-up involves both chest and tail coming up off the water. This emphasises the colouring on the male's neck and breast, as well as the black and white pattern on the tail.

Raised wing is another action where the male tucks his head behind the raised wing, as if to preen. This really serves to expose a blue-green bar (speculum) edged with white, along the rear of the wing.

Though not actually involved in the courtship rituals, this male (4) is alerted to the proceedings and quacks in response. When there is a surplus of males, they continue to court females already paired.

self off to be the brightest and largest bird present, and therefore the most suitable to fertilise her eggs.

Choice of nest site Mallards tend to choose nest sites on the ground, where they will be concealed in marshy vegetation; but they also adapt to all kinds of artificial situations – including nest boxes and holes in, and even under, buildings. They may nest a trifle precariously in the crowns of pollarded willows, and even on broad branches many metres off the ground. One much-publicised site was in a window box of the house next-door to the Iranian Embassy in London, facing on to Hyde Park. The duck sat through the trauma of the 1980 siege and rescue, apparently without budging from her nest.

Nest construction When nesting off the ground, the female mallard uses little or no nest material because she cannot carry things in her bill. On the ground, however, the duck constructs a shallow cup of such vegetation as it can reach from the nest, pulling and pushing stems and leaves into a circular rim.

2 head-up tail-up

female

1 grunt whistle

The female (above) remains passive prior to pairing but once she has a mate she sometimes 'incites' him to drive off contending suitors. She dabs her head and bill in the direction of the interloper, while quacking noisily.

As the mother begins to lay the clutch of seven to eleven eggs, she also begins to pluck down from her breast. This process starts slowly with a few bits at a time, but by the end of the egg-laying – she usually manages one egg per day – there is a thick layer of pale greyish down under and around the eggs. The down serves two functions: first it insulates the eggs from the cold, and often damp, ground; secondly, when the female leaves the eggs for her twice daily feed and bathe, she pulls the down and some of the nest material over the eggs, concealing them completely from any passing predator.

Incubating the eggs The drake takes no part in the incubation, and rarely has any contact with the female once she finishes laying and begins to sit on the eggs all day. Sometimes he waits nearby to meet her when she comes off the nest. He also keeps watch while she has a hasty feed, but only does this for a week or so. In fact this is just as well: the female's mottled brown plumage is perfect camouflage, and fits in with the nest surroundings, but the contrasting green, purple and white plumage of the male could catch the eye of a fox or crow, and lead such predators to the nest with its precious clutch of eggs.

Brooding the chicks The female incubates the eggs for 26-28 days. The young hatch out over a short period – all within 24 hours. Depending on the time of day and the weather, the female will brood them in the nest for

3 raised wing

4 alert, quacking

several hours, during which their down dries, and they become fluffy and active. Then she leads them off the nest, and takes them to the nearest stretch of suitable water where they can find food. Most nests are within a hundred metres of water, but some ducks may have to trek double that distance, and even cross roads to get there.

The young can run and swim as soon as they leave the nest, and also feed themselves, pecking instinctively at any small object. They quickly learn to distinguish between small seeds and insects which are good to eat, and surface debris, which is of no value to them. The town park mallard eats crusts and scraps, but the true diet of those living in more

157

atural surroundings includes seeds of rushes
nd grasses, a wide variety of insects and the
ps of leaves and stems of growing plants.

The mother broods her young at night or
uring rainy periods, defending them against
redators. However, many of the ducklings
ll prey to pike and rats and, during a cold
et spell, they may even starve. From a brood
f ten young, perhaps four or five survive to
ie flying stage. They reach this all important
age in about six weeks, and may incur
irther losses while they learn to fly properly.
evertheless the number of young mallard
ared each year is ample to compensate for
sses of adult birds, and the overall popula-
on is buoyant.

Population In December and January there
e usually between 600,000-700,000 mal-
rds in the country. Many of these are
igrants coming from northern Europe to
verwinter, but when they depart in the
ring, about 100,000 pairs of mallard stay
hind to breed.

Although most of the town park lakes in
ritain only hold small numbers of mallard,
few hundred at most, there are some notable
ncentrations–over 8000 have been seen
gether on the estuary of the Humber near
ull, and nearly 6000 on the floods of the
iver Derwent. Counts of 4000 to 5000 have
en made on Abberton reservoir in Essex,
d on the Ouse Washes in Norfolk.

Distribution Mallard occur throughout the
orthern hemisphere, in Europe, Asia and
orth America. They have also been intro-
iced into Australia and New Zealand.
hose that breed in the British Isles are com-
etely sedentary, rarely moving more than

30 miles throughout their lives. Those that
migrate from Scandinavia on the other hand,
move considerable distances.

The breeding range for birds wintering in
Britain extends north from southern Sweden
and Finland to the Arctic Circle and deep into
the Soviet Union to the east. The majority of
these birds leave Britain in March and move
north-east in a series of short hops, to reach
their breeding quarters by the end of April.
Once the female is sitting safely on her eggs,
the male may start to move back south-west
as early as July.

Many males pause for some weeks on large
lakes and reservoirs while they undergo their
annual moult, changing all their feathers, and
actually becoming flightless for a couple of
weeks. They then continue their migration,
arriving back in Britain in September. The
females and the young stay on the breeding
grounds until well into August.

Above: The male mallard
(called the drake) is a
handsome bird with a bottle-
green head and neck. A neat
white collar separates the
purple-brown chest and pale
grey back. Small black
feathers curl above the tail.

Mallard (*Anas
platyrhynchos*), one of the
most widely distributed of
our breeding birds.
50-65cm (20-25in) long.

Opposite page: Female
mallard duck in full flight.

Below: The female is a
subdued mottled brown all
over, which makes her well
camouflaged for sitting on
the eggs and nest.

DIVING DUCKS OF STILL WATERS

Two of our most attractive diving ducks, the pochard and its close relative the tufted duck, are becoming increasingly common on Britain's lakes and reservoirs. Many are now breeding here, but most are winter visitors from northern Europe.

Above: A male tufted duck. The female has a much less pronounced tuft.

Tufted duck (*Aythya fuligula*). Resident duck, breeding next to lakes, gravel pits and reservoirs throughout much of lowland Britain. Length 43cm (17in).

Pochard (*Aythya ferina*). Resident duck, but far less common in the breeding season than the tufted duck and confined mostly to natural lakes. Length 46cm (18in).

As with so many species of duck, male pochard and tufted duck are strikingly coloured birds. The females, on the other hand, are dull by comparison since they need to be well camouflaged when they incubate their eggs and raise the young.

The male tufted duck has black upperparts set off by brilliant white sides and belly. It gets its name from the tuft on the back of its head, although this feature is not always conspicuous. The female tufted duck has only a rudimentary tuft and is brown with slightly paler sides. Sometimes, she has a pale patch at the base of her bill. In flight, both sexes show a long white bar on the upper side of each wing.

The pochard is larger and more heavily built than the tufted duck. The male is unmistakable, his pale grey body contrasting sharply with a black chest and dark chestnut neck and head. From a distance, the male seems to have a uniformly dark head, neck and breast, and a pale body. The female resembles a larger version of the female tufted duck, but she has a paler back and buff markings around the bill and eye. In flight, the pochard shows pale grey wing-bars, the only species of duck with this feature.

Winter visitors The numbers of tufted duck and pochards breeding in Britain has increased considerably during the last hundred years—in the case of the tufted duck the increase has been spectacular—yet most of the birds seen in Britain are still winter visitors from other parts of Europe. It estimated that there are between 50,000 and 60,000 of each species wintering in Britain compared to the summer breeding figures of about 7000 pairs of tufted duck and only 1 pairs of pochard. It is, therefore, not surprising that they are our commonest diving ducks to be seen on lakes, reservoirs and gravel pits during winter.

Many tufted duck wintering in Britain arrive here from Iceland, the rest coming from northern Scandinavia and northern and Arctic Russia. The former population winter mostly in Scotland, western England and Ireland; the latter usually settles in southern nd eastern England. Flocks of several thousand may gather, particularly on large areas of water such as the reservoirs around London.

Our wintering pochard come to us from Russia, though further south than the tufted duck's breeding grounds. Like the tufted duck, pochard form huge flocks numbering several thousand. One notable gathering point, Duddington Loch, a tiny pool lying within the city limits of Edinburgh, used to hold a staggering 8000 pochard crowded together, but current numbers have fallen to less than 100. The Ouse Washes still host large winter populations, while several London reservoirs continue to support hundreds every year.

Favourite foods During winter, large numbers of both pochard and tufted duck happily coexist on the same lake or reservoir–happily, because they are not in direct competition with each other since they have different food preferences. Generally, the tufted duck is carnivorous and the pochard is herbivorous. However, both species feed on the other's food if it is abundant. The main food source for the pochard is the stoneworts and pondweeds; the tufted duck feeds mainly on insects and shellfish.

Both species feed by diving, usually beginning with a slight upward jump to give them impetus to dive deeper. Once under water they swim with their feet alone, keeping their wings tightly closed. The dives last for about

With its striking black and white plumage and tuft, the male tufted duck is far more distinguished than its dull brown and white female. After mating, the male adopts a characteristic 'bill-down' posture.

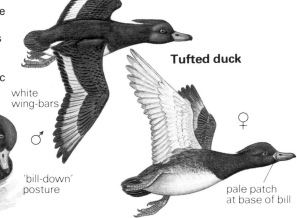

Tufted duck

white wing-bars

tuft

♂

'bill-down' posture

♀

pale patch at base of bill

Right: The head of a male tufted duck is black but, in certain lights, its glossiness can give it a purplish tinge. Notice the bright yellow iris, a characteristic shared by the female.

Below: Pochards and tufted ducks share the same habitat but rarely compete with each other for food since they have different preferences. Tufted ducks generally feed on animals, whereas pochards concentrate more on plants.

15-20 seconds and the birds emerge close to where they submerged.

Segregated flocks In both species, the winter flocks consist predominantly of one sex or the other, rather than being evenly mixed. The reason for this is that the males leave the breeding grounds well before the females and so arrive at their wintering grounds much earlier. By the time the females arrive the more northerly wintering sites (the ones nearest to the breeding grounds) may already be full of males, so the females have to move on further south.

Even if a flock comprises males and females it is noticeable how often the sexes remain separated. The males tend to feed in deeper water further from the shore. Being larger, they can dive deeper and stay submerged for longer, up to 20 seconds compared to the females' 15 seconds. By feeding in deeper water the males reduce the competition for food by exploiting a different source.

Resident tufted ducks Most pochards and tufted ducks migrate in spring back to their summer breeding grounds, but increasing numbers are now breeding in Britain. The earliest recorded instance of tufted ducks breeding in Britain was as recent as 1849, when a pair bred in Yorkshire. Other records

quickly followed; the speed of their increase can be gauged from the breeding record at Loch Leven, where the first pair bred in 1875 but only five years later there were more than a hundred breeding pairs.

The excavation of numerous gravel pits in lowland parts of southern England has provided the tufted duck with large areas of new habitat, and there are now few pits without nesting pairs. The presence of an island in the gravel pits is a great advantage since the birds are then safe from foxes.

The tufted duck's nest is a hollow on dry ground near water, hidden in grass or rushes and lined with grass, down and feathers. The usual clutch of eggs is between seven and twelve. Only the female incubates the eggs; the male leaves to congregate with other males, his part in the breeding cycle having now been completed. The eggs hatch after about 24 days, and the female leads the young chicks down to a shallow sheltered area of water close to the shore, where she rears them.

The young take about six weeks to fledge, but they are often abandoned by the mother two or three weeks beforehand. The reason for this is that the female moults immediately after the breeding season; by leaving the brood early she gives herself more time to carry out the moult.

head-throw display
crouch display
neck-stretch display

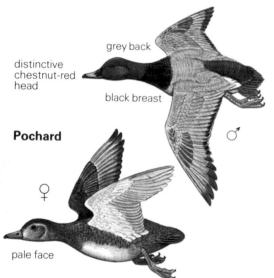
grey back
distinctive chestnut-red head
black breast

Pochard

♂

♀

pale face

Above: Male pochards have several unusual courtship displays. The commonest is the neck-stretch display, where the male's neck is held upright and appears thickened, possibly due to its feathers ruffling out. It may also perform the head-throw display, in which it whips its head far back and then forwards again while calling, and the crouch display, in which its neck is pulled in.

Left: A male pochard. During winter, male and female pochards often form separate flocks. If they stay within the same flock they are likely to feed in different parts of the lake.

Left: The characteristic chestnut brown head of a male pochard contrasts sharply with its black chest and pale grey wings and back. The female pochard is dull brown.

Below: A female tufted duck with chicks. The chicks fledge after six weeks, but the mother often abandons them before that.

Resident pochards Pochards have bred in Britain in small numbers for centuries. However, as with the tufted duck, their population began to grow during the latter half of the 19th century. Pochards now breed in most parts of Britain, except upland areas, though they are still much less common than tufted ducks. This is probably due to their breeding habits, which are much more restricting than those of the tufted duck. Instead of nesting on dry land, the pochard builds its nest close to, or actually in the water, and so it needs dense stands of vegetation growing in shallow water. Its natural habitat used to be marshlands but, as these have been drained and reclaimed, the pochard has had to find alternative sites. Unlike the tufted duck, the pochard has not yet been able to colonize recently established gravel pits and reservoirs since the margins still lack the necessary vegetation.

The breeding habits of the pochard are broadly the same as those of the tufted duck. The female alone incubates the clutch of six to eleven eggs and rears the brood. But she does not abandon the chicks before they can fly (at about seven weeks old). Possibly, this is because pochards nest earlier than tufted ducks and so have more time for moulting.

WATER RAILS: HEARD BUT RARELY SEEN

Detailed studies by ornithologists have shown that the water rail, one of our most secretive water birds, is far commoner in Britain and Ireland than was first suspected. Despite its cautious nature, the water rail often advertises its presence among waterside vegetation with its loud, raucous call.

Water rail distribution

The water rail enjoys a somewhat undeserved reputation as one of the rarities among British and Irish birds. It is, without doubt, one of our most secretive birds, avoiding disturbance of any kind, and its reputation for rarity has discouraged many people from seeking the water rail, leaving it relatively undisturbed in its marshy haunts. The reputation is undeserved however, because water rails were found in 25% of the 3862 10km squares mapped in the breeding season surveys carried out to provide data for the *Atlas of Breeding Birds in Britain and Ireland*. This was far more than most bird-watchers expected, and led to estimates of a breeding population of between 2000 and 4000 pairs, comparable, for example, to our great crested grebe, heron and mute swan populations.

Watching the water rail To see a water rail well requires one or more of a number of factors operating in your favour: luck, which is probably as important as patience; a good hide overlooking a suitable habitat; or else a spell of bitter, freezing weather extending over several days, which forces hungry water rails to come out into the open to forage for

Above: Few counties in Britain and Ireland are without water rails. Because of its generally wetter landscape, Ireland, though smaller, probably holds as many pairs as Britain, and possibly even more.

Below: A close-up view of a water rail – a rare and exciting moment.

dark brown-black back

Moorhen

white wing flash

foot has a short hind toe and three very long front toes

red frontal shield

green legs

streaked dark brown back

short, pale bill

Corncrake

narrow, laterally compressed body

long, slightly down-curved red bill

streaked brown back

lead-grey face, throat and belly

black and white barred flanks

Water rail

Water Rail (*Rallus aquaticus*); dwells in reedbeds and other dense marsh vegetation. Resident population, swollen by migrants from Europe in winter. Length 28cm (11in).

Below left: A water rail in winter. The birds clearly suffer in cold weather: they lose weight and are easier to see since they are forced to come out of seclusion to feed. Their normal diet is extremely varied, including almost any small aquatic animals from insects to fish, as well as plant roots, tubers, seeds and berries. In cold weather they venture on to stubble in search of grain, and also turn predator—reed buntings, chaffinches and wrens may come within reach of a swift dash and stab of the water rail's long beak.

Below: Looking for a nest site. As would be expected, the nest is a secluded affair deep in the vegetation, and often further concealed by being placed in the heart of a tussock of dead grass, sedge or reed. The vegetation meets in a 'roof' over the deep nest cup. Breeding begins early, with first clutches often laid at the start of April. Clutch sizes range normally from about 6 to 11 eggs; there may be two broods a year.

what food they are able to discover.

A first glimpse of this secretive bird gives the impression of a rather tall, brown moorhen. Part of this impression comes from the tail, which is up-cocked (in 'giant wren' fashion) just like a moorhen's, and which presents a bold patch of white undertail coverts to the observing eye as the tail is regularly flicked—again, like a moorhen's tail.

Unlike a moorhen, however, the water rail has a rich brown back, all the feathers having darker centres and thus giving a streaked appearance. In the adult the face, throat and belly are a pure lead-grey, a colour otherwise seen only on the breast of the dunnock among British and Irish birds. In immature water rails, and sometimes in winter adults, this grey is blotchy, with alternating pale and dark bands. The flanks carry conspicuous vertical bars of black and white that are slightly curved. The beak, considerably longer than that of the moorhen, is also slimmer and slightly down-curved. It is blood-red, with varying degrees of brown or black towards the tip.

The legs are long—hence the appearance of height—and pinkish-brown, ending in a short hind toe and three immensely long front toes. With these feet, water rails can cross soft mud and floating vegetation, and swim surprisingly well with them, too.

A marshland bird The most startling feature of a water rail is how easily it vanishes into nearby vegetation. Even if this consists of densely packed reed stems, the water rail walks straight in, without a pause, like the fabled ghost walking through a wall. A close head-on view shows the origin of this ability, as the water rail is 'compressed laterally' or flattened from side to side—a case of adaptive evolution to the habitat.

For such a skulking bird, the water rail has an extremely raucous voice and an unusually distinctive, though certainly not attractive, range of loud calls. The commonest call and, once you know it, one of the easiest ways of locating water rails, starts off like the grunting of a pig and ends in a horrific series of squeals as if that pig were being slaughtered. Other calls include a staccato 'kek-kek-kek' which may be repeated monotonously for long into the spring evening, interspersed with occasional whinnying trills that resemble those of the dabchick.

From its name, and from the structural adaptation already described, it is clear that

the water rail is a bird of densely vegetated marshland, extensive reedbeds and swamps. It is quite tolerant of brackish-water habitats such as the reed-fringed dykes of coastal marshes. Occasional pairs breed on overgrown ponds or beside meandering streams, and outside the breeding season water rails may be seen on sewage farms and watercress beds–locations where they would not normally nest.

These wetland habitats are among the most threatened parts of today's countryside. The extensive drainage, not just of marshes and fens, but also of millions of acres of sedge-covered swampy fields in the process of land 'improvement' for farming, must by now have reduced water rail numbers considerably. Certainly this reduction must be far more than has been compensated for by modern man-made wetland 'replacements' such as overgrown disused canals or gravel pits.

Intrepid flight Water rails seem so suited to life on the ground, or for occasional sorties on the water, that it comes as no surprise to see how small their wings are, nor to watch their fluttering, feeble flight, legs trailing, low over the water.

Therefore it is a surprise to discover, from the results of ringing, that the water rails on the Continent are migrants, and often long-range migrants at that. There is as yet little evidence to show whether or not British and Irish breeding birds regularly migrate, but there are now dozens of ringing recoveries showing a marked westerly or south-westerly migration of water rails from the Continent to Britain in autumn. In spring, water rails ringed in Britain during the winter are seen migrating eastwards and south-eastwards to the Continent. Some have been reported from as far afield as Sweden, Poland and Czechoslovakia.

Above: The young hatch after three weeks of incubation by both parents. They look like tiny balls of black fluffy down, alert as soon as they are dry. They are tended at the nest by both parents for the first few days, but then venture farther afield in the company of one or other parent. Here the parent has found a food item to offer to the chick.

Migration mystery The fact that the birds fly south-east in spring, rather than north-east, is intriguing and difficult to explain. As a reverse of the autumn arrivals, one might reasonably expect to see the Continental water rails returning north-east and east towards Scandinavia and north Germany. Yet these mysterious ringing results are completely endorsed by accounts of birds seen at the bird observatories along the east coast: the northerly observatories all report peak numbers in autumn, while the southerly ones (particularly Dungeness in Kent) show a pronounced spring peak.

A risky life Ringing results also show a relatively short life-span for a bird of this size, for the average post-fledging survival time is about 20 months. Considering their sheltered existence and their versatility as feeders, post-fledging (and probably pre-fledging) mortality appears to be surprisingly high; this is reflected in their apparent fecundity at the egg-producing stage, which can be seen as an evolutionary response to the high mortality. Known causes of death are, as usual, varied, including a high proportion killed by predators, and the toll taken by frost and ice in winter. Among man-made hazards are overhead electric power lines.

Many birds caught for ringing are also weighed, and the water rail proves remarkable at all times of year for its extreme variability in weight. The maximum weight recorded in a recent study was 190gm (6½oz), the minimum only 63gm (2½oz). The latter was during hard weather, but otherwise it is difficult to pinpoint any single cause for such interesting variability.

FAR-AWAY PHALAROPES

Phalaropes are rare birds with the unusual distinction of having reversed sexual roles: the females are brightly coloured, and the duller males hatch and raise the young.

There are three species of phalarope: the red-necked, the grey, and Wilson's phalarope. Although they are classified as waders, these birds spend much of their time swimming. They have wide lobes on their toes, as do grebes and the coot, and it is these that make them such efficient swimmers. Two of the species (the red-necked and the grey) spend the whole of the winter far out in tropical oceans—an astonishing feat for such delicate-looking birds.

Birds of the island fringe Of the three species of phalarope only one, the red-necked phalarope, breeds in Britain and Ireland, and even this has only a slender foothold, with perhaps 20 pairs breeding each year. However, this is not surprising since, in both the Old and the New World, they prefer to breed in the treeless tundra zone, between latitudes 60° and 70° north. Thus mainland Britain is well to the south of their main breeding range; only the Shetland Isles are sufficiently far north. Despite this, red-necked phalaropes also breed on the Orkneys, Hebrides and on the west coast of Ireland. They are loyal to traditional breeding colonies, but several colonies, after an existence of many years, are now in danger of extinction. Indeed, there was once a colony in Ireland with 50 pairs or more, but fewer and fewer phalaropes returned each year until, in 1972, no pairs bred there at all.

Efficient breeding The most remarkable

Above: A male red-necked phalarope incubating. It is less conspicuous than the female, whose red plumage extends down the neck.

Red-necked phalarope (*Phalaropus lobatus*); summer visitor; female 20cm (8in), male smaller.

Grey phalarope (*Phalaropus fulicarius*); migrant; female 20cm (8in), male smaller.

Wilson's phalarope (*P. tricolor*); accidental; female 23cm (9in), male smaller.

characteristic of all species of phalaropes is the way they divide nesting duties between male and female—for they are among the tiny minority of birds with reversed sexual roles. In most species of birds, the male sings and displays in order to claim and defend a territory and attract a mate; often he takes only a minor part in nest-building, incubation and caring for the young. He is more aggressive and has more striking plumage than his mate.

The female phalarope, on the other hand, is larger and more brightly coloured than the male; she sings and displays, lays the eggs and then leaves incubation and caring for the chicks entirely to her mate. The male, in keeping with his more secretive role, has dull, well-camouflaged plumage.

The phalarope's breeding system is a beneficial adaptation, enabling each pair to raise the maximum possible number of young each year. At their Arctic and sub-Arctic breeding grounds, the summer is short and cool: speed and economy of reproduction is essential. For the adults, egg-laying and incubation are the most difficult, energy-sapping tasks (the chicks are largely self-sufficient). Many waders share the incubation thus reducing the burden on the female's meagre reserves, but the phalarope's method, where only the male incubates, allows the female to recoup her lost energy reserves unhindered, often gathering with others on nearby pools. The only other British bird to

Summer plumage

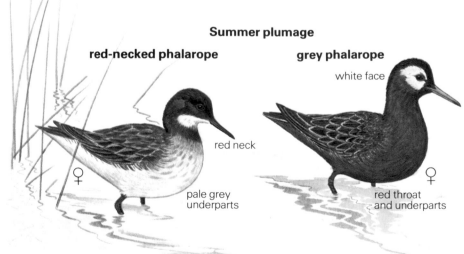

red-necked phalarope

grey phalarope

white face

red neck

pale grey underparts

red throat and underparts

adopt this strategy is another wader, the dotterel, which breeds on high mountain tops in Scotland.

Nesting in marshes Red-necked phalaropes are among our latest spring migrants. The earliest birds, usually females eager to claim the best territories, arrive in mid-May–a time when some of our resident lowland waders already have their first brood of chicks–while the latest may not appear until mid-June.

They have a variety of calls, of which the most distinctive is the female's trilling 'chip, chip, chip, chip', uttered during her display flight. Her plumage is decorative: white throat and underparts, slate-grey head and upperparts, and a bright orange-red stripe down the side of her neck, from which the name of the species derives. Both wings and back have buff-coloured markings forming, in a rear view, a double V shape. The male is browner and duller and his red neck-stripe is less extensive.

Wet, marshy areas with scattered, reedy pools, often only a few metres wide, provide ideal habitats for breeding phalaropes; they feed on the pools and nest among nearby tussocky grass. Some use bays and inlets of large inland or seaside lochs.

Both sexes scrape nesting hollows in suitable well-hidden spots, and in one of these the female lays her eggs–usually four in number. Like those of many ground-nesting

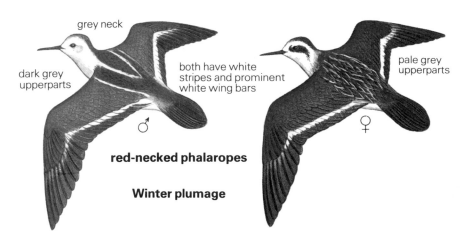

grey neck

dark grey upperparts

both have white stripes and prominent white wing bars

pale grey upperparts

♂

red-necked phalaropes

Winter plumage

♀

red-necked phalarope distribution

Left: The grey phalarope breeds in the Arctic zone, in Siberia, North America and on some north European islands. It is sometimes seen in Britain, on passage to its summer haunts in the tropical Atlantic. Wilson's phalarope, the third species, breeds only in North America, and a mere handful are seen in this country in autumn, blown off course across the Atlantic.

Below: A pair of red-necked phalaropes–the female is on the right.

birds, their eggs are well camouflaged, being buffish and irregularly blotched with brown.

Phalaropes are sometimes polyandrous–that is, the female (since she is freed from further parental duties) is sometimes able to find a second mate. By making a second nest, often only a short distance from the first, and laying a second clutch, she can double the number of her offspring without spending any more time in the breeding grounds.

The phalarope chicks hatch after about 20 days. Their first coat of down provides marvellous camouflage, as it is striped and mottled with various shades of yellow, brown, black and white.

And so to sea With the arrival of autumn, phalaropes leave the icy waters of the north to head south, and many pass along our coasts. A combination of their slim build, needle-fine bill, swimming habit and a conspicuous black mark through the eye is sufficient to distinguish them from other waders. At a distance and in flight, they have a noticeably white head and a large white wing bar.

The wintering range of our phalaropes is poorly known; much of their time is spent out of sight of land. However, red-necked phalaropes are seen in the tropical regions of all three southern oceans–the Indian, Pacific and Atlantic–and our birds probably winter off the coast of West Africa, 8000km (5000 miles) south of Scotland.

Spinning on the water In their remote breeding areas, as well as out at sea during winter, phalaropes do not normally come into contact with people, and perhaps as a result of this they are surprisingly tame: they allow very close approach without showing any sign of concern.

Occasionally they feed on land, trotting over seaweed washed up by the tide, for example; but they prefer to wade–or, better still, swim. They have the amusing habit of swimming in tight circles, or even spinning like a top, creating a little whirlpool which stirs up the water and underlying sediments, and brings food to the surface. As well as insects, they eat tiny snails and worms, and a variety of marine organisms.

167

SNIPE: LONG-BILLED WADERS

Snipe, noticeable for their long, straight bills, are small wading birds most often seen in inland marshy areas, damp meadows and river valleys.

The two species of snipe regularly seen in the British Isles are both birds of rank vegetation in damp, fresh-water areas. Both birds have richly mottled and striped brown body plumage, with characteristic creamy stripes along each side of the back. The jack snipe is known only as a winter visitor and is the smaller of the two species, with a shorter beak. The common snipe is a widespread breeding species, and its numbers are augmented during winter by an influx of larger birds from the rest of Europe; it has a very long bill.

Common snipe breed in damp meadows, river valleys, coastal fresh-water marshes, bogs, and over damp moorland throughout the British Isles. They are thinly scattered in the more populated areas of south-eastern England but become increasingly common in western and northern Britain. There are particularly large breeding populations in the boglands of central Ireland, over much of the Highlands of Scotland and on many Scottish islands, especially the remote St Kilda group. The birds are quite small – roughly the size of a starling, but look much longer as they have 6cm (2½in) long bills.

'Drumming' flight It is easy to discover that common snipe are holding territory, as the birds have a conspicuous aerial display called 'drumming'. The displaying bird flies above its territory, periodically swooping down with its outer tail feathers pushed

Above: The jack snipe is a winter visitor that breeds in the north-eastern parts of Europe and western Siberia. It is smaller than the common snipe but less shy; if approached it does not fly away until the last possible moment.

Jack snipe
(*Lymnocryptes minimus*), 19cm (7½in) from beak to tail. Shorter bill and rounder wings than common snipe and no white on tail. Sept-April visitor.

Common snipe
(*Gallinago gallinago*), 27cm (10½in) from beak to tail. Very long bill. Resident.

Above: Common snipe feeding in marshland – their typical habitat. You usually see them in groups, probing with their exceptionally long bills for worms and other food. They also take insects from the surface.

out into the passing airstream. The feathers are strengthened and stiff so that they whirr as the air passes them, causing the 'drumming' sound. In fact, to most people the sound is not so much a drumming noise as a bleat, sounding rather like a goat. Such displaying birds also utter a 'chippering' note.

These noisy displays may take place at any time of day but are most usual early in the morning or during the evening; some birds display at night as well if there is a bright moon. There is another territorial call, generally given from an elevated perch such as a fence post or tree stump, and this is a sharp, loud 'tock'.

Territorial displays may take place as

Left: When flushed out of the vegetation in which it hides, the common snipe twists as it rises steeply away, but the jack snipe flies slowly in a broad loop and usually for a shorter distance.

early as February in southern England – at least a good two months earlier than the displays of the birds living in the Highlands and Islands of northern Scotland. The snipe makes its well-concealed nest on the ground. The chicks are most attractive, with striking markings. They are able to fly after 18-20 days but, like all waders, they leave their nest within a few hours of hatching. In some areas two broods may be reared, but most pairs are thought to be single brooded.

Long sensitive bills The common snipe's long bill is used to obtain food from deep in the ground. It is a precise and sensitive tool and a bird can insert the whole length of the bill into soft ground and still open the tip to take worms or other food. Snipe take food items from the surface as well.

When the marshy areas where snipe normally feed freeze rock hard, they are adept at finding areas which have not frozen, such as where a spring has kept the ground open. Here they may congregate in large numbers. Flocks of snipe, known as wisps, flushed out from the marshes by shooting parties, usually number fewer than 10 birds, but in freezing weather favoured areas might provide flocks of 50-100 birds. If frosts persist native birds may be forced to move to warmer places.

The jack snipe is much rarer than the common snipe and is a native breeding species of the north-easternmost parts of Europe and western Siberia. The wintering birds reach the British Isles in October and leave again in March or early April. The birds are superficially similar to common snipe, but their bills are shorter and they are, overall, about two-thirds the size of the common snipe. Their choice of habitat is much the same, but they allow a closer approach, and when they fly off they do not

Common snipe

twisting flight

Jack snipe

short hopping flight

very long bill with sensitive tip

Common snipe

Jack snipe

usually call or 'jink' in flight. Indeed, they often pitch again within a few dozen yards. They are quite often found along the edges of paths or ditches in marshy areas, and may sometimes be in small flocks – especially shortly after they have just arrived in autumn on the east coast.

The great snipe is the only other snipe found regularly in the British Isles. A handful is recorded each winter as visitors from the breeding areas of north-east Europe. They are difficult to distinguish from the common snipe, although they are actually plumper and show more white on their tails in flight. The great snipe is the long-distance migrant record holder for the group. Many are recorded in Africa in winter.

Fair game All snipe are liable to be shot during autumn and winter, both in the British Isles and in other European countries. Game species such as pheasants and grouse are shot in a highly organised fashion, but most snipe are shot by people walking through marshland, accompanied by dogs. The birds are disturbed as they rise and jink away. They

Above: The superbly marked fluffy snipe chicks leave their nest just a few hours after hatching. Their basic ground colour is a dark, rich chestnut, spangled with gold and silver markings.

Right: The nest is usually made within a grassy tussock in freshwater marshy surroundings, and four eggs are laid. Like those of most wading birds, the eggs are pointed, with dark blotches on an olive backgroud. They are incubated by the female alone for about 20 days.

Below: A parent snipe guards a newly hatched chick. Most pairs of snipe rear only one brood a year, though some may manage two.

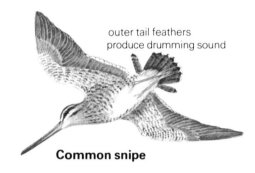

outer tail feathers produce drumming sound

Common snipe

cambered outer tail feather
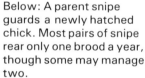

are always difficult to kill, and at present there is no evidence that the population is suffering through shooting. Indeed, there are records of much more intense shooting pressures in the past than now. Drumming birds are, of course, safe from being shot as they display only during the close season, which starts at the beginning of February and lasts until 11 August.

However, it is not possible to be complacent about these birds and their chances in the future as their habitats are under increasing pressure. In southern Britain areas of marshland are being drained and taken into arable agriculture, and many of the smaller field ponds that in the past provided shelter and food for one or two birds during winter have been filled in. Old-fashioned sewage farms, with their large settling ponds with muddy margins, have been replaced by systems with little, if any, chance for snipe to feed. As fresh-water wetlands are drained, what are now commonplace birds could become rare over the span of just a few decades.

REED AND LAPLAND BUNTINGS

The reed and Lapland buntings are found over much of Europe and northern and eastern Asia. The reed bunting is a well established resident in Britain and Ireland, while the Lapland bunting only recently began tentative breeding in Scotland.

Above: A female reed bunting broods the young. The nestlings' diet consists mostly of insects; the young birds leave the nest once they become capable of flight, some 12 days after hatching.

Buntings tend to be unfairly neglected by many birdwatchers. Two superficially similar species are the reed and Lapland buntings. The former is a common resident throughout Britain and Ireland, while the Lapland bunting is a scarce winter visitor and passage migrant to the east coast and, in an exciting new development, a recent colonist in some Scottish hills. Both are sparrow-sized birds, their thick bills signifying their seed-eating habits. In both species the male has a black head in the breeding season which is at least partly concealed in winter and is completely lacking, in all seasons, from the female. In all plumages, both sexes show conspicuous white outer tail feathers.

Reed bunting The reed bunting, the more familiar of the two species, can be found in almost any marshland area in lowland Britain, but is rather scarcer in upland areas. In spring and summer the male sports a pure black head and bib, separated by a white moustachial stripe; and it has a more or less complete white collar round the back of the neck. The underparts are pale, almost white, with some streaking on the flanks. The back and wing coverts have rich dark brown mottling and striping, sometimes almost black. The female is never a striking bird, although she has a pale stripe over the eye and a faint moustachial stripe too.

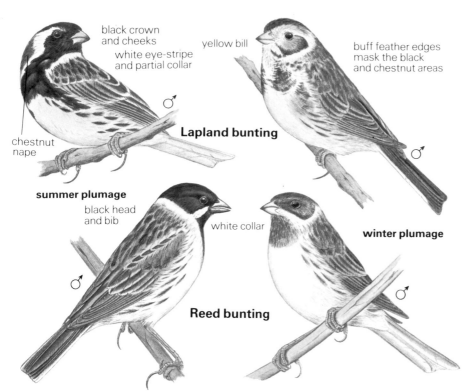

black crown and cheeks

white eye-stripe and partial collar

chestnut nape

Lapland bunting

yellow bill

buff feather edges mask the black and chestnut areas

♂

summer plumage

♂

black head and bib

white collar

Reed bunting

winter plumage

♂

Reed bunting (*Emberiza schoeniclus*); resident bird of reed-beds and swamps, roaming farmland in winter. Length 15cm (6in).

Lapland bunting (*Calcarius lapponicus*); scarce winter visitor and vagrant in coastal farmland, moors and saltings; a few pairs breed in Scotland. 15cm (6in).

Below: A female Lapland bunting incubating. The clutch of four, five or six pale but reddish-spotted eggs hatch after some 14 days, and the young are fed on the rich variety of insects found in the Arctic summer. They leave the nest within eight to ten days, while still unable to fly.

Nest building The pairs come together on the breeding territory in April and eggs may be found from late in that month through to early July, with two broods (possibly sometimes three) being reared.

The nest is generally sited on or near the ground in a tuft of grass or among a thicket of brambles, reeds or sedges. Some nests have been found up to 3m (10ft) high, but these are exceptional. The female does most if not all of the building, using a variety of grasses to make the rather untidy nest; this is always delicately lined with the finest of grasses, horsehair and occasionally 'pappus' (fluffy hairs) from the seeds of reeds or poplars. The normal clutch is four or five eggs; these show a brown-olive ground colour with dark streaks and spots superimposed.

Local pockets The marshes and reedbeds where they breed are productive areas, and the reed buntings may be thick on the ground. In one location on the overgrown fringes of a series of mature gravel pits, the average territory occupied less than half a hectare (about an acre) of land and emergent vegetation. However, other studies in mixed farmland have shown a density of about one pair per 25 hectares (60 acres), with large areas completely devoid of the species and small pockets, coinciding with ideally suitable habitat, of much denser populations. Over the last 25 years or more the reed bunting, in Britain, has steadily colonized new areas and can now be found in a much wider variety of habitats than formerly. Pairs now breed in tangled vegetation in totally dry habitats—for example chalkland scrub and even in the middle of cereal growing districts, nesting in the crops where an adjacent hedge or fence gives the males the possibility of songposts for territorial advertisement.

Moving in flocks Although the reed buntings are with us throughout the year, there is quite a lot of local movement at different times of the year. After the breeding season fairly large flocks of locally bred young birds may be formed, exploiting abundant autumn food supplies of freshly matured seeds. Later in October and November, after some of these food resources have been used up, the birds tend to move from site to site and reed buntings may be found flocking with finches and other buntings along hedgerows or in flocks feeding in fields. Often the reed buntings continue to roost in reedbeds, preferably over water so that they have additional protection from predators. One characteristic is that when the weather becomes particularly severe they are often found visiting gardens and seeking food at bird feeding stations. However, once the weather improves, they are no longer seen in these places.

Bird ringing has shown that during the winter and early spring the population of reed buntings in a given locality may be very transient: roosts that have room for 100 birds at most on any one evening may be used by 300 individuals passing through during the course of six or eight weeks. Often the females form the majority among these roving birds, for the males do not move so far; it seems likely that they remain in the vicinity of the breeding territories in order to be able to reclaim them as soon as the weather becomes warmer in spring.

Arctic replacement The reed bunting is, in world terms, a very widespread bird. Our populations in Britain and Ireland are on the species' western flank, and the same species can be found over almost all of the rest of Europe and across Asia to northern Japan and Kamchatka in the USSR. In some areas the birds are highly migratory—as, for example, in Arctic Scandinavia—and some birds from Norway reach the east coast of Britain during the winter. This is a feature the species has in common with the much rarer Lapland bunting. This species is very much a high Arctic replacement for the reed bunting and

during the breeding season it is found all
round the North Pole with populations in
Greenland and over the whole of Arctic
Canada to Alaska.

The male Lapland bunting looks similar to
the male reed bunting but has a striking chestnut nape. One of the easiest ways to identify
it is from the cheerful 'turrit' or 'tick, tick,
iew' calls, which are reminiscent of the calls
of skylarks or even turnstones. They are most
often seen in small flocks on coastal marshland, and may even be found in the company
of snow buntings.

Nesting in tundra In spring the Lapland
buntings migrate to the open tundra of northern Europe, where the males begin to sing and
display. The tundra seldom has suitable song
posts and so, unlike reed buntings, they utter
their song in circling flight after the manner of
the skylark.

Since the Arctic summer is so short, only a
single brood can be raised and all populations
are migratory, for the breeding areas would
be untenable during the winter. Apart from
those that reach Britain, other birds may be
found in the Netherlands and north Germany
and across southern Europe and Russia to
the coasts of the China Sea. The autumn
passage starts in September, but it seems that
many of the migrants wintering in Britain
start their return to the breeding grounds
quite early in spring. By the middle of March,
many of their traditional haunts are devoid of
the species.

The Scottish pairs The recent records of
breeding in Scotland have been most exciting.
In 1974 a pair was found and may have bred;
but proof, in the form of a male with two
females and two successful nests, came in
1977. Besides this proven case, up to 14 other
pairs of Lapland buntings at five other sites
may have bred. During the next two years up

to five sites were occupied, and 13 pairs were
proved to have bred. More records of polygamous males (with more than one mate)
were reported, including one considered to
have four females. During the 1980s evidence
of breeding pairs became increasingly scarce
and the species can no longer be described as a
regular breeder in the British Isles.

Climatic change This new colonization was
not a total surprise, for a wide range of northern species have colonized northern Britain in
recent years as a result of longterm climatic
trends. The best examples are the goldeneye,
sanderling and purple sandpiper; a particularly spectacular but less successful example
is the snowy owl, which bred here for nine
years from 1967-75 but not since then.

Apart from the snowy owl, these northern
colonizers are not particularly eye-catching,
and their breeding attempts have not, in most
cases, been disturbed by birdwatchers or anyone else.

Above: The male reed
bunting's song is rather
monotonous: although
males vary in the choice of
phrase they sing, each tends
to repeat his one phrase
interminably. One of the
most usual consists of three
single phrases and a terminal
flourish: 'tsik, tsik tsik,
tsissisik'. The singing bird
defends quite a small
territory and is very
conservative in his choice of
song-posts. These may, in
the middle of a marsh, be no
more than prominent
tussocks of grass, but
elsewhere posts, bushes or
trees may be used. He
returns regularly to each of
his posts, and local
birdwatchers can easily learn
exactly where to find him.

Right: A male Lapland
bunting brings food to his
chicks. This nest is
situated in moorland
vegetation that is typical
of the Arctic tundra, as
well as the mountainous
habitat of the few Scottish
breeding pairs. The male
looks quite like the male
reed bunting, but has a
striking chestnut nape to
his neck and is darker on
the breast and flanks. He
lacks the reed bunting's
moustachial stripe, but has
pale buff stripe from the
nape to above the eye. The
female has a residual
partial chestnut patch on
the nape of the neck, though
this is not easy to see.
Juveniles, like the one being
fed here, have lighter
plumage and a light stripe
across the crown from front
to back.

A TRIO OF WETLAND WARBLERS

Three small songbirds that live in our waterside habitats in summer are the reed, marsh and sedge warblers, welcome visitors which come to breed in Britain each year.

Warblers are a large, world-wide family of insect-eating birds, most of which migrate south to Africa in autumn, returning in spring to breed. During their few months in this country, most British warblers are inconspicuous, tending to stay hidden within trees and bushes–one reason why many people are not familiar with them. There are three main groups in this country–'leaf', 'bush' and 'reed-bed' warblers; the reed, marsh and sedge warblers belong to the last of these groups.

The 'reed-bed' warblers have a characteristic shape and appear to be pointed at both ends. At one end the fine, relatively long bill merges smoothly with the head. At the other, the graduated tail with shorter outer feathers is supported by unusually long tail coverts (the small feathers that lie above and below the tail). In colour the birds are generally sandy brown above and creamy white below.

Broadly speaking, the group contains streaked and unstreaked species. Sedge warblers, with contrasting colours on the head, back and wings, are streaked. Reed and marsh warblers are typical of the unstreaked category, although both have a pale, indistinct stripe above the eye. These two species are so similar that they can only be safely distinguished by the colour of their plumage if a very good view is obtained.

Adult marsh warblers have more olive upper parts, while reed warblers tend to be more rusty in colour. Ornithologists have to catch the young birds before they can positively identify them, and even then some are indistinguishable.

Habitat Reed-bed warblers tend to stay within thick cover. When they fly they rarely cover much distance, although their wings flap rapidly, before diving back into the vegetation. Consequently even sedge warblers may not be easy to identify. Often the habitat is of little help since there is considerable overlap and all three species may

left: The sedge warbler can be identified by the creamy stripe with a dark outline above the eye; its wing feathers have pale edges. The nest is cup-shaped and rather bulky, and attached to supporting reed stems.

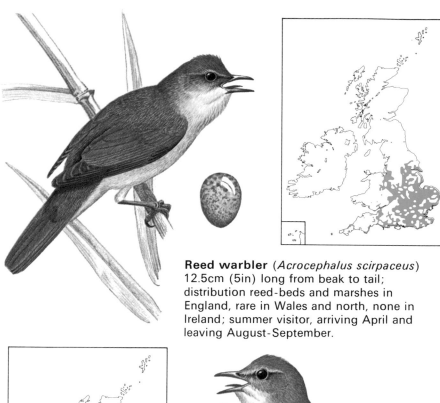

Reed warbler (*Acrocephalus scirpaceus*) 12.5cm (5in) long from beak to tail; distribution reed-beds and marshes in England, rare in Wales and north, none in Ireland; summer visitor, arriving April and leaving August-September.

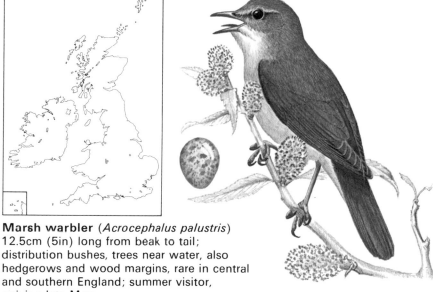

Marsh warbler (*Acrocephalus palustris*) 12.5cm (5in) long from beak to tail; distribution bushes, trees near water, also hedgerows and wood margins, rare in central and southern England; summer visitor, arriving late May.

Sedge warbler (*Acrocephalus schoenobaenus*) 13cm (5¼in) long from beak to tail; distribution widespread in waterside habitats, bushes, hedgerows and crop fields throughout British Isles; summer visitor, arriving early April.

In general, reed-bed warblers sing in a rather unpunctuated manner with repetitive 'chirruping' and 'chirring' for several seconds at a time. These phrases are interspersed to a variable extent with more musical notes. At one extreme, the reed warbler often chatters slowly and methodically, repeating each phrase two or three times in succession with little more than regular changes of pitch for variety. Sedge warblers are less repetitive and frequently utter high-pitched trills and clear musical phrases in their rather hurried delivery.

Both birds will imitate the songs and calls of other species, which can give rise to confusion with the marsh warbler that has, without doubt, the most musical and varied song. Its rich and diverse warblings often give the impression that a variety of birds are all singing within the same bush, for its ability to mimic others is quite remarkable. Over 50 species may be imitated, although any single bird will have a much smaller repertoire. Other calls, often scolding 'chirrs' and 'rattles', are uttered when danger threatens, for example when someone approaches the nest.

Breeding The nests of reed warblers are often supported by two or three vertical reed stems, and the female does the bulk of the building. The nest is particularly deep cupped, and cylindrical to ensure that egg and nestlings do not fall out when strong winds cause the reeds to sway. Many build nests low down over the water where wind is not a problem. Marsh warbler nests are similar in construction but sited in dense vegetation such as nettles, while sedge warblers build nests low down in deep cover.

Sedge warblers lay six or seven eggs, while broods of five or six are quite common among their unstreaked relatives. The eggs of the

nest together.

Perhaps reed warblers are the most aptly named, since they are frequently found among stands of common reeds, close to water. Their ability to cling to vertical reed stems is obvious as they slide up and down, one foot always higher than the other. Sedge warblers are less dependent on water and inhabit overgrown hedges and marshy ground with bushes and ditches, as well as reed-beds. Marsh warblers require vigorous undergrowth of plants such as nettle, willowherb and meadowsweet, although they will also inhabit reedy places with bushes. All three are found in colonies in a suitable habitat; the edges of lakes and flooded gravel pits are favoured.

Migration All three species leave Britain in August or September to winter in Africa, choosing the risks of long-distance migration rather than the high probability of acute food shortage in Britain. While there, they moult all their feathers, even though the body feathers were replaced before the autumn migration. When they return, the earliest arrivals – in April – are always sedge warblers, followed by reed warblers about a fortnight later, although some individuals of both species do not arrive at their breeding sites until late May or even June. Marsh warblers, one of our latest migrants, are rarely recorded before late May, although most arrive before mid-June.

Above: A marsh warbler feeds his mate on the nest they have woven together; the nest is attached to the reeds with a kind of basket weave. Unlike reed warblers, these birds rarely build over water.

Song-flight
Of the three species only the sedge warbler (left) has a true song-flight. Singing boldly, the bird flutters up for a metre or so before parachuting down again. More usually the song is delivered from the cover of vegetation or in the sedge from an exposed perch, particularly by marsh warblers. Reed and sedge warblers often also sing at night.

sedge warbler are generally mottled brown, quite different from the off-white, brown-blotched eggs of the reed and marsh warblers. Also, incubation is chiefly by the female sedge warbler, while both parents of the other species share this duty. When parents are feeding young, both sexes can be seen flying to and fro over the reeds, each carrying beakfuls of food. It takes a full month to lay and incubate the eggs and then rear the nestlings.

After leaving the nest, the young birds rely on their parents for food for a while. Marsh warblers, many of which leave the country by mid-August, have insufficient time to rear two broods. Early arriving sedge warblers, and reed warblers in southern England, do produce a second brood.

Diet The breeding birds collect much of their food outside the defended territory, but marsh-haunting and aquatic insects and their larvae form the bulk of the diet. The birds do take other animal foods, such as spiders, worms and slugs, and in autumn some berries are eaten. Reed-dwelling aphids are known to be important before migration. At this time some sedge warblers double their weight in southern England; the extra fat provides the energy needed for the long flight south.

Distribution One striking difference between the three species is their distribution within the British Isles. Sedge warblers occur in every county and are common even in

Above: The reed warbler, similar in appearance to the marsh warbler, does not have the conspicuous marking of the sedge warbler. It is pale brown above and buff white below. Male and female reed warblers have the same colouring so are difficult to tell apart.

Left: The female reed warbler builds a deep, cup-shaped nest among common reeds. The sides are woven round the reed stems. Here it is feeding time for the chicks.

northern Scotland and western Ireland, where most other warblers are scarce. Only in upland areas and in Shetland are they thin on the ground. In contrast, the reed warbler is confined largely to the south and east of England and Wales, with perhaps a tenth as many breeding pairs. Sadly the best songster, the marsh warbler, is rare.

While shortage of habitat may be partly responsible for these differences, a study of the European distributions is revealing. Sedge warblers, for example, occur farther north than all European warblers except the willow and arctic, and therefore might be expected to be common throughout the British Isles. Reed warblers have a more southerly range and seem to need warm, dry summers, which prevents colonization of the north and west, even where suitable habitats appear to exist.

British-breeding marsh warblers are on the extreme western fringe of their range and, unless the European population extends westwards, our population is unlikely to increase significantly.

BEARDED TITS: REED DWELLERS

Britain's population of the bearded tit is small, with some 600 pairs; but it is resilient, recovering from near extinction after the winter of 1946-47.

Above: A male bearded tit, with the 'beard' to which its name refers. This would more aptly be described as a black moustache, which begins between the eye and beak and extends to the sides of the throat. His head is lilac-blue, and he has a bright yellow bill.

Below: The female has a brown head and bill, and lacks the black moustache. The bill colour helps to tell the sexes apart, even at the nestling stage.

The bearded tit is instantly detected in its reed-bed habitat by the sound of its sharp, pinging call. Despite its common name, it is not a tit at all and many ornithologists prefer the old country name, the bearded reedling. Its nearest relatives are a group of birds known as parrotbills, which occur mainly in China.

This attractive bird breeds in the reed-beds of eastern and southern England and is rarely seen outside these sites. Like many small birds, the bearded tit is severely affected by hard winters such as in 1946-47. Indeed, after that winter the British population was reduced from some hundreds of pairs to only about half a dozen pairs in Suffolk and Norfolk. In earlier times it suffered an additional hardship, for it used to be an irresistible target for the Victorian fowler's gun—not to be eaten, but simply to be stuffed and mounted as ornament. Later it became popular as a cage bird, and this is still true today. However, since 1954 it has been protected under law and courts can impose heavy fines on anyone caught and convicted of molesting this bird.

Alternating diet One of the most remarkable features of the bearded tit concerns its diet. During the summer, like so many other small birds, it lives mainly on insects and other small invertebrates. Most other birds which feed in this manner migrate to warmer countries during the winter and hence continue to find similar food. The bearded tit stays in its breeding grounds or occupies another reed-bed, and adapts its way of life to feed on seeds—primarily those of the common reed. Such a change in diet involves a radical change in the digestive system: the bearded tit's stomach, in converting itself to the seed-eating way of life, swells to twice its summer size. This far-reaching adaptation takes place over a short period in the autumn, when days are shortening, and is reversed during the lengthening days of spring.

Populations of bearded tits can survive the cold weather of winter provided they can still find the seeds of the reed. If there is heavy snow they may find sufficient seeds in among the reeds where the snow layer is held off the ground by the vegetation. However, if the weather is very severe the reed-heads themselves can be encased in ice; then the birds may well starve. This is thought to be the reason why the winter of 1946-47 did so much more harm to bearded tits than the winter of 1962-63. In the former, glazed frosts were more prevalent and coated the reed-heads in ice, but this was not so widespread in 1962-63.

Recovery from disaster The bearded tit has a remarkable ability to recover from losses after bad winters. Breeding begins as early as April in good years, and pairs can rear up to three or even four broods in one season. Each clutch, laid in a nest deep in the reed-bed, may have six eggs and so the population will quickly multiply if conditions are good. It is thought

that the young birds of the year may help their parents (or neighbours) to raise later broods by bringing food.

Change in behaviour At times when their numbers are fairly small, bearded tits remain in the area of their particular reed-bed. But when their numbers increase beyond the capacity of the reed-bed, they cease to be sedentary and set off to explore the country-side in travelling flocks, looking for sites in which to start new colonies. This was observed in the British Isles in 1965 and subsequent years: despite their potential for quick population growth, their numbers had been so badly reduced in 1947 that it took some 18 years for them to outgrow their established colonies in the reed-beds of East Anglia. Observers in the autumn of these years in the mid-1960s noticed excited parties of bearded tits flying back and forth over the reed-beds, calling continually. It soon became clear that the birds were preparing to move out of their breeding grounds, at least for the winter. By ringing individual birds, it was shown that they travelled in their newly formed flocks for distances up to several hundred kilometres. Some subsequently returned to their native areas, while others established new colonies all over England, as well as in Wales and even, in recent years, in Ireland.

This behavioural change was also seen in the Netherlands, where a population of some 700-1400 pairs of bearded tits is resident.

Left: A male pauses on a reed stem before returning to his nest with a beak full of food. Also seen here is the long tail, which is made up of finely graduated feathers—shortest on the outside, longest in the middle. The closest resemblance in British birds is to the long-tailed tit.

Bearded tit or **bearded reedling** (*Panurus biarmicus*). Resident in reed-beds. Length 17cm (6½in).

Bearded tit distribution

Birds of the reed-bed

Beds of the common reed (*Phragmites communis*) have always attracted birdwatchers, as they hold so many interesting birds–small ones such as the reed warblers in even the smallest reed-beds, and others such as the bittern or marsh harrier in larger beds. Each species has its own favoured nest site within this habitat. Those of the bittern and marsh harrier are made on the ground at the bases of reeds, often at the water's edge. The nests of the water rail and reed bunting are also on the ground but within the tangle of vegetation of the reed-bed. The bearded tit's nest is usually constructed low in the thicker parts of the reed-bed while the deep cup-shaped nest of the reed warbler is set quite high in the reed stems. Reed-beds, however, are a constantly changing habitat: if left undisturbed, they take only a few years to fill in and become dry land. To maintain the richness of bird life, the reed-beds need constant cycles of partial cutting and removal of reeds.

1 Marsh harrier	4 Bearded tit
2 Reed warbler	5 Water rail
3 Bittern	6 Reed bunting

Mammals of lake, pond and marsh

Water is not generally a natural habitat for mammals – various special adaptations, such as waterproof fur or webbed feet for swimming, are necessary if they are to exist for the greater part of their lives in water. Seals, for instance, which inhabit the sea, are very highly adapted for the life they lead. Nevertheless, a number of British mammals are attracted to the rich habitats surrounding our lakes, rivers and ponds. Although only three of our inland species are really aquatic, a surprising number of other species can swim well in pursuit of prey or if circumstances force them to take to the water.

The three truly aquatic mammals in Britain are the otter, the water vole and the tiny water shrew. The otter is an elegant and graceful carnivore, more at home when moving sleekly through the water after fish than on land. Sadly, the otter has become fairly rare because of water pollution and loss of habitat. The water vole is a delightful creature, rather like an aquatic guinea-pig; it feeds solely on aquatic and waterside vegetation, and may fall prey both to aquatic predators such as the pike and to terrestrial predators such as the fox. The water shrew, though tiny, is a ferocious predator with a need for a tremendously high food intake, which means that it is constantly on the move in search of prey.

Many other mammals, though not specifically adapted to water, are attracted to the waterside because of the greater amounts of food, especially invertebrates, to be found there. Several species of bats, for example, feed avidly over water at dusk and into the night on caddisflies, mayflies and any other flying insects. The introduced mink takes readily to water in pursuit of fishes or any other prey, including birds. Voles, rats, weasels and some deer – particularly the Chinese water deer – and others are all attracted to the water margins, either to feed directly on the aquatic plants or animals, or to feed on the other mammals that come to make use of the habitat. Some, such as the hedgehog and the brown rat, are even good swimmers and will propel themselves through a barrier of water if they have no other way of crossing it.

Left: The water vole inhabits ponds and lakes with well-vegetated banks, into which it digs its burrows. It swims by rapidly paddling with all four feet at once and feeds on grasses and roots.

Left: A water shrew dives after prey. A fierce predator, its high metabolic rate means that it must hunt constantly to satisfy its food needs. Though only about 140mm (5⅝in) long, including its tail, it can kill fish and even frogs, as well as worms, small spiders and insect larvae. It must paddle fast when it dives, because water trapped under its fur makes it buoyant.

181

MAMMALS OF WETLAND HABITATS

The wetlands and inland waterways of Britain provide an abundance of food and shelter that has been exploited by many species of mammals.

The wetlands and inland waterways of Britain are rich in plant and animal life. Freshwater habitats, whether fast-moving rivers, man-made canals and reservoirs, or the marshy edges of lakes and ponds, provide a source of food and shelter that has been exploited by many of our mammals.

Only three native mammals of inland Britain are truly aquatic: the otter, the water vole and the water shrew. They spend most of their lives in and around water and usually build homes in a waterside bank. However, more essentially land-living native mammals also live in close association with water for parts of the year, seeking food and refuge in fertile areas around the wetlands. And one introduced mammal, the mink, is now firmly established in inland freshwater habitats.

Freshwater habitats The wetlands and inland waterways can be divided into two main types: flowing water (rivers, canals and streams), and still water (lakes, ponds, marshes and fens). Water circulates in the atmosphere in the form of rain, and arrives in these habitats as a result of drainage from surrounding land, carrying with it dissolved nutrients that make it a medium suitable for plants, and hence animals, to colonize. The composition of wildlife is determined by such factors as the flow rate of the water, its temperature, chemicals and nutrients.

High in the mountains the water flows too fast for flowering plants to take root. Algae, mosses and liverworts mainly grow underwater and the most common animals here are insect larvae. Further downstream becks and deep pools harbour many species of fishes. Reed beds line the margins of slower lowland stretches of river and streams, and here many small aquatic mammals, such as water voles and water shrews, make their homes. Larger mammals are frequent visitors.

In lakes most animal life flourishes in the shallows where sunlight penetrates to the bottom enabling rooted plants to grow and provide oxygen. Lakes and ponds are relatively independent worlds with their own constantly changing balance of plants and animals. Their edges and shores provide homes for water voles and shrews, and for

many plant-eating mammals and the carnivores, especially weasels and stoats, that prey upon them. In summer the insect life of old-established ponds and wooded lakes attracts bats during the early evening.

Marshes and fens are waterlogged areas overgrown with reeds and other plants that flourish in patches of standing water. Marshes, often sited at the edge of a pond or lake, provide shelter for voles, mice and shrews, while the otter lives in fens which have deep-sided channels and flooded dykes. Canals—man-made habitats—are often supplemented by large reservoirs, and have most of the characteristics of shallow ponds and lakes because the flow of water into them is slow and usually only just sufficient to

Above: None of our essentially terrestrial mammals has taken to water quite so well as the brown rat. From areas of dense ground cover it enters the water regularly and is often mistaken for a water vole. It tends to keep to the surface, however, whereas the vole dives if disturbed. The vole can also be identified by its short tail.

Some wetland mammals

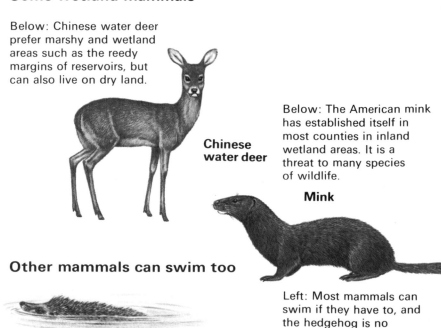

Below: Chinese water deer prefer marshy and wetland areas such as the reedy margins of reservoirs, but can also live on dry land.

Chinese water deer

Below: The American mink has established itself in most counties in inland wetland areas. It is a threat to many species of wildlife.

Mink

Other mammals can swim too

Hedgehog

Left: Most mammals can swim if they have to, and the hedgehog is no exception. It often swims in garden ponds, but moves to dry land when possible.

Above: Although the otter is a land mammal, it spends a great deal of its life in water, especially at dusk and during the night when it is feeding. It relies on its good eyesight and sensitive whiskers to detect the movements of passing fishes. It makes numerous short, sharp dives, and eats small fishes in water. Larger prey is taken to the shore. Here two otters are mating. The young are born on land and they learn to swim at about three months old.

maintain the water level.

Waterside dwellers Our most easily seen aquatic mammal is the water vole (often incorrectly called the water rat). Patches of bank where the plants have been bitten off and piles of chopped grasses and reeds on small rocks or patches of mud at the water's edge are all good indications that water voles are present. Unlike land-living voles, they catch and eat many animals such as snails, worms, fish and spawn. Water voles live in complex burrow systems in the banks of canals, lakes, slow-moving rivers and marshes, with entrances above and below water level.

The otter is much more difficult to see. Not only is it much rarer than it was, but it is shy and secretive, lying up in burrows, drains, root cavities and reed beds during the day, and preferring stretches of river with good ground cover on the banks. It hunts over enormous distances both in water and

overland.

The water shrew is the smallest of our water-living mammals. Although it is only a fraction of the size of the otter, it is just as ferocious and determined a hunter. Like all shrews, it needs enormous amounts of food to maintain its high metabolic rate and it eats its own body weight of living prey every 24 hours. It lives in a variety of watery habitats but is also found in woodland up to 3km (2 miles) away from water.

Waterside visitors The rushes, shrubs, grasses and trees of the fertile areas around wetlands and waterways have been described as 'biological crossroads' where land-dwelling animals mix with those that spend most of their lives in water. Small mammals such as short-tailed voles, mice and shrews are attracted to the rich plant and insect life, and they in turn attract predators such as foxes and badgers – their tracks are often quite clear in the mud. Deer also feed on the vegetation.

During the warmer months of the year the insect life above slow moving and still water attracts the Daubenton's bat, sometimes called the water bat. It can occasionally be seen at dusk, flying low and taking aquatic insects on the wing. Prey is eaten in flight. Our most common bat, the pipistrelle, also hunts over water, usually near old deciduous woodland. It takes prey in a similar manner to the Daubenton's bat, but does not keep so constantly close to the surface of the water.

Moles and polecats, two mammals that one would not necessarily associate with water, are in fact quite at home in damp areas. Even a pine marten has been known to live in a riverbank burrow, very far from its normal habitat.

Introduced mammals During the early part of this century three introduced mammals

Left: The Chinese water deer was introduced to Woburn Abbey in 1900. It stands about 50cm (20in) high and can be recognised by the long upper canine teeth which protrude from the jaw, especially in the male. In its native China and Korea the deer inhabits swampy country, reedbeds and grassland. In Britain it is found in open grassland and woodland in parts of Bedfordshire, Buckinghamshire and Hertfordshire, especially in wetland areas. It has bred successfully in the fenland areas of Norfolk and Cambridgeshire. Look out for the distinctive tracks and areas of flattened reed where the deer have been lying up during the day.

Adaptations for life under water

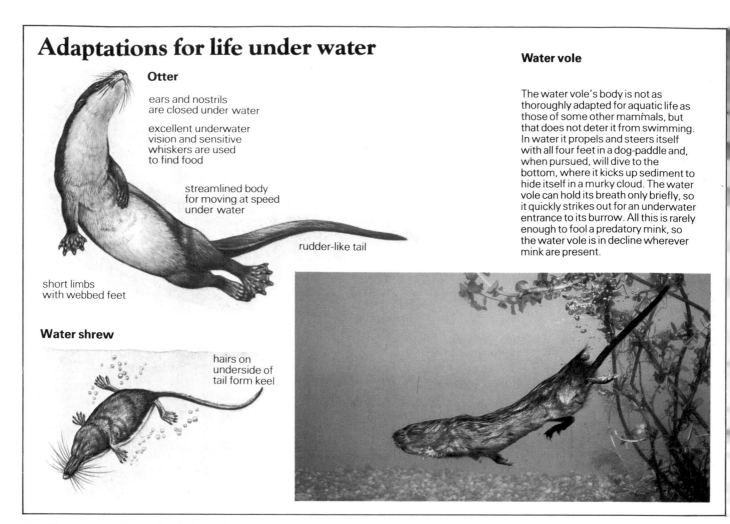

Otter

ears and nostrils
are closed under water

excellent underwater
vision and sensitive
whiskers are used
to find food

streamlined body
for moving at speed
under water

rudder-like tail

short limbs
with webbed feet

Water shrew

hairs on
underside of
tail form keel

Water vole

The water vole's body is not as
thoroughly adapted for aquatic life as
those of some other mammals, but
that does not deter it from swimming.
In water it propels and steers itself
with all four feet in a dog-paddle and,
when pursued, will dive to the
bottom, where it kicks up sediment to
hide itself in a murky cloud. The water
vole can hold its breath only briefly, so
it quickly strikes out for an underwater
entrance to its burrow. All this is rarely
enough to fool a predatory mink, so
the water vole is in decline wherever
mink are present.

that live near wetlands in their native countries began to escape from captivity and form
feral communities. These were the Chinese
water deer, the American mink and the
coypu. The Chinese water deer is a grazer
rather than a browser and causes little damage
to vegetation, but the other two species have
had a great effect on the ecology of British
wetlands. They were originally introduced for
fur production. Some species of waterfowl
have now vanished from mink-infested areas,
and where mink are hunting water voles
desert their burrows for higher ground. The
coypu, a vegetarian, used to damage crops,
especially sugar-beet.

Little competition exists overall between
the various mammal species. Our native
aquatic mammals co-exist well, and the
presence of such predators as weasels and
stoats ensures that the numbers of rodents
and small mammals in the surrounding areas
are kept in check. However, the introduction
of alien species has upset this balance. The
mink occupies a feeding niche not previously
occupied by our native carnivores because it
is both aquatic and terrestrial. In addition to
harming waterfowl, it is now thought to be
partly responsible for the decline of the otter,
because it competes for the same food.

Changed habitats Natural changes, such as
sudden torrential rain, can endanger mammals. The mole, for example, has to evacuate
its burrow if it becomes flooded and swim for

safety to higher ground. Smaller mammals
may be drowned or chilled if their fur becomes
waterlogged.

Man has the greatest effect on our wetland
mammals. The drainage of land, the increasing use of waterways for recreation, disturbance by Water Authorities, pollution,
and hunting have all contributed to the decline of the otter, to give the most dramatic
example. And pollution from whatever source
makes the water uninhabitable and is a direct
threat to mammal populations everywhere.

Below: The mole finds the
damp marginal land around
fens ideal for burrowing
and a rich source of
earthworm and insect prey,
although it tends to avoid
marshy and heavily
waterlogged ground. The
mole is an excellent swimmer
and its front feet are
equally well adapted for
swimming and for digging.

BRITAIN'S BIGGEST VOLE

Not to be confused with a rat, the water vole (below) is an expert swimmer, using its feet in a kind of dog-paddle. It can be spotted, day or night, near lakes, streams and rivers.

Water voles are readily distinguishable by their large size from the mouse-sized bank and field voles which live only on land. In some parts of Europe water voles live as land voles; and because it was thought that the two types were different species, each was given its own scientific name. It is now known, however, that the large voles, both water and land-loving, are all the same species and must therefore have the same name. This is why Britain's water voles have the apparently contradictory name of *Arvicola terrestris; terrestris* refers to the terrestrial habits of their continental cousins.

Water-lovers Although water voles feed almost entirely on land plants, they nearly always live close to water, especially on the densely vegetated banks of lakes, slow-flowing rivers, streams and ponds, as well as by canals and drainage ditches all over Britain. There are just a few places in Britain where water voles are common away from water, where they burrow like moles in pasture. The colony of water voles on Read's Island in the estuary of the River Humber, for example, has flourished because there are no rats on the island to prey upon them.

Ratty Kenneth Grahame's book *Wind in the Willows* calls Mole's friend Ratty—although the pictures show him to be a vole. If you see a brown or black mammal, about 30-45cm (12-17½in) in length, swimming with just the top of its head, back and tail breaking the surface, it is either a rat or a vole. A vole is distinguished by its rounded face (which resembles that of a small guinea

WATER VOLE
(*Arvicola terrestris*)
Size Males 19cm (7½in) head and body plus 12cm (4¾in) tail. Females 18cm (7in) head and body plus 11cm (4¼in) tail. Adult weight in breeding season 230-260g (8-9oz).
Colour dark brown shaggy fur, lighter brown or brownish grey underneath. Black varieties common in N Scotland.
Breeding season from April to September.
Gestation period 3 weeks.
No of young 2-3 litters of 5 per female each year.
Lifespan 12-18 months.
Food Vegetable matter, especially the stems of waterside grasses and other green plants.
Predators Pike, heron, weasels, stoats, mink and most other predatory mammals, especially brown rats, and birds of prey.
Distribution All over Britain, but rare in NW Scotland; not Ireland.

Water vole or brown rat?

Brown rat

Water vole

Above: The water vole (left) is often confused with the brown rat (right), which also lives along riverbanks and swims just as well. The vole has been called a 'water rat', but rats have a longer tail, longer ears and a more pointed face.

Below: Water voles plunge into the water to escape predators. All four feet are used in a dog-paddle. The under-fur is protected by long 'guard' hairs, which give water voles a shaggy appearance.

pig), smaller eyes, shorter muzzle and shorter ears which project just beyond its fur. A rat's tail is as long as its head-and-body length, while a vole's is about half or three-quarters of the total length of the head and body.

Enemies The greatest threat to the survival of the water vole is probably represented by brown rats. Rats can kill and eat baby voles and may even overpower a young vole. In areas where rats have become common on riverbanks, water voles have become rare or disappeared completely.

Apart from rats, all the usual predators of small mammals – such as weasels, stoats, mink and birds of prey – eat water voles. The water voles' habit of swimming and diving to escape danger helps protect them from these land-based predators, but exposes them to other predators which include heron and pike.

Dive for survival Swimming and diving are the chief ways in which water voles can escape danger – and in these they are therefore expert although they normally only use them as a means of escape. They swim, steer and dive using all four feet in a dog-paddle. When scared, they dive to the bottom and stir up mud with their forefeet so that they are more difficult to spot. Voles can only hold their breath for about 20 seconds, so once they have dived they swim quickly to one of the underwater entrances to their burrow system.

Any swimming mammal has to keep its body surface as dry as possible so that it does not lose too much body heat. Water voles have a thick, warm layer of under-fur which traps air near the body surface; the warm air insulates the animal. The vole is further protected by long, greasy guard hairs, which project above the under-fur and so prevent it getting wet when the vole dives.

The home range If you see several water voles together, they are probably a family group, as they are generally unfriendly to other individuals. Both males and females have their own home ranges, which include a complex system of burrows. The ranges are marked and both males and females try to exclude other voles of the same sex as themselves.

Water voles mark the boundaries of their range in two ways: firstly, by the smell of their droppings, which are usually confined to the latrine sites at the edge of the range; and, secondly, by a scent that is produced by glands under the skin of the flank. The scent exudes on to the skin surface where it is transferred to the feet of the voles when they scratch themselves. From the feet, the scent reaches the ground and marks the voles' runways. Male voles have larger ranges to mark and so have bigger and more easily visible scent glands. The scent organ is located on each flank in the form of an oval of naked skin.

Voles' ranges vary greatly in size depending on the nature of the habitat. But Dr Michael Stoddart, in his detailed study of voles in Scotland, found that a male's range averaged 130m (142yd) of riverbank. He also discovered that the female range is only about half that length.

Males usually stay in their home range for the whole of their adult life. Females sometimes move to new areas, however, particularly when they are pregnant with the second or third litter in the breeding season.

Signs of activity Although water voles will dive for cover if disturbed, there are several signs you can look for. Burrows in the middle of a circular, grazed 'lawn' – usually of a radius of about 15-20cm (6-8in) – are caused by voles staying in the mouth of the burrow while they feed. These are a good indication that voles have been at work. There may be several holes, or entrances, to the burrows; and while those are often below water level, you may well see some above.

Other signs are the piles of nibblings, which voles drop as they bite bits off a grass stem, or the white inner pith left in spring and summer from rushes. Voles droppings are usually made in special latrine sites at the extremity of their range. Each dropping is cylindrical, 10-12mm (about 0·4in) in length and khaki to light green in colour.

If you hear a rasping 'crick-crick' sound, it may well be a vole nearby that has been frightened. Otherwise, water voles are usually silent.

Although active both day and night, water voles are generally busiest by day. So if you watch quietly by a riverbank, where signs of voles are present, you may often be rewarded by a sighting.

Feeding Water voles are almost complete vegetarians, their main diet being the stems and leaves of grasses and other waterside plants. When they eat, they assume a characteristic hunch-backed stance, holding the food with their forepaws.

They do not usually feed more than 2m (6ft) from the water's edge, so that they can dive for cover if disturbed, and will often swim along or across the river from their

home burrow to get to a feeding site.

Breeding Water voles mate first in early spring, the first litter being born in April or May after a gestation period of three weeks. A female vole may have two or three litters in a summer.

The nests are usually made below ground in the burrow system, or at the base of rushes in marshlands. If the nest is disturbed when the babies are very young, the mother will carry them off, one by one, in her mouth, to a new nest site. By the time the young are two weeks old, they are weaned and within one month they are trying to establish home ranges of their own. By this time, the mother is likely to be pregnant with her next litter.

Above: A female water vole with young in a disturbed nest. There are usually about five to each litter. The young are born naked, with eyes closed. At birth, they weigh about 5g ($\frac{1}{5}$oz), increasing by one gramme a day for the first week and slightly more in the second week. At five days, the young voles have fur; their eyes open after eight days.

Water voles' riverbank home

Within their home range, water voles make quite complex burrows in riverbanks. The several entrances can be either below or above water level. Underground, the burrow leads to a nest chamber with a nest built of chewed and shredded grass. If it is a breeding nest, the adult vole may block the above-ground entrances with mud or grass for security.

Water voles do not hibernate, coming out instead to feed the whole year round. In autumn, however, they often take plant stems into their burrow system and store them in chambers or on the floor of the burrow. These food stores are probably used as a supplement in winter when fresh food is difficult to find. Water voles often stay in the entrance of feeding burrows, eating what they can reach without coming right into the open. However, if you see burrows in the middle of a small, circular grazed 'lawn', you will know that voles are around.

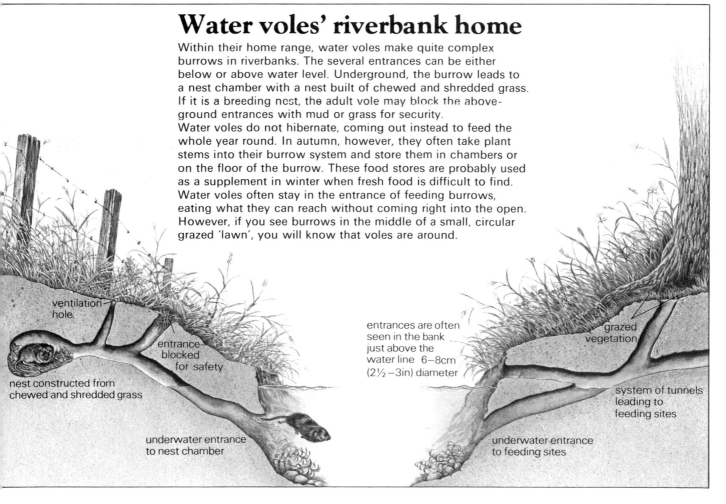

ventilation hole

entrance blocked for safety

nest constructed from chewed and shredded grass

underwater entrance to nest chamber

entrances are often seen in the bank just above the water line 6–8cm (2½–3in) diameter

grazed vegetation

system of tunnels leading to feeding sites

underwater entrance to feeding sites

CHINESE WATER DEER
(*Hydropotes inermis*)
Size of adult Male about 60cm (24in); weighs 13.6kg (30lb). Female 55cm (22in); weighs 11.7kg (26lb).
Breeding season Rut takes place in November and December. Fawns, born late May and early June are browny-fawn with rows of white spots along each side of body which fade as the fawn grows.
Gestation period 180-210 days.
No of young Litter size unusually large for deer, up to five or six in China, but fewer usually born in the British Isles.
Lifespan 15 years.
Food Grasses, small plants.
Predators Man, cats, dogs, foxes, stoats.
Distribution Bedfordshire, Cambridgeshire, Chilterns, Hertfordshire, Oxfordshire.

Left: A Chinese water deer buck, showing the tusk-like canine teeth which are his fighting weapons. The female also has tusks, but they are barely visible.

Below: In their native countries of eastern China and Korea, Chinese water deer inhabit reed beds and estuarine swamps. In England the deer visit pools and streams to drink but they rarely, if ever, swim.

PETITE CHINESE WATER DEER

The Chinese water deer was introduced to Britain from China early this century. It does not bear antlers, being equipped instead with sabre-like sharp canine teeth.

The Chinese water deer, one of the smallest species of deer in the world, is only slightly larger than a fox. Like the muntjac, it was introduced to England by the Duke of Bedford early this century when he was collecting various species for Woburn Park. Some species did not survive over the years in a foreign environment, but the Chinese water deer thrived and multiplied in all but the severest weather. Although it is shy, nervous and independent of man, this deer has gradually become established in the countryside in Bedfordshire, Cambridgeshire, Hertfordshire, the Chilterns and Oxfordshire. However, this species is nowhere near as numerous as the muntjac.

One factor which makes it more difficult to spot Chinese water deer is that they spend much of the day under cover. However, they probably make use of regular routes and set territories in the areas where they have become established, and traces of such paths may sometimes be seen in woodland undergrowth or reed beds. Droppings and tracks can be seen in marshlands and reed beds.

Appearance The buck and doe look similar until the buck develops his distinctive canine tusks at the age of one and a half years. When seen head-on, the Chinese water deer is particularly attractive: it looks rather like a teddy bear with pricked ears high on the head, its nose and eyes appearing as three black buttons in its face. The adult has a plain coat which is reasonably uniform in thickness all over, but paler in colour on the belly and on the insides of the legs. The coat of both male and female is a reddish-sandy colour in summer, and a brownish-sandy colour, flecked with grey, in winter. The legs are short and slender and well proportioned to the body, and the feet are small with cloven hoofs and dew claws. From the rear the deer appears to have no tail: in fact the tail is about 9cm (3½in) long and thick, and in colour blends well with the rump.

Social life Most deer species congregate in herds for at least part of the year, but the Chinese water deer is mainly solitary. During late November and December the buck establishes his rutting territory by scent marking with faeces and urine, fraying plant stems with his teeth, and driving out any other competing bucks. He makes a deep bird-like chattering sound when herding the does.

Again unlike the other deer species, the Chinese water deer produces two or three fawns together. (Up to five or six are common in China.) They are usually born in June and for the first few days they lie tightly curled up together in grassland. After about a week they are able to jump up and run off if disturbed. For the next three months the doe is accompanied by her fawns, and is occasionally seen with another doe or a yearling doe. After six months the buck and doe are sexually mature, but usually the buck is not yet strong enough to compete for territory with older males, and he rarely mates before the following season. The female becomes pregnant when she is six months old and she gives birth for the first time when she is one year old.

Behaviour The Chinese water deer is most often seen on grassland where it feeds, rests

and breeds. Sometimes it browses for fruits and seeds on the fringes of woodland. Its eyesight appears poor and if the animal is disturbed it tends to flick its head round every few degrees as though it is trying to focus on the passing object. It often stands quite still in long grass, apart from this head movement. If it is alarmed, it often turns on itself so sharply that it falls over, only to scramble up and run off at high speed, with the curious action of throwing up its hind legs much higher than its back every two or three strides.

In Woburn Park and the surrounding areas Chinese water deer are regularly struck by road vehicles, especially during the dark. If a fawn is handled by a human and then left, the doe associates the smell on her fawn with the scent of a predator and leaves it to die. Anyone who finds a fawn in the countryside should therefore leave it well alone. More often than not the doe is close at hand, waiting for the opportunity to claim her fawn and take it to a safer area, such as the long grass on the edges of woodland where the species is most often found.

Above: A Chinese water deer in the snow, well protected by its thick coat. This coat, very thick for such a small animal, enables it to withstand extremes of temperature. There is little change in colour and thickness in spring and autumn, compared with other deer species.

Below: A Chinese water deer fawn has a dark brown coat with creamy white spots which last for the first three to four months. For the first six months male and female fawns appear similar, until the male develops his canine tusks.

The entries listed in **bold** type refer to main subjects. The page numbers in *italics* indicate illustrations. Medium type entries refer to the text.

ACKNOWLEDGEMENTS

Photographers' credits Heather Angel 8, 10 (upper middle), 13, 16 (top), 17 (bottom), 18 (bottom), 21 (top), 26 (middle), 28 (middle, bottom), 30 (bottom), 33 (top), 34 (middle), 37 (middle), 41 (bottom), 42 (middle), 44 (bottom), 46 (bottom left, bottom right), 47 (middle), 48-9 (top), 52, 53 (middle, bottom), 54 (bottom), 56 (bottom), 57 (middle), 58 (bottom left), 60-1, 62, 63 (top right), 65 (middle), 69 (bottom), 70 (top, lower middle), 73 (bottom right), 74 (top), 76, 77, 78, 83, 84, 96 (bottom), 97, 99 (bottom), 100, 104, 105, 109 (bottom), 110 (top), 116, 117, 118, 119 (top), 120, 122 (bottom), 126, 127, 129 (bottom), 131 (top), 139, 159 (bottom), 160, 177 (bottom), 184 (bottom), 186: Aquila Photographics/H Kinloch 150; Wayne Lankinen 144; M Leach 183 (top); EK Thompson 106; DS Whitaker 155 (bottom); MC Wilkes 12, 163: Ian Beames 18 (middle), 131 (bottom), 157, 161 (bottom): Biofotos/J Thomas 33 (middle): Bob Gibbons Photography/R Fletcher 22 (bottom), 75; Bob Gibbons 41 (top), 131 (middle); Peter Wilson 170 (top): Bruce Coleman Ltd/Mark N Boulton 130; Jane Burton 63 (bottom), 124, 188 (top), 188-9 (bottom); Bruce Coleman 154 (bottom), 165 (bottom), 178 (top); AJ Deane 148 (top); Gordon Langsbury 146; J Markham 187; SC Porter 153; Hans Reinhard 136, 137, 151, 156; Kim Taylor 119 (bottom); R Tidman 162 (bottom); J van Wormer 158; F Vollmar 114-15; Peter Ward 161 (middle); Roger Wilmshurst 171; Gunter Zies front cover, 145, 148 (bottom), 179: Raymond E Chaplin 189 (top, middle): Michael Chinery 113: JPA Clare 149: John Clegg 10 (lower middle), 11, 50 (middle, bottom), 54 (top), 122 (middle): David Corke 63 (top left): Dennis Green 18 (top), 21 (bottom), 142,

143 (bottom), 155 (top): Melvin Grey 173 (bottom): Nigel Holmes 70 (upper middle), 72, 73 (bottom left): J Horsefall 165 (top): George Hyde 70 (bottom), 74 (bottom): Michael Leach 59: John Mason 22 (top), 26 (top), 32-3 (bottom), 68, 99 (top), 107 (bottom), 108 (top), 111 (top), 129 (top); 135: M King & M Read 40-1 (top): Geoff Dore 82 (top right); M Read 16 (bottom): RT Mills 152 (bottom), 169, 170 (middle), 182: John Mitchell 66, 67, 87 (bottom): Colin Molyneux 35, 37 (top): Pat Morris 39, 58 (top), 183 (bottom): Natural History Photographic Agency/J & M Bain 82 (bottom); AP Barnes 42 (top); L Campbell 71; S Dalton 25, 58 (bottom right), 90-1, 92 (bottom), 95 (top), 103, 180-1; J Goodman 138; F Greenaway 96 (top), 102; SJ Harris 170 (bottom); B Hawkes 28 (top), 172; EA Janes 27; J Kett 92 (top); KG Preston-Mafham 50 (top), 109 (top), 110 (bottom), 112; R Shaw 80; A Wharton 73 (top): Nature Conservancy Council/John Ratcliffe 47 (top); John Riggall 44-5 (top): Nature Photographers/ T Andrewartha 51; A Beamish 79; SC Bisserot 10 (bottom), 15 (bottom), 101; FV Blackburn 88 (top left), 147, 174, 176 (top); D Bonsall 6-7, 53 (top); N Brown 57 (bottom); NA Callow 45 (bottom); K Carlson 166; A Cleave 46 (top), 88 (bottom); C Grey-Wilson 24 (middle); EA Janes 93; C & J Knights 95 (middle); P Knights 164 (bottom left); MDF Oates 20 (top); Owen Newman 128, 152 (middle); WS Paton 162 (middle); D Sewell 9; D Smith 17 (middle), 86; P Sterry 10 (top), 24 (top), 107 (top), 121, 167 (middle); EK Thompson 143 (top); R Tidman 55 (bottom), 154 (top); N Wilmore 55 (top): Naturfoto/S Christoffersen 176 (bottom): WS Paton 26 (bottom): Premaphotos Wildlife/KG Preston-Mafham 20 (bottom), 24 (bottom), 36, 64, 65 (top), 69, 82 (top left),

87 (top), 111 (bottom), 123: Press-tige Pictures/ D Avon & T Tilford 120 (bottom), 132, 140-1, 167 (bottom), 168, 173 (top), 177 (top), 178 (bottom), 184 (middle), 185; T Howes 29; R Jones 30 (bottom); Geoff Nobes 89: Richard Revels 56-7 (top), 81: John Robinson 14, 30 (middle), 32 (top), 95 (bottom), 133, 134: Royal Society for the Protection of Birds/M Richards 31: David Sewell 159 (top): A Shay 15 (top): MWF Tweedie 98, 108 (bottom): Gerald Wilkinson 34 (top): Woodfall Wildlife Pictures/D Woodfall 43.

Artists' credits Graham Allen/Linden Artists 180, 182, 184, 186: Fred Anderson/The Garden Studio 131: Norman Arlott 157, 175 (images): Russell Barnett 29, 42 (line), 65 (middle), 93 (top), 111, 117 (line): Trevor Boyer/Linden Artists 154: Rhoda Burns/Drawing Attention 38: Sarah De Ath/Linden Artists 67, 72-3: Elisabeth Dowle 60: Eugene Fleury 23 (colour): Wayne Ford 140, 144, 147, 148, 151, 152, 161, 164, 166, 167 (top), 169, 170, 172: Hayward Art Group 11 (line), 78-9, 84-5, 132 (map), 138 (map), 175 (maps), 187: Kristin Jakob/ The Garden Studio 65 (bottom), 89: Ian Lewington title page: Richard Lewington/The Garden Studio 97, 105, 107, 113, 122, 123: Keith Linsell 132 (bottom), 133, 135, 139: Paul Nesbitt 93 (bottom): Denys Ovenden 114, 117 (colour), 120, 125, 126, 127, 137: Sandra Pond 21, 23 (line), 47, 69, 76: Bob Press 87: Andrew Riley 90, 98, 99, 101, 102: Nina Roberts/The Garden Studio 48-9: Colin Salmon 11 (colour), 17, 42 (colour), 128, 143, 145, 155, 163, 167 (map), 179 (map): Phil Weare/Linden Artists 94, 179.

Index compiled by Richard Raper of Indexing Specialists, Hove, East Sussex.

Typesetting PHOTOCOMP LTD, BIRMINGHAM; Printing & Binding PRINTER INDUSTRIA, GRÁFICA S.A. BARCELONA;
Separations YORK HOUSE GRAPHICS, HANWELL; COLOURSCAN OVERSEAS CO PTE LTD, SINGAPORE;
Paper KNP MILL, HOLLAND